STERLING
Test Prep

AP Biology

Practice Questions

4th edition

Customer Satisfaction Guarantee

Your feedback is important because we strive to provide the highest quality prep materials. Email us questions, comments or suggestions.

info@sterling–prep.com

We reply to emails – check your spam folder

4 3 2 1

ISBN-13: 979-8-8855703-5-0

Sterling Test Prep materials are available at quantity discounts.

Contact info@sterling–prep.com

Sterling Test Prep
6 Liberty Square #11
Boston, MA 02109

Published by Sterling Test Prep

 Printed in the U.S.A.

STERLING
Test Prep

Thousands of students use our preparation materials to achieve high AP scores!

Scoring well on AP exams is essential to earn placement credits and admission into competitive colleges, positioning you for success. This book helps you develop and apply knowledge to choose the correct answers quickly. Solving targeted practice questions builds your understanding and is more effective than mere memorization.

This book has 990 high-yield AP biology practice questions. Experienced biology instructors analyzed test content and developed the practice material that builds knowledge and skills crucial for success on the test. Our test preparation experts structured the content to match the current test requirements.

The detailed explanations teach the scientific foundations and details of essential biology topics needed to answer exam questions. They describe why an answer is correct, and another attractive choice is wrong. By reading these explanations, you will learn essential biology principles and understand how they apply to questions.

With this practice material, you will significantly improve your test score.

230428akp

What some students say about this book

★★★★★ ***I was prepared for the exam***

Great AP biology practice questions...questions are challenging and the explanations are very helpful. My teacher told the class...I was prepared for the AP biology exam.

Helen (Amazon verified purchase)

★★★★★ ***Great book to learn AP biology***

Great prep book for the AP biology exam... Much better than the other books I compared it to from my library. I'm also using the Sterling Test AP physics I book. Both books are excellent - great practice and clear explanations. The big difference is the detailed solutions. I learned so much from these books.

Steve F. (Amazon verified purchase)

★★★★★ ***Very good material***

These practice questions have extensive explanations that walk you through many biology concepts... The questions cover a broad range of concepts within each topic, are not repetitive and range from easier ones to more difficult and complex. I learned a lot of biology from this book and can recommend it to others.

FJ (Amazon verified purchase)

★★★★★ ***a must have AP biology***

Great results on the AP biology exam thanks to this book. I learned so much more from practicing the questions and reading the explanations than I did from my textbook.

Bridgette (Amazon verified purchase)

★★★★★ ***good combination with the review book from sterling***

used this ap biology practice questions book with the review book.

Mike S. (Amazon verified purchase)

★★★★★ ***Got a 5 by using this book***

Great book to prepare for the AP biology exam. Questions and explanations are excellent and targeted for the actual exam.

Kelsey Sandler (Amazon verified purchase)

If you benefited from this book, we would appreciate if you left a review on Amazon, so others can learn from your input. Reviews help us understand our customers' needs and experiences while keeping our commitment to quality.

Advanced Placement (AP) prep books

Biology Practice Questions

Biology Review

Physics 1 Practice Questions

Physics 1 Review

Physics 2 Practice Questions

Physics 2 Review

Environmental Science

Psychology

U.S. History

World History

European History

U.S. Government and Politics

Comparative Government and Politics

Human Geography

Visit our Amazon store

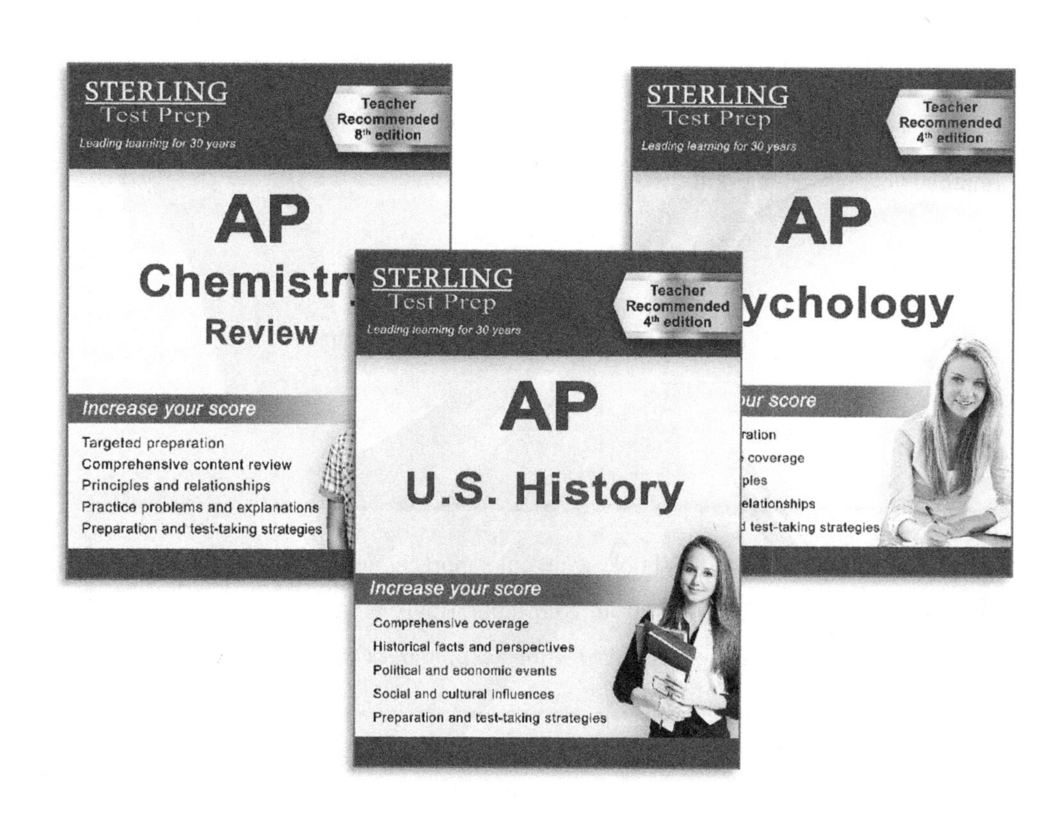

College Level Examination Program (CLEP)

Biology Review

Biology Practice Questions

Chemistry Review

Chemistry Practice Questions

Introductory Business Law Review

College Algebra Practice Questions

College Mathematics Practice Questions

History of the United States I Review

History of the United States II Review

Western Civilization I Review

Western Civilization II Review

Social Sciences and History Review

American Government Review

Introductory Psychology Review

Visit our Amazon store

College study aids

Cell and Molecular Biology Review

Organismal Biology Review

Cell and Molecular Biology Practice Questions

Organismal Biology Practice Questions

Physics Review

Physics Practice Questions

Organic Chemistry Practice Questions

General Chemistry Review

General Chemistry Practice Questions

Environmental Science

United States History

American Government & Politics

Comparative Government & Politics

Visit our Amazon store

Table of Contents

Table of Contents *(continued)*

AP Biology Preparation and Test-Taking Strategies

Test preparation strategies

The best way to do well in AP Biology is to be good at biology. There is no way around knowing the subject; proper preparation is key to success. Prepare to answer with confidence as many questions as possible.

Study in advance

Devote 3 to 6 months to studying. The information is manageable by studying regularly before the test.

Cramming is not a successful tactic. However, do not study too far in advance. Studying more than six months ahead is not advised and may result in fatigue and poor knowledge retention.

Develop a realistic study and practice schedule

Cramming eight hours a day is unfeasible and leads to burnout, which is detrimental to performance.

Commit to a realistic study and practice schedule.

Remove distractions

During this preparation period, temporarily eliminate distractions.

However, balance is critical, and it is crucial not to neglect physical well-being and social or family life.

Prepare with full intensity but do not jeopardize your health or emotional well-being.

Develop an understanding over memorization

When studying, devote time to each topic.

After a study session, write a short concept outline to clarify relationships and increase knowledge retention.

Make flashcards

Avoid commercial flashcards because making cards help build and retain knowledge.

Consider using self-made flashcards to develop knowledge retention and quiz what you know.

Find a study partner

Occasionally studying with a friend to prepare for the test can motivate and provide accountability.

Explaining concepts to another improves and fine-tunes your understanding, integrates knowledge, bolsters competence, and identifies deficiencies in comprehension.

Take practice tests

Do not take practice tests too early.

First, develop a comprehensive understanding of concepts.

In the last weeks, use practice tests to fine-tune your final preparation. If you are not scoring well on practice tests, you want time to improve without undue stress.

Alternate studying and practicing to increase knowledge retention and identify areas for study.

Taking practice tests accustoms you to the challenges of test-taking.

Test day strategies

Be well-rested and eat the right foods

Get a full night's sleep before the test for proper mental and physical capacity. If you are up late the night before, you will have difficulty concentrating and focusing on the test.

Avoid foods and drinks that lead to drowsiness (carbohydrates and protein).

Avoid drinks high in sugar, causing glucose to spike and crash.

Pack in advance

Check what you are allowed to bring to the test. Pay attention to the required check-in items (e.g., confirmation, identification).

Pack the day before to avoid the stress of not frantically looking for things on test day.

Arrive at the testing center early

Starting right is an advantage. Allow time to check in and remain calm before the test begins.

Plan your route to the center correctly without additional challenges and unnecessary stress. Map and test the route to the center in advance and determine needed parking.

If you are unfamiliar with the test location, visit before the test day to practice and avoid travel errors.

Maintain a positive attitude

Avoid falling into a mental spiral of negative emotions. Too much worry leads to underperformance.

If you become anxious, chances are higher for lower performance in preparation and during the test.

Inner peace helps during preparation and the high-stakes test.

To do well on the test requires logical, systematic, and analytical thinking, so relax and remain calm.

Focus on progress

Do not be concerned with other test-takers. Someone proceeding rapidly through the exam may be rushing or guessing on questions.

Take breaks

Do not skip the available timed breaks. Refreshing breaks help you finish strong.

Eat a light snack to replenish your energy. Your mind and body will appreciate the available breaks.

The best approach to any test is *not* to keep your head down the whole session.

While there is no time to waste, breathe deeply for a few seconds between questions.

Momentarily clear your thoughts to relax your mind and muscles.

Time management strategies

Timing

Besides good preparation, time management is the critical strategy for the exam.

Timed practice is not the objective at this stage.

While practicing, note how many questions you would have completed in the allotted time.

Average time per question

In advance, determine the average time allotted for each question.

Use two different approaches depending on which preparation phase you are working.

During the first preparation phase, acquire, fortify, and refine your knowledge.

During final practice, use the time needed to develop analytical thought processes related to specific questions.

Work systematically

Note your comprehension compared to the correct answers to learn and identify conceptual weaknesses.

Do not overlook explanations to questions as a source of content, analysis, and interdependent relationships.

During the second preparation phase, do not spend more than the average allotted time on each question when taking practice tests.

Pace your response time to develop a consistent pace and complete the test within the allotted time.

If you are time-constrained during the final practice phase, work more efficiently, or your score will suffer.

Focus on the easy questions and skip the unfamiliar

Easy or difficult questions are worth the same points. Score more points for three quickly answered questions than one hard-earned victory.

Answer the familiar and easy questions to maximize points if time runs out.

Identify strengths and weaknesses

Skip unfamiliar questions in the first round, as challenging questions require more than average time.

In the second review, questions you cannot approach systematically or lack fundamental knowledge will not be answered through analysis.

Use the elimination and educated guessing strategy to select an answer and move on to another question.

Do not overinvest in any question

Some questions consume more time than the average and make you think of investing more time.

Stop thinking that investing more time in challenging questions is productive.

Do not get entangled with questions while losing track of time.

The test is timed, so do not spend too much time on any questions.

Look at every question on the exam

It is unfortunate not to earn points for a question you could have quickly answered because you did not see it.

If you are in the first half of the test and spending more than the average on a question, select the best option, note the question number, and move on.

Do not rush through the remaining questions, causing you to miss more answers.

If time allows, return to marked questions and take a fresh look.

However, do not change the original answer unless you have a reason to change it.

University studies on students show that hastily changing answers often replace correct and incorrect answers.

Multiple-choice questions

Answer all questions

How many questions are correct, not how much work went into selecting the answers matters. An educated guess earns the same points as an answer known with confidence.

On the test, you need to think and analyze information quickly.

The skill of analyzing information quickly cannot be gained from a college course, prep course, or textbook.

Working efficiently and effectively is a skill developed through focused effort and applied practice.

Strategic approach

Strategies, approaches, and perspectives for answering multiple-choice questions help maximize points.

Many strategies seem like common sense. However, these helpful approaches might be overlooked under the pressure of a timed test.

While no strategy replaces comprehensive preparation, apply probability for success on unfamiliar questions.

Understand the question

Know what the question is asking before selecting an answer.

It is surprising when students do not read (and reread) carefully and rush to select the wrong answer.

The test-makers anticipate hasty mistakes, and many enticing answers include specious choices.

A successful student reads and understands the question precisely before looking at the answers.

Focus on the answer

Separate the vital information from distracters and understand the design and thrust of the question.

Answer the question and not merely pick a factually accurate statement or answer a misconstrued question.

Rephrasing the question helps articulate precisely what the correct response requires.

When rephrasing, do not change the question's meaning; assume it is direct and to the point as written.

After selecting the answer, review the question and verify that the choice selected answers the question.

Answer the question before looking at choices

This valuable strategy is applicable if the question asks for generalized factual details.

Form a thought response first, then look for the choice that matches your preordained answer.

Select the predetermined statement as it is likely correct.

Factually correct, but wrong

Questions often have incorrect choices that are factually correct but do not answer the question.

Predetermine the answer and do not choose merely a factually correct statement.

Verify that the choice answers the question.

Do not fall for the familiar

When in doubt, it is comforting to choose what is familiar. If you recognize a term or concept, you may be tempted to pick that choice impetuously.

However, do not go with familiar answers merely because they are familiar.

Before selecting the answer and how it relates to the question, think about it.

Experiments questions

Determine the purpose, methods, variables, and controls of the experiment.

Understanding the presented information helps answer the question.

With multiple experiments, understand variations of the same experiment by focusing on the differences.

For example, focus on changes between the first and second experiments, second and third, and first and third.

Direct comparison between experiments helps organize and apply the information to the answer.

Words of caution

The words *"all," "none,"* and *"except"* require attention. Be alert with questions containing these words, as the answer may not be apparent on the first read of the question.

Double-check the question

After selecting an answer, return to the question to ensure the selected choice answers the question as asked.

Fill the answers carefully

Many mistakes happen when filling in answers.

Filling answers correctly is simple but crucial.

Be attentive to the question number and enter the answer accordingly. If you skip a question, skip it on the answer sheet.

Elimination strategies

If the correct answer is not immediately apparent, use the process of elimination.

Use the strategy of educated guessing by eliminating one or two answers.

Usually, at least one answer choice is easily identified as wrong. Eliminating one choice increases the odds of selecting the correct one.

Process of elimination

Eliminate choices:

- Use proportionality for quantitative questions to eliminate choices too high or too low.
- Eliminate answers that are *almost right* or *half right*.

  Consider *half right* as *wrong* since distractor choices are purposely included.
- If two answers are direct opposites, the correct answer is likely one of them.

  However, note if they are direct opposites or another reason to consider them correct. Therefore, eliminate the other choices and narrow the search for the correct one.
- For numerical questions, eliminate the smallest and largest numbers (unless for a reason).

Roman numeral questions

Roman numeral questions present several statements and ask which is/are correct.

These questions are tricky for most test-takers because they have more than one potentially correct statement.

Roman numeral questions are often included in combinations with more than one answer.

Eliminating a wrong Roman numeral statement eliminates all choices that include it.

Educated guessing

Correct ways to guess

Do not assume you must get every question right; this will add unnecessary stress during the exam.

You will (likely) need to guess for some questions.

Answer as many questions correctly as possible without wasting time.

For challenging questions, random guessing does not help. Use educated guessing after elimination.

Playing the odds

Guessing is a form of "partial credit" because while you might not be sure of the correct answer, you have the relevant knowledge to identify some wrong choices.

There is a 25% chance of correctly guessing random responses since questions have four choices. Therefore, the odds are guessing 1 question correctly to 3 incorrectly.

Guessing after elimination of answers

After eliminating one answer as wrong, you have a 33% chance of a lucky guess. Therefore, your odds move from 1 question right to 2 questions wrong.

While this may not seem like a dramatic increase, it can make an appreciable difference in your score.

Confidently eliminating two wrong choices increases the chances of guessing correctly to 50%!

When using elimination:

- Do not rely on gut feelings alone to answer questions quickly.

  Understand and recognize the difference between *knowing* and *gut feeling* about the answer.

  Gut feelings should sparingly be used after the process of elimination.

- Do not fall for answers that sound "clever," and choose "bizarre" answers.

  Choose them only with a reason to believe they may be correct.

Eliminating Roman numeral choices

A workable strategy for Roman numeral questions is to guess the wrong statement.

For example: A. I only

B. III only

C. I and II only

D. I and III only

Notice that statement II does not have an answer dedicated to it. This indicates that statement II is likely wrong and eliminates choice C, narrowing your search to three choices.

However, if you are confident that statement II is the answer, do not apply this strategy.

Free-response questions

Free-response questions typically require processing information into existing conceptual frameworks.

There are some personal choices for writing the desired response.

Free-response question skills

Be able to present and discuss relevant examples. Practice clarifying or evaluating principles.

Perform detailed analysis of relationships and respond to stimulus materials such as charts or graphs.

Understand the question

As with the multiple-choice questions, understand what the question asks. Assume that the question, as written, is direct and to the point.

Mental rephrasing should not add or alter the meaning or essence of the question.

Answer the questions in order of competence

You are not bound to answer the questions in their sequence. Survey all questions and decide which requires minimal effort or time.

Avoid getting entangled and frustrated to use time efficiently and maximize points.

Do not write more than needed

Additional work beyond the question's stated directives does not earn a higher score or result in extra credit.

For time management and keeping responses relevant, answer the question but avoid superfluous responses.

Organize thoughts

Before writing, brainstorm the questions' topics. Outline your thoughts on scratch paper during the composition process. Essential definitions, ideas, examples, or names are valid details when relevant.

Organized thoughts produce a coherent response. With practice, balance time between brainstorming and writing.

Follow the structure

Structure responses to match the order specified in the question for a grader-friendly answer.

The reader/grader should not need to search for topics used in the grading criteria. A well-structured essay has complete sentences and paragraphs.

A formal introduction and conclusion are unnecessary; they go directly into answering the question.

Answer questions in their entirety

It is essential to answer questions thoroughly, not just partially. For example, some questions ask to identify and explain. Performing only one step is inadequate and will be graded accordingly.

Task verbs

Below are *task verbs* common for free-response questions – underline directives on practice questions and exams.

Refer to these tasks and verify when completed. Do not overlook them when writing a comprehensive response.

Compare – provide a description or explanation of similarities or differences.

Define – provide a specific meaning for a word or concept.

Identify – provide information about a specified topic without elaboration or explanation.

Describe – provide the relevant characteristics of a specified concept.

Develop an argument – articulate a claim and support it with evidence.

Explain – provide how (or why) relationships, processes, patterns, or outcomes occur, using evidence and reasoning.

Conclude – use available information to formulate an accurate statement demonstrating understanding based on evidence.

How questions typically require analyzing the relationship, process, pattern, or outcome.

Why questions typically require analyzing motivations or reasons for the relationship, process, or outcome.

Write legibly

The reader must decipher your writing so responses are scored appropriately.

Practice writing under a time limit to produce a readable response.

Ask a friend to read a sample response to understand the words expressed if this issue exists.

Consider printing key phrases or highlighting them cleanly (e.g., asterisk, underline) in your response.

Use plain language

All claims should be directly stated. You do not want the graders to guess how something demonstrates a point.

Regardless of if they correctly guess your intentions, you will be graded critically for ambiguities.

Present relevant information clearly and concisely to demonstrate the argument's primary points.

Use facts to bolster arguments

Written responses should include specific facts and avoid unsubstantiated claims.

Do not use long, meandering responses filled with loosely-related facts regarding specific concepts.

Avoid contradictions, circular definitions, and question restatements.

Review and correct answers

If questions are completed and time remains, review each response.

Assess if anything is needed to be added or requires correction.

Put a simple strikethrough through the error for a mistake, so the grader disregards that portion.

If you add content, insert an asterisk (*) and refer the reader to the end of the essay. Thoughtful revisions earn crucial points.

AP Biology

Practice Questions

Macromolecules

1. The linear sequence of amino acids along a peptide chain determines its:

A. primary structure
B. secondary structure
C. tertiary structure
D. quaternary structure

2. There are [ ] different types of major biomolecules used by humans.

A. a few dozen
B. four
C. several thousand
D. several million

3. Amino acids are linked to one another in a protein by which bonds?

A. amide bonds
B. carboxylate bonds
C. ester bonds
D. amine bonds

4. Insulin is an example of a(n):

A. hormone
B. storage protein
C. structural protein
D. enzyme

5. Which protein structure corresponds to a spiral alpha-helix of amino acids?

A. primary
B. secondary
C. tertiary
D. quaternary

6. Proteins are characterized by:

A. always has a quaternary structure
B. retaining their conformation above 35-40 °C
C. a primary structure formed by covalent linkages
D. composed of a single peptide chain

7. Members of which class of biomolecules is the building block of proteins?

A. fatty acids
B. amino acids
C. glycerols
D. monosaccharides

8. All the bonds stated are apparent in the secondary and tertiary structure of a protein, EXCEPT:

A. electrostatic interactions
B. peptide bonds
C. hydrogen bonding
D. hydrophobic interactions

9. Proteins are polymers. They consist of monomer units which are:

A. keto acids
B. amide
C. amino acids
D. ketones

10. Why might a change in pH cause a protein to denature?

A. The hydrogen bonds between the hydrophobic portions of the protein collapse due to extra protons
B. The disulfide bridges open
C. The functional groups that give the protein its shape becomes protonated or deprotonated
D. The water hardens and causes the protein's shape to change

11. Hydrophobic interactions help stabilize the [ ] structure(s) of a protein.

A. primary
B. secondary
C. secondary and tertiary
D. tertiary and quaternary

12. Collagen is an example of a (an):

A. storage protein
B. transport protein
C. enzyme
D. structural protein

13. The coiling of a chain of amino acids describes protein:

A. primary structure
B. secondary structure
C. tertiary structure
D. quaternary structure

14. The laboratory conditions typically used to hydrolyze a protein are:

A. dilute acid and room temperature
B. dilute base and room temperature
C. concentrated acid and heat
D. concentrated base and heat

15. Which is an essential amino acid?

A. aniline
B. valine
C. glycine
D. serine

16. What is the localized bending and folding of a polypeptide backbone?

A. primary structure
B. secondary structure
C. tertiary structure
D. quaternary structure

17. Which macromolecule is composed of polypeptides?

A. amino acids
B. proteins
C. carbohydrates
D. fats

18. What is the purpose of the plasma membrane?

A. Storing of the genetic material of the cell
B. Retaining water in the cell to prevent it from dehydrating
C. Acting as a cell wall to give the cell structure and support
D. Acting as a boundary, but also letting molecules in and out

19. These fatty acids contain sixteen to eighteen carbons and range from saturated to three double bonds. Which has the lowest melting point?

A. palmitic acid (saturated)
B. oleic acid (one double bond)
C. linoleic acid (two double bonds)
D. linolenic acid (three double bonds)

20. Which statements correctly describe the relationship between fatty acid structure and its melting point?

I. Saturated fatty acids melting points increase gradually with the molecular weights
II. As the number of double bonds in a fatty acid increase, its melting point decreases
III. The presence of a *trans* double bond in the fatty acid has a greater effect on its melting point than does the presence of a *cis* double bond

A. I only
B. II only
C. III only
D. I and II only

21. The hydrocarbon end of a soap molecule is:

A. hydrophilic and attracted to grease
B. hydrophobic and attracted to grease
C. hydrophilic and attracted to water
D. hydrophobic and attracted to water

22. It is important to have cholesterol in one's body because:

A. it breaks down extra fat lipids
B. it serves as the starting material for the biosynthesis of most other steroids
C. it is the starting material for the building of glycogen
D. the brain is made almost entirely of cholesterol

23. Cholesterol belongs to the [ ] group of lipids.

A. prostaglandin
B. triacylglycerol
C. saccharides
D. steroid

24. In chemical terms, soaps are best described as:

A. simple esters of fatty acids
B. mixed esters of fatty acids
C. salts of carboxylic acids
D. long-chain acids

25. The function of cholesterol in a cell membrane is to:

A. function as a precursor to steroid hormones
B. take part in the reactions that produce bile acids
C. maintain structure due to its flat rigid characteristics
D. attract hydrophobic molecules to form solid deposits

26. Which fatty acid is a saturated fatty acid?

A. oleic acid
B. linoleic acid
C. arachidonic acid
D. myristic acid

27. Commercially, liquid vegetable oils are converted to solid fats such as margarine by:

A. oxidation
B. hydration
C. hydrolysis
D. hydrogenation

28. The biochemical roles of lipids are:

A. short-term energy storage, transport of molecules, and structural support
B. storage of excess energy, component of cell membranes, and chemical messengers
C. catalysis, protection against outside invaders, motion
D. component of cell membranes, catalysis, and structural support

29. Which molecule is an omega-3 fatty acid?

A. oleic acid
B. linolenic acid
C. linoleic acid
D. palmitic acid

30. Which of the following is a lipid?

A. lactose
B. aniline
C. nicotine
D. estradiol

31. Which term best describes the interior of a soap micelle in water?

A. hard
B. saponified
C. hydrophobic
D. hydrophilic

32. Lipids are compounds soluble in:

A. glucose solution
B. organic solvents
C. distilled water
D. normal saline solution

33. Which statement regarding fatty acids is NOT correct? Fatty acids:

A. are always liquids
B. are long-chain carboxylic acids
C. are usually unbranched chains
D. usually have an even number of carbon atoms

34. Unsaturated triacylglycerols are usually [ ] because [ ]?

A. liquids … they have relatively short fatty acid chains
B. liquids … the kinks in their fatty acid chains prevent their fitting closely
C. liquids … they contain impurities from their natural sources
D. solids … they have relatively long fatty acid chains

35. Triacylglycerols are compounds with:

A. cholesterol and other steroids
B. fatty acids and phospholipids
C. fatty acids and glycerol
D. fatty acids and choline

36. Oils are generally [ ] at room temperature and obtained from [ ]:

A. liquids … plants
B. liquids … animals
C. solids … plants
D. solids … animals

37. Lipids are naturally occurring compounds that all:

A. contain fatty acids as structural units
B. are water-insoluble but soluble in nonpolar solvents
C. contain ester groups
D. contain cholesterol

38. Hydrogenation of vegetable oils converts them into which molecule?

A. esters
B. ethers
C. hemiacetals
D. saturated fats

39. Saturated fats are [ ] at room temperature and are obtained from [ ]?

A. liquids; plants
B. liquids; animals
C. solids; plants
D. solids; animals

40. Which is NOT in a lipid wax?

A. saturated fatty acid
B. long-chain alcohol
C. glycerol
D. ester linkage

41. How many fatty acid molecules are needed to produce one fat or oil molecule?

A. 1
B. 1.5
C. 2
D. 3

42. When dietary triglycerides are hydrolyzed, the products are:

A. glycerol and fatty acids
B. carbohydrates
C. amino acids
D. alcohols and lipids

43. How many fatty acids are in a phospholipid molecule?

A. 0
B. 1
C. 2
D. 3

44. Which is NOT a function of lipids?

A. cushioning to prevent injury
B. insulation
C. energy reserve
D. precursor for glucose catabolism

45. Which lipid is an example of a simple lipid?

A. oil
B. wax
C. fat
D. terpene

46. Which statement describes most monosaccharides?

A. They are unsaturated compounds
B. They are rarely monomers in nature
C. They are composed of carbon, hydrogen, and oxygen, with each carbon bound to at least one oxygen
D. They are insoluble

47. The three elements in all carbohydrates are [ ], [ ] and [ ]:

A. nitrogen, oxygen, hydrogen
B. carbon, hydrogen, oxygen
C. carbon, hydrogen, water
D. nitrogen, oxygen, carbon

48. Fructose does not break apart into smaller units because it is a(n):

A. monosaccharide
B. polysaccharide
C. hexose
D. aldose

49. Which molecule is a disaccharide?

A. lactose
B. cellulose
C. amylose
D. glucose

50. What is the primary biological function of the glycogen biomolecule?

A. It is used to synthesize disaccharides
B. It is the building block of proteins
C. It stores glucose in animal cells
D. It is a storage form of sucrose

51. A carbohydrate that gives two molecules when it is completely hydrolyzed is a:

A. polysaccharide
B. starch
C. monosaccharide
D. disaccharide

52. Which group of carbohydrates can NOT be hydrolyzed to give smaller molecules?

A. oligosaccharides
B. trisaccharides
C. disaccharides
D. monosaccharides

53. A carbohydrate can be defined as a molecule with:

A. carbon atoms bonded to water molecules
B. amine and carboxylic acid groups bonded to a carbon skeleton
C. mainly hydrocarbons and soluble in non-polar solvents
D. tan aldehyde or ketone with more than one hydroxyl group

54. Disaccharides are best characterized as:

A. two monosaccharides linked by a nitrogen bond
B. two peptides linked by a hydrogen bond
C. two monosaccharides linked by an oxygen bond
D. two amino acids linked by a peptide bond

55. Which molecule has the highest lipid density?

A. very-low-density lipoprotein (VLDL)
B. low-density lipoprotein (LDL)
C. high-density lipoprotein (HDL)
D. chylomicron

56. Which choice is the correct statement about lipids?

A. They are composed of elements C, O, N & H
B. Their secondary structure is composed of α helices and β pleated sheets
C. They are molecules used for long-term energy storage in animals
D. Elements of C:H:O are in the ratio of 1:2:1

57. Which nutrients yield four calories per gram?

A. glucose and proteins
B. fats and glucose
C. proteins and lipids
D. lipids and sugars

58. Which is NOT an end product of digestion?

A. amino acids
B. lactose
C. fructose
D. fatty acids

59. During digestion, fats are catabolized when fatty acids are detached from glycerol, while proteins are digested into amino acids. What do these two processes have in common?

A. Both involve the addition of H_2O to break bonds (hydrolysis)
B. Both occur as intracellular processes in most organisms
C. Both are catalyzed by the same enzyme
D. Both require the presence of hydrochloric acid to lower the pH

60. The two strands of DNA in the double helix are held by:

A. dipole–dipole attractions
B. metallic bonds
C. ionic bonds
D. covalent bonds

61. What happens to DNA when placed into an aqueous solution at physiological pH?

A. Individual DNA molecules repel each other due to the presence of positive charges
B. DNA molecules bind to negatively charged proteins
C. Individual DNA molecules attract each other due to the presence of positive and negative charges
D. Individual DNA molecules repel each other due to the presence of negative charges

62. What is the term for how a DNA molecule synthesizes a complementary single strand of RNA?

A. translation
B. transcription
C. replication
D. duplication

63. Consider compounds:

I. amino acid
II. nitrogen-containing base
III. phosphate group
IV. five-carbon sugar

From which of the compounds are the monomers (i.e., nucleotides) of nucleic acids formed?

A. I only
B. I and II only
C. II and IV only
D. II, III and IV only

64. The nucleotide sequence, T–A–G, stands for

A. threonine-alanine-glutamine
B. thymine-adenine-guanine
C. tyrosine-asparagine-glutamic acid
D. thymine-adenine-glutamine

65. The two new DNA molecules formed in replication:

A. contain one parent and one daughter strand
B. contain only the parent DNA strands
C. contain only two new daughter DNA strands
D. are complementary to the original DNA

66. Which is in an RNA nucleotide?

I. phosphoric acid
II. nitrogenous base
III. ribose sugar

A. I only
B. II only
C. I and II only
D. I, II and III

67. If one strand of a DNA double helix has the sequence AGTACTG, what is the sequence of the other strand?

A. GACGTCA
B. AGTACTG
C. GTCATGA
D. TCATGAC

68. The leading role of DNA is to provide instructions on how to build:

I. lipids
II. carbohydrates
III. proteins

A. I only
B. II only
C. III only
D. I and II only

69. Nucleic acids are polymers of [ ] monomers.

A. monosaccharide
B. fatty acid
C. DNA
D. nucleotide

70. During DNA transcription, a guanine base on the template strand codes for which base on the growing RNA strand?

A. guanine
B. thymine
C. adenine
D. cytosine

71. What intermolecular force connects strands of DNA in the double helix?

A. hydrogen bonds
B. ionic bonds
C. amide bonds
D. ester bonds

72. How are codons and anticodons related?

A. Codons are the base pairs on a tRNA that bind to complementary strands of DNA and produce proteins
B. Anticodons are the codons on the mRNA used to bind to DNA
C. Codons start the process of transcription; anticodons end the process
D. Codons and anticodons are complementary base pairs that encode an amino acid

73. Which biological compound is a polymer of sugar, a base, and phosphoric acid?

A. nucleic acid
B. lipid
C. carbohydrate
D. protein

74. What is the term for a DNA molecule synthesizing an identical DNA molecule?

A. transcription
B. translation
C. duplication
D. replication

75. The bonds that link the base pairs in the DNA double helix are [ ] bonds?

A. hydrophobic
B. hydrogen
C. peptide
D. ionic

76. Translation is the process whereby:

A. protein is synthesized from DNA
B. protein is synthesized from mRNA
C. DNA is synthesized from DNA
D. DNA is synthesized from mRNA

77. What is the primary structural difference between the sugar of RNA compared to the sugar of DNA?

A. It stabilizes the RNA outside the nucleus
B. It acts as an energy source to produce proteins
C. It allows the RNA to be easily digested by enzymes
D. It keeps the RNA from binding tightly to DNA

78. The double helix of DNA is stabilized mainly by:

A. hydrogen bonds
B. covalent bonds
C. ion–dipole bonds
D. ester bonds

79. Which is the correct listing of DNA's constituents in the order of increasing size?

A. Nucleotide, codon, gene, nucleic acid
B. Nucleic acid, nucleotide, codon, gene
C. Nucleotide, codon, nucleic acid, gene
D. Gene, nucleic acid, nucleotide, codon

80. The number of adenines in a DNA molecule equals the number of thymines because:

A. adenines are paired opposite of guanine in a DNA molecule
B. of the strong attraction between the nucleotides of adenine and thymine
C. the structure of adenine is similar to uracil
D. adenine is paired to cytosine in a DNA molecule

81. What is the sugar component in RNA?

A. fructose
B. galactose
C. glucose
D. ribose

82. What is the process when the DNA double helix unfolds, and each strand serves as a template for synthesizing a new strand?

A. translation
B. replication
C. transcription
D. complementation

83. Which illustrates the direction of flow for protein synthesis?

A. RNA → protein → DNA
B. DNA → protein → RNA
C. RNA → DNA → protein
D. DNA → RNA → protein

84. The three-base sequence in mRNA specifying the amino acid is:

A. rRNA
B. an anticodon
C. a codon
D. tRNA

85. Which is an RNA codon for protein synthesis?

I. GUA II. CGU III. ACG

A. I only
B. II only
C. I and II only
D. I, II and III

86. During DNA replication, an adenine base on the template strand codes for which base on the complementary strand?

A. thymine
B. guanine
C. cytosine
D. adenine

87. Which is NOT part of a nucleotide?

A. cyclic nitrogenous base
B. fatty acid
C. phosphate group
D. cyclic sugar

88. Which linkage is in a nucleic acid?

A. phosphate linkage
B. ester linkage
C. glycoside linkage
D. peptide linkage

89. Which codes for an amino acid during protein synthesis?

A. RNA nucleotide
B. RNA trinucleotide
C. DNA nucleotide
D. DNA trinucleotide

90. How does RNA differ from DNA?

A. RNA is double-stranded, while DNA is single-stranded
B. RNA is a polymer of amino acids, while DNA is a polymer of nucleotides
C. RNA contains uracil, while DNA contains thymine
D. In RNA, G pairs with T, while in DNA, G pairs with C

91. The one cyclic amine base that occurs in DNA but not in RNA is:

A. cystine
B. guanine
C. thymine
D. uracil

92. In the synthesis of mRNA, an adenine in the DNA pairs with:

A. guanine
B. thymine
C. uracil
D. adenine

93. Nucleic acids determine the:

A. quantity and type of prions
B. number of mitochondria in a cell
C. sequence of amino acids
D. pH of the cell nucleus

94. DNA is a(n):

A. peptide
B. protein
C. nucleic acid
D. enzyme

95. Which amine base is NOT in DNA?

A. adenine
B. cytosine
C. guanine
D. uracil

96. In transcription:

A. the mRNA contains the genetic information from DNA
B. uracil pairs with thymine
C. a double helix containing one parent strand and one daughter strand is produced
D. the mRNA produced is identical to the parent DNA

97. The two strands of the double helix of DNA are held by:

A. disulfide bridges
B. ionic bonds
C. hydrogen bonds
D. covalent bonds

Notes for active learning

Eukaryotic Cell: Structure and Function

1. Facilitated transport is differentiated from active transport because:

A. active transport requires a symport
B. facilitated transport displays saturation kinetics
C. active transport displays sigmoidal kinetics
D. active transport requires an energy source

2. The cell is the basic unit of function and reproduction because:

A. subcellular components cannot regenerate whole cells
B. cells can move in space
C. single cells can sometimes produce an entire organism
D. cells can transform energy to do work

3. Which can NOT readily diffuse through the plasma membrane without a transport protein?

I. water
II. small hydrophobic molecules
III. small ions
IV. neutral gas molecules

A. I only
B. I and II only
C. I and III only
D. III and IV only

4. During a hydropathy analysis of a recently sequenced protein, a researcher discovers that the protein has several regions containing 20-25 hydrophobic amino acids. What conclusion is drawn from this finding?

A. Protein would be specifically localized in the mitochondrial inner membrane
B. Protein would be targeted to the mitochondrion
C. Protein is likely to be an integral protein
D. Protein is probably involved in glycolysis

5. If a membrane-bound vesicle with hydrolytic enzymes is isolated, likely it is a:

A. vacuole
B. lysosome
C. chloroplast
D. phagosome

6. A DNA damage checkpoint arrests cells in:

A. M/G2 transition
B. S/G1 transition
C. G1/S transition
D. anaphase

7. If a segment of a double-stranded DNA has a low ratio of guanine-cytosine (G-C) pairs relative to adenine-thymine (A-T) pairs, it is reasonable to assume that this nucleotide segment:

A. requires less energy to separate the two DNA strands than a comparable segment with a high C-G ratio
B. requires more energy to separate the two DNA strands than a comparable segment with a high C-G ratio
C. contains more cytosine than guanine
D. contains more adenine than thymine

8. In general, phospholipids contain:

A. a glycerol molecule
B. saturated fatty acids
C. unsaturated fatty acids
D. a cholesterol molecule

9. The overall shape of a cell is determined by:

A. cell membrane
B. cytoskeleton
C. nucleus
D. cytosol

10. Which molecule generates the greatest osmotic pressure when placed into water?

A. 300 m*M* NaCl
B. 250 m*M* $CaCl_2$
C. 500 m*M* glucose
D. 600 m*M* urea

11. Which cellular substituent is produced within the nucleus?

A. Golgi apparatus
B. lysosome
C. ribosome
D. rough endoplasmic reticulum

12. In the initial stages of the cell cycle, progression from one phase to the next is controlled by:

A. p53 transcription factors
B. anaphase-promoting complexes
C. cyclin–CDK complexes
D. pre-replication complexes

13. Which is the correct sequence during polypeptide synthesis?

A. DNA generates tRNA → tRNA anticodon binds the mRNA codon in the cytoplasm → tRNA is carried by mRNA to the ribosomes, causing amino acids to join in a specific order
B. DNA generates mRNA → mRNA moves to the ribosome → tRNA anticodon binds the mRNA codon, causing amino acids to join in their appropriate order
C. Specific RNA codons cause amino acids to line up in a specific order → tRNA anticodon attaches to mRNA codon → rRNA codon causes a protein to cleave into specific amino acids
D. DNA regenerates mRNA in the nucleus → mRNA moves to the cytoplasm and attaches to the tRNA anticodon → operon regulates the sequence of amino acids in the appropriate order

14. Prokaryotes and eukaryotes contain:

I. a plasma membrane II. ribosomes III. peroxisomes

A. I only
B. II only
C. I and II only
D. II and III only

15. RNA is NOT expected to be in which structure?

A. nucleus
B. mitochondrion
C. vacuole
D. ribosome

16. Phosphotransferase is needed to form the mannose-6-phosphate tag that targets hydrolase enzymes to their lysosomal destination. Defective phosphotransferase causes I-cell disease, whereby the defective organelle which gives rise to this condition is the:

A. nucleus
B. cell membrane
C. Golgi apparatus
D. smooth ER

17. Mitochondria and chloroplasts are unusual organelles because they:

A. synthesize all their ATP using substrate-level phosphorylation
B. contain cytochrome C oxidase
C. are devoid of heme-containing proteins
D. contain nuclear-encoded and organelle-encoded proteins

18. All statements are true about cytoskeleton, EXCEPT that it:

A. is not required for mitosis
B. maintains the cell's shape
C. gives the cell mechanical support
D. is composed of microtubules and microfilaments

19. Inside the cell, critical events in the cell cycle include:

I. DNA damage repair and replication completion
II. centrosome duplication
III. assembly of the spindle and attachment of the kinetochores to the spindle

A. I and III only
B. I, II and III
C. I and II only
D. II and III only

20. A researcher labeled *Neurospora* mitochondria with a radioactive phosphatidylcholine membrane component and followed cell division by autoradiography in an unlabeled medium, allowing enough time for one cell division. What results did this scientist observe before concluding that pre-existing mitochondria give rise to new mitochondria?

A. Daughter mitochondria are labeled equally
B. Daughter mitochondria are all unlabeled
C. One-fourth of daughter mitochondria are labeled
D. Some daughter mitochondria are unlabeled, while some are labeled

21. Which involves the post-translational modification of proteins?

A. peroxisomes
B. vacuoles
C. Golgi complex
D. lysosomes

22. The width of a typical animal cell is closest to:

A. 1 millimeter
B. 20 micrometers
C. 1 micrometer
D. 10 nanometers

23. Which organelle is identified by the sedimentation coefficient – S units (Svedberg units)?

A. peroxisome
B. ribosome
C. mitochondrion
D. nucleolus

24. Which is NOT involved in osmosis?

A. H_2O spontaneously moves from a hypertonic to a hypotonic environment
B. H_2O spontaneously moves from an area of high solvent to low solvent concentration
C. H_2O spontaneously moves from a hypotonic to a hypertonic environment
D. Diffusion of H_2O

25. During cell division, cyclin B is marked for destruction by:

A. p53 transcription factor
B. anaphase-promoting complex
C. CDK complex
D. pre-replication complex

26. When a female mouse with a defective mitochondrial protein required for fatty acid oxidation is crossed with a wild-type male, all progeny (male and female) are wild-type. Which statement is correct?

A. Mice do not exhibit maternal inheritance
B. The defect is a result of a nuclear gene mutation
C. The defect is a result of an X-linked recessive trait
D. The defect is a result of a recessive mitochondrial gene

27. The smooth ER is involved in:

A. substrate-level phosphorylation
B. exocytosis
C. synthesis of phosphatidylcholine
D. allosteric activation of enzymes

28. Which organelle is in plants but not in animals?

A. ribosomes
B. mitochondria
C. nucleus
D. plastids

29. Mitochondrial mutations are often limited to one tissue type. If an individual does not produce blood calcium-decreasing hormone calcitonin, which tissue is likely to carry the mitochondrial mutation?

A. thyroid
B. kidney
C. parathyroid
D. liver

30. The rough ER is involved in:

A. oxidative phosphorylation
B. synthesis of plasma membrane proteins
C. endocytosis
D. post-translational modification of enzymes

31. The best definition of active transport is the movement of:

A. solutes across a semipermeable membrane down an electrochemical gradient
B. solutes across a semipermeable membrane up against a concentration gradient
C. substances across a membrane by the Donnan equilibrium
D. solutes via osmosis across a semipermeable membrane from high to low concentration

32. Overexpression of cyclin D:

A. increases contact inhibition
B. decreases telomerase activity
C. activates apoptosis
D. promotes unscheduled entry into S phase

33. A failure in which the spermatogenesis stage produces nondisjunction resulting in a male XXY karyotype?

A. prophase I
B. metaphase
C. anaphase I
D. telophase

34. Protein targeting occurs during the synthesis of which proteins?

A. nuclear proteins
B. secreted proteins
C. cytosolic proteins
D. mitochondrial proteins

35. The difference between "free" and "attached" ribosomes is that:

I. Free ribosomes are in the cytoplasm, while attached ribosomes anchor to the endoplasmic reticulum
II. Free ribosomes produce proteins in the cytosol, while attached ribosomes produce proteins inserted into the ER lumen
III. Free ribosomes produce proteins exported from the cell, while attached ribosomes make proteins for mitochondria and chloroplasts

A. I only
B. II only
C. I and II only
D. I, II and III

36. The concentration of growth hormone receptors reduces after selective destruction of which structure?

A. nucleolus
B. nucleus
C. cytosol
D. plasma membrane

37. These processes are ATP-dependent, EXCEPT:

A. export of Na^+ from a neuron
B. influx of Ca^{2+} into a muscle cell
C. movement of urea across a cell membrane
D. exocytosis of the neurotransmitter at a nerve terminus

38. The loss of function of p53 protein results in:

A. blockage in the activation of the anaphase-promoting complex
B. increase of contact inhibition
C. elimination of the DNA damage checkpoint
D. activation of apoptosis

39. Which organelle is most closely associated with exocytosis of newly synthesized secretory protein?

A. peroxisome
B. ribosome
C. lysosome
D. Golgi apparatus

40. Plant membranes are more fluid than animal membranes because plant membranes:

A. contain substantial amounts of cholesterol
B. have higher amounts of unsaturated fatty acids in the membranes of animals
C. have lower amounts of unsaturated fatty acids in the membranes of animals
D. are only in the inner membrane of the mitochondria

41. Which organelles are enclosed in a double membrane?

I. nucleus II. chloroplast III. mitochondrion

A. I and II only
B. II and III only
C. I and III only
D. I, II and III

42. Proteins are marked and delivered to specific cell locations through:

A. specific protein transport channels
B. regulation signals released by the cell's cytoskeleton
C. post-translational modifications occurring in the Golgi
D. compartmentalization of the rough ER during protein synthesis

43. The presence of which element differentiates a protein from a carbohydrate molecule?

A. carbon
B. hydrogen
C. nitrogen
D. oxygen

44. What change occurs in the capillaries when arterial blood is infused with the plasma protein albumin?

A. Decreased movement of H_2O from the capillaries into the interstitial fluid
B. Increased movement of H_2O from the capillaries into the interstitial fluid
C. Decreased permeability to albumin
D. Increased permeability to albumin

45. The retinoblastoma protein controls:

A. contact inhibition
B. transition from G1 to S phase
C. activation of apoptosis
D. expression of cyclin D

46. All processes take place in the mitochondrion, EXCEPT:

A. oxidation of pyruvate
B. Krebs cycle
C. electron transport chain
D. glycolysis

47. Which is the most abundant lipid in the body?

A. teichoic acid
B. peptidoglycan
C. glycogen
D. triglycerides

48. What is the secretory sequence in the flow of newly synthesized protein for export from the cell?

A. Golgi → rough ER → smooth ER → plasma membrane
B. Golgi → rough ER → plasma membrane
C. smooth ER → rough ER → Golgi → plasma membrane
D. rough ER → Golgi → plasma membrane

49. Digestive lysosomal hydrolysis would affect all the following, EXCEPT:

A. proteins
B. minerals
C. nucleotides
D. lipids

50. Recycling of organelles within the cell is accomplished through autophagy by:

A. mitochondria
B. peroxisomes
C. nucleolus
D. lysosomes

51. All the following are lipid derivatives, EXCEPT:

A. carotenoids
B. albumins
C. waxes
D. steroids

52. Defective attachment of a chromosome to the spindle:

A. blocks activation of the anaphase-promoting complex
B. activates exit from mitosis
C. prevents overexpression of cyclin D
D. activates sister chromatid separation

53. Which stage is when human cells with a single unreplicated copy of the genome form?

A. mitosis
B. meiosis II
C. meiosis I
D. interphase

54. Which organelle in the cell is the site of fatty acid, phospholipid, and steroid synthesis?

A. endosome
B. peroxisome
C. rough endoplasmic reticulum
D. smooth endoplasmic reticulum

55. Which eukaryotic organelle is NOT membrane-bound?

A. nucleus
B. plastid
C. centriole
D. chloroplast

56. During which mitotic division do spindle fibers split the centromere and separate the sister chromatids?

A. anaphase
B. telophase
C. prophase
D. metaphase

57. All the following are correct about cyclic AMP (cAMP), EXCEPT:

A. the enzyme that catalyzes the formation of cAMP is in the cytoplasm
B. membrane receptors can activate the enzyme that forms cAMP
C. ATP is the precursor molecule in the formation of cAMP
D. adenylate cyclase is the enzyme that catalyzes the formation of cAMP

58. Which molecule, and its associated protein kinase, ensures a proper progression of cell division?

A. oncogene
B. tumor suppressor
C. cyclin
D. histone

59. Placed in a hypertonic solution, erythrocytes will undergo:

A. crenation
B. expansion
C. plasmolysis and rupture
D. no change

60. Tiny organelles abundant in the liver containing oxidases and detoxify substances (e.g., alcohol and hydrogen peroxide) are:

A. peroxisomes
B. lysosomes
C. endosomes
D. rough endoplasmic reticulum

61. Microtubules can function independently or form protein complexes to produce structures like:

I. flagella
II. actin and myosin filaments in muscle cells
III. mitotic spindle apparatus

A. I, II, and III
B. I and III only
C. II and III only
D. I and II only

62. About a cell that secretes much protein (e.g., a pancreatic exocrine cell), it can be assumed that this cell has:

I. an abundance of rough endoplasmic reticulum
II. a large Golgi apparatus
III. a prominent nucleolus

A. I only
B. I and III only
C. II and III only
D. I, II and III

63. A cell division when each daughter cell receives a chromosome complement identical to that of a parent is:

A. mitosis
B. non-disjunction
C. meiosis
D. replication

64. Which would be affected the LEAST by colchicine, which interferes with microtubule formation?

A. organelle movement
B. pseudopodia for amoeboid motility
C. mitosis
D. cilia

65. Which process is NOT an example of apoptosis?

A. Reabsorption of a tadpole's tail during metamorphosis into a frog
B. Formation of the endometrial lining of the uterus during the menstrual cycle
C. Formation of the synaptic cleft by triggering cell death in brain neuronal cells
D. Formation of fingers in the fetus by the removal of tissue between the digits

66. Cells that utilize large quantities of ATP for active transport (e.g., epithelial cells of the intestine) have:

A. many mitochondria
B. high levels of DNA synthesis
C. high levels of adenylate cyclase
D. polyribosomes

67. Clathrin is a protein collected on the cytoplasmic side of cell membranes and functions in the coordinated pinching off membrane into receptor-mediated endocytosis. It is predicted that a lipid-soluble toxin that inactivates clathrin results in:

A. increased ATP consumption
B. increased protein production on the rough endoplasmic reticulum
C. increased secretion of hormone into the extracellular fluid
D. reduced delivery of polypeptide hormones to endosomes

68. Cells respond to peptide hormones through membrane receptors and kinase activation biochemical reactions. For cells to respond, the first and second messengers communicate because:

A. peptide hormones pass through the cell membrane and elicit a response
B. the hormone-receptor complex moves into the cytoplasm as a unit
C. hormones alter cellular activities directly through gene expression
D. the G protein acts as a link between the first and second messengers

Notes for active learning

Microbiology

1. What is the *major* distinction between prokaryotic and eukaryotic cells?

   A. prokaryotic cells do not have DNA, and eukaryotic cells do
   B. prokaryotic cells do not have a nucleolus, but eukaryotic cells do
   C. eukaryotic cells are smaller than prokaryotic cells
   D. prokaryotic cells have not prospered, while eukaryotic cells are evolutionarily advanced

2. Which statement describes the actions of penicillin?

   A. it is a reversible competitive inhibitor
   B. it is an irreversible competitive inhibitor
   C. it activates transpeptidase that digests the bacterial cell wall
   D. it is an effective antiviral agent

3. Which statement applies to all viruses?

   A. They have RNA genome
   B. They have DNA genome
   C. They have chromosomes
   D. They cannot replicate outside of the host cell

4. The replica plating technique of Joshua and Esther Lederberg demonstrated that:

   A. mutations are usually beneficial
   B. mutations are usually deleterious
   C. streptomycin caused the formation of streptomycin-resistant bacteria
   D. streptomycin revealed the presence of streptomycin-resistant bacteria

5. Operons:

   A. are a common feature of the eukaryote genome
   B. often coordinate the production of enzymes that function in a single pathway
   C. have multiple translation start and stop sites used by the ribosome
   D. usually undergo alternative splicing

6. Which is TRUE for the life cycle of sexually-reproducing *Neurospora* fungus?

   A. Only mitosis occurs
   B. Fertilization and meiosis are separated
   C. Meiosis quickly follows fertilization
   D. Fertilization immediately follows meiosis

7. Which is in prokaryotic cells?

A. mitochondria
B. chloroplasts
C. nuclei
D. enzymes

8. Which organelle is the site of protein modification and carbohydrate synthesis?

A. Golgi apparatus
B. lysosomes
C. peroxisomes
D. smooth ER

9. What is likely if a suspension of Hfr cells is mixed with an excess of F^- cells?

A. Most F^- cells are transformed into F^+ cells
B. The F^- cells produce sex pili that attach to the Hfr cells
C. Hfr chromosomal DNA is transferred to F^- cells by conjugation
D. Hfr cells replicate the F factor independently of their chromosomes

10. What carcinogen and mutagen test looks for an increased reversion frequency in a His^- bacteria strain?

A. *Salmonella* reversion test
B. Ames test
C. mutagen test
D. amber test

11. The type of bacteria NOT able to grow on minimal media due to mutations affecting metabolism:

A. auxotrophs
B. chemotrophs
C. heterotrophs
D. prototrophs

12. Which statement is TRUE?

A. Endospores are for reproduction
B. Endospores allow a cell to survive environmental changes
C. Endospores are easily stained with Gram stain
D. Cell produces one endospore and keeps growing

13. Most fungi spend the biggest portion of their life cycle as:

A. haploid
B. haploid and diploid
C. diploid
D. polyploid

14. An aerobic bacteria culture that has been exposed to cyanide gas is infected by bacteriophages. However, the replication of viruses does not occur. What is cyanide's mechanism of action?

A. Binding to viral nucleic acid
B. Denaturing bacteriophage enzymes
C. Inhibiting aerobic ATP production
D. Destroying bacteriophage binding sites on the bacterial cell wall

15. Recipient cells acquire genes from free DNA molecules in the surrounding medium by:

A. transformation
B. conjugation
C. transduction
D. recombination

16. Viruses can have a genome that is:

A. single-stranded DNA
B. single-stranded RNA
C. double-stranded RNA
D. all the above

17. Which assumption must be true to map the order of bacterial genes on the chromosome in a Hfr strain?

A. Bacterial genes are polycistronic
B. A given Hfr strain always transfers its genes in the same order
C. The rate of chromosome transfer varies between bacteria of the same strain
D. Different mechanisms replicate the inserted F factor and bacterial genes

18. Which statement about prokaryotic cells is generally FALSE?

A. They have a semirigid cell wall
B. They are motile using flagella
C. They possess 80S ribosomes
D. They reproduce by binary fission

19. All the following events play a role in the life cycle of a typical retrovirus, EXCEPT:

A. injection of viral DNA into the host cell
B. integration of viral DNA into the host genome
C. reverse transcriptase gene is transcribed, and mRNA is translated inside the host cell
D. viral DNA incorporated into the host genome may be replicated along with the host DNA

20. All the following are true for viruses, EXCEPT:

A. Genetic material may be single-stranded or double-stranded RNA
B. The virus may replicate in a bacterial or eukaryotic host
C. The virus may replicate without a host
D. The protein coat of the virus does not enter a host bacterial cell

21. DNA transfer from a bacterial donor cell to a recipient cell by cell-to-cell contact is:

A. conjugation
B. transformation
C. transduction
D. recombination

22. On the overnight agar plates with *E. coli*, replication of a virus is marked by:

A. no visible change
B. bacterial colonies on the agar surface
C. growth of a smooth layer of bacteria across the plate
D. growth of bacteria across the plate except for small clear patches

23. Which of the following about gram-negative cell walls is FALSE?

A. They protect the cell in a hypotonic environment
B. They have an extra outer layer of lipoproteins, lipopolysaccharides, and phospholipids
C. They are toxic to humans
D. They are sensitive to penicillin

24. All the following may be in a mature virus found outside the host cell, EXCEPT:

A. core proteins
B. RNA and DNA
C. protein capsid
D. phospholipid bilayer envelope

25. All the following are correct about *lac* operon, EXCEPT:

A. The repressor protein binds to the operator, halting gene expression
B. The promoter is the binding site of RNA polymerase
C. *Lac* operon is in eukaryotes
D. Three structural genes encode functional proteins

26. Phage DNA integrated into the chromosome is:

A. lytic phage
B. specialized transducing phage
C. lysogenic phage
D. prophage

27. Many RNA copies of the retrovirus RNA genome are synthesized by:

A. host cell DNA polymerases
B. reverse transcriptase
C. host cell RNA polymerases
D. host cell ribosomes

28. In the laboratory, *E. coli* are grown at a temperature of 37 °C because:

A. *E. coli* strain is a 37 °C temperature-sensitive mutant
B. *E. coli* reproduce most rapidly at this temperature
C. lower temperatures inhibit conjugation
D. *E. coli* are obligate aerobes

29. Some bacteria can propel themselves through the liquid using:

A. flagellum
B. centriole
C. centrosome
D. peptidoglycan

30. When most viruses infect eukaryotic cells:

A. their capsid does not enter the host cell
B. they replicate independently of the host cell during a lysogenic infection
C. they can enter the cell via endocytosis
D. they do not need to have host-specific proteins to infect the target cell

31. Which organelle(s) is/are NOT in bacteria?

I. peroxisomes
II. nucleolus
III. ribosomes
IV. flagellum

A. I only
B. II only
C. I and II only
D. I, II, and III

32. A bacterial cell carrying a prophage is:

A. lysogen
B. temperate
C. exconjugant
D. transformant

33. All the following are true of prokaryotic translation, EXCEPT:

A. mRNA is not spliced before initiation
B. N-terminal amino acid of nascent polypeptides is formylated
C. mRNA chain being translated may not be fully transcribed before translation begins
D. Hydrogen bonds between amino acids and mRNA codons are necessary for translation

34. Prokaryotes are about how many times smaller in diameter than a typical eukaryote?

A. two
B. ten
C. 100
D. 10,000

35. Which structures are in prokaryotes?

I. A cell wall containing peptidoglycan
II. A plasma membrane with cholesterol
III. Ribosomes

A. I only
B. II only
C. I and II only
D. I and III only

36. Which of the following is characteristic of viruses?

A. membrane-bound organelles
B. protein coat
C. peptidoglycan cell wall
D. phospholipid bilayer membrane

37. An F-plasmid that can integrate into the bacterial chromosome by homologous recombination is:

A. episome
B. virion
C. endoconjugate
D. lytic

38. The RNA genome of a retrovirus is converted to double-stranded DNA by:

A. host cell DNA polymerases
B. reverse transcriptase
C. host cell RNA polymerases
D. host cell ribosomes

39. Which statement is true about T4 infection of *E. coli*?

A. T4 mRNA is translated by bacterial ribosomes while being transcribed from DNA
B. One of the first genes expressed during viral infection is a lysozyme that facilitates cell lysis
C. The final stage for lytic cycles of infection is the viral assembly after the virus leaves the cell
D. T4 buds via endocytosis through the plasma membrane to leave the cell

40. Which statement about a gram-positive cell wall is FALSE?

A. It maintains the shape of cell
B. It is sensitive to lysozyme
C. It protects the cell in a hypertonic environment
D. It contains teichoic acids

41. Which statement is correct about the lipopolysaccharide layer outside the peptidoglycan cell wall of a Gram-negative bacterium?

A. It allows the bacterium to attach to solid objects
B. It does not contain a phospholipid membrane
C. It protects the bacterium against antibiotics
D. It absorbs and holds Gram stain

42. DNase added to a bacterial cell causes hydrolysis of the cell's DNA, preventing protein synthesis and cell death. Some viruses pretreated with DNase continue to produce new proteins following infection because:

A. viral genome contains multiple copies of their genes
B. viral genome is comprised of RNA
C. viral genome contains multiple reading frames
D. icosahedral protein coat of the virus denatures DNase

43. In a mating between Hfr and F^- cells, the F^- recipient:

A. becomes Hfr
B. becomes F′
C. remains F^-
D. becomes F^+

44. The unique feature of the methionine residue used for prokaryotic initiation of translation is that it is:

A. formylated
B. hydrophilic
C. methylated
D. acetylated

45. Which statement describes a bacterial cell in a 35% solution of a large polysaccharide (e.g., dextran)?

A. NaCl moves into the cell from a higher to a lower concentration
B. The cell undergoes plasmolysis
C. H_2O moves out of the cell
D. H_2O moves into the cell

46. If the Gram stain method stains a Gram-positive bacterium, it appears:

A. deep purple because of a thicker peptidoglycan cell wall
B. deep purple because of a thinner peptidoglycan cell wall
C. red or pink because of a thicker peptidoglycan cell wall
D. red or pink because of a thinner peptidoglycan cell wall

47. Which enzyme replicates the F factor in F^+ bacteria before conjugation?

A. DNA polymerase
B. reverse transcriptase
C. DNA ligase
D. integrase

48. In a mating between Hfr and F^- cells, the Hfr donor:

A. becomes F′
B. remains Hfr
C. becomes F^+
D. becomes F^-

49. Which statement(s) is/are TRUE regarding retrotransposons?

I. They are never between genes in the human genome
II. They comprise close to half of the human genome
III. They can cause mutations by inserting themselves into genes

A. I and II only
B. II and III only
C. I and III only
D. I, II and III

50. Which is TRUE about plasmids?

I. They are small organelles in the bacterial cytoplasm
II. They are transcribed and translated simultaneously
III. They are replicated by bacterial enzymes

A. I only
B. II and III only
C. I and III only
D. I, II, and III

51. Which has a cell wall?

A. protoplasts
B. fungi
C. L forms
D. viruses

52. Which statement about a prokaryotic cell is correct?

A. It contains a range of different organelles
B. It uses glycolysis to produce ATP
C. It contains cell walls composed of chitin
D. It has a nuclear membrane that encloses a nucleus

53. Which statement applies to a bacteriophage and retrovirus?

A. They are capable of infecting human cells
B. They act as immunosuppressive agents
C. They integrate their genetic material into the genome of the host cell
D. They have genes that encode for reverse transcriptase

54. Integration of the phage DNA into the bacterial chromosome is facilitated by:

A. DNA polymerase encoded in the host genome
B. topoisomerase encoded in the phage
C. site-specific recombinase encoded in the phage
D. site-specific recombinase encoded in the host genome

55. After digested by restriction enzymes, how is DNA ligated into a plasmid in two different directions?

A. Both ends of a DNA fragment produced by a restriction enzyme are identical if rotated 180°

B. The existing DNA strands serve as primers for DNA polymerase

C. DNA ligase enzymes can link any two pieces of DNA

D. Plasmid DNA is single-stranded, so the ligated strands form double-stranded segments

56. Virulent phage:

I. is capable only of lytic growth

II. can only undergo a process called lysogeny

III. needs different proteins for incorporation into the bacterial chromosome

A. I and II only

B. III only

C. II only

D. I only

57. Which statement best describes the promoter in an operon?

A. It activates the repressor-inducer complex to permit transcription

B. It is a molecule that inactivates the repressor and turns on the operon

C. It is the binding site for RNA polymerase

D. It is the binding site for the repressor

Notes for active learning

Cellular Metabolism and Enzymes

1. The atom generating a hydrogen bond to stabilize the α-helical configuration of a polypeptide is:

A. peptide bond atom
B. atom in the R-groups
C. hydrogen of the carbonyl oxygen
D. hydrogen of the amino nitrogen

2. The ATP molecule contains three phosphate groups, two of which are:

A. bound as phosphoanhydride
B. bound to adenosine
C. never hydrolyzed from the molecule
D. cleaved off during most biochemical reactions

3. Which attractive force by the side chains of nonpolar amino acids interacts with other nonpolar amino acids?

A. ionic bonds
B. hydrogen bonds
C. hydrophobic interaction
D. disulfide bonds

4. Fermentation yields less energy than aerobic respiration because:

A. it requires a greater expenditure of cellular energy
B. glucose molecules are not completely oxidized
C. it requires more time for ATP production
D. oxaloacetic acid serves as the final H^+ acceptor

5. How does the reaction kinetics of an enzyme and its substrate change if an anti-substrate antibody is added?

A. The antibody binds to the substrate, which increases the V_{max}
B. The antibody binds to the substrate, which increases K_m
C. No change because K_m and V_{max} are independent of antibody concentration
D. The antibody binds the substrate, which decreases V_{max}

6. Metabolism is:

A. consumption of energy
B. release of energy
C. all conversions of matter and energy taking place in an organism
D. production of heat by chemical reactions

7. During alcoholic fermentation, all the following occurs, EXCEPT:

A. release of CO_2
B. oxidation of glyceraldehyde-3-phosphate
C. oxygen is not consumed in the reaction
D. ATP synthesis because of oxidative phosphorylation

8. When determining a protein's amino acid sequence, acid hydrolysis causes partial degradation of tryptophan, conversion of asparagine into aspartic acid, and glutamine into glutamic acid. Which statement is NOT correct?

A. Glutamine concentration is related to the level of aspartic acid
B. Glutamic acid levels are an indirect indicator of glutamine concentration
C. Tryptophan levels cannot be estimated accurately
D. Asparagine levels cannot be estimated accurately

9. What is the correct sequence of energy sources used by the body?

A. fats → glucose → other carbohydrates → proteins
B. glucose → other carbohydrates → fats → proteins
C. glucose → other carbohydrates → proteins → fats
D. glucose → fats → proteins → other carbohydrates

10. Enzymes act by:

A. lowering the overall free energy change of the reaction
B. decreasing the distance reactants must diffuse to find each other
C. increasing the activation energy
D. decreasing the activation energy

11. For the following reaction, which statement is TRUE?

ATP + Glucose → Glucose-6-phosphate + ADP

A. reaction results in the formation of a phosphodiester bond
B. reaction is endergonic
C. reaction is part of the Krebs cycle
D. free energy change for the reaction is approx. –4 kcal

12. Which is the correct cAMP classification because cAMP-dependent protein phosphorylation activates hormone-sensitive lipase?

A. DNA polymerase
B. lipoproteins
C. glycosphingolipids
D. second messenger

13. Which statement is NOT true about the Krebs cycle?

A. Krebs cycle is the single greatest direct source of ATP in the cell
B. Citrate is an intermediate in the Krebs cycle
C. Krebs cycle produces nucleotides such as NADH and $FADH_2$
D. Krebs cycle is linked to glycolysis by pyruvate

14. The rate of V_{max} is related to:

I. Enzyme concentration
II. Substrate concentration
III. Concentration of a competitive inhibitor

A. I, II, and III
B. I and III only
C. I and II only
D. I only

15. A reaction in which the substrate glucose binds the enzyme hexokinase, and the conformation of both molecules changes, is an example of:

A. lock-and-key mechanism
B. induced-fit mechanism
C. competitive inhibition
D. allosteric inhibition

16. A researcher studies an enzyme that catalyzes a reaction with a free energy change of +5 kcal. If they double the amount of enzyme in a reaction mixture, what would be the free energy change for the reaction?

A. –10 kcal
B. –5 kcal
C. 0 kcal
D. +5 kcal

17. Glucokinase and hexokinase catalyze the first glycolysis reaction; glucokinase has a higher K_m. Which is a correct statement if K_m equals [Substrate] = $1/2V_{max}$?

A. hexokinase is always functional and is not regulated by negative feedback
B. hexokinase and glucokinase are not isozymes
C. glucokinase is not a zymogen
D. glucokinase becomes active from elevated levels of fructose

18. α-helices and β-pleated sheets are characteristic of which level of protein folding?

A. primary
B. secondary
C. tertiary
D. quaternary

19. Coenzymes are:

A. minerals such as Ca^{2+} and Mg^{2+}
B. small inorganic molecules that work with an enzyme to enhance the reaction rate
C. small organic molecules that work with an enzyme to enhance the reaction rate
D. small molecules that do not regulate enzymes

20. Hemoglobin is an example of a protein that:

A. is initially inactive in the cell
B. has a quaternary structure
C. carries out a catalytic reaction
D. has only a tertiary structure

21. The site of the TCA cycle in eukaryotic cells, as opposed to prokaryotes, is:

A. mitochondria
B. endoplasmic reticulum
C. cytosol
D. nucleolus

22. All the following are metabolic waste products, EXCEPT:

A. lactate
B. pyruvate
C. CO_2
D. H_2O

23. When measuring the reaction velocity as a function of substrate concentration, what is likely if the enzyme concentration changes?

A. V_{max} changes, while K_m remains constant
B. V_{max} remains constant, while V changes
C. V_{max} remains constant, while K_m changes
D. V_{max} remains constant, while V and K_m change

24. A holoenzyme is:

A. inactive enzyme without its cofactor
B. inactive enzyme without its coenzyme
C. active enzyme with its cofactor
D. active enzyme with its coenzyme

25. *Clostridium butyricum* is a heterotrophic anaerobe that grows on glucose and converts it to butyric acid as a product. If the free energy for this reaction is –50 kcal, the maximum number of ATP that this organism can synthesize from one molecule of glucose is approximately:

A. 5 ATP
B. 36 ATP
C. 7 ATP
D. 38 ATP

26. Which amino acid is directly affected by dithiothreitol (DTT), known to reduce and break disulfide bonds?

A. methionine
B. leucine
C. glutamine
D. cysteine

27. Which choice represents a correct pairing of aspects for cellular respiration?

A. Krebs cycle – cytoplasm
B. fatty acid degradation – lysosomes
C. electron transport chain – inner mitochondrial membrane
D. glycolysis – inner mitochondrial membrane

28. An apoenzyme is:

A. inactive enzyme without its cofactor
B. inactive enzyme without its inorganic cofactor
C. active enzyme with its cofactor
D. active enzyme with its coenzyme

29. Several forces stabilize the tertiary structure of proteins. Which participates in this stabilization?

A. glycosidic bonds
B. disulfide bonds
C. peptide bonds
D. anhydride bonds

30. In the non-oxidative branch of the pentose phosphate pathway, transketolase is a reaction catalyst enzyme, and its activity depends on a prosthetic group. Which bond is used by a prosthetic group to attach to its target?

A. van der Waals interactions
B. covalent bond
C. ionic bond
D. hydrogen bond

31. The process of $C_6H_{12}O_6 + O_2 \rightarrow CO_2 + H_2O$ is completed in:

A. plasma membrane
B. cytoplasm
C. mitochondria
D. nucleus

32. In a hyperthyroidism patient, the oxidative metabolism rate measured by basal metabolic rate (BMR) is:

A. indeterminable
B. below normal
C. above normal
D. normal

33. Cofactors are:

I. small inorganic molecules that work with an enzyme to enhance the reaction rate
II. small organic molecules that work with an enzyme to enhance the reaction rate
III. small molecules that regulate enzyme activity

A. I only
B. I and II only
C. II and III only
D. I, II and III

34. All proteins:

A. are post-translationally modified
B. have a primary structure
C. have catalytic activity
D. contain prosthetic groups

35. After being gently denatured with the denaturant removed, proteins can recover significant activity because recovery of the structure depends on?

A. 4° structure of the polypeptide
B. 3° structure of the polypeptide
C. 2° structure of the polypeptide
D. 1° structure of the polypeptide

36. All statements about glycolysis are true, EXCEPT:

A. end-product can be lactate, ethanol, CO_2, and pyruvate
B. $FADH_2$ is produced during glycolysis
C. one molecule of glucose is converted into two molecules of pyruvate
D. net total of two ATPs are produced

37. Vitamins are:

A. necessary components in the human diet
B. in plants but not in animals
C. absent in bacteria within the gastrointestinal tract
D. all water-soluble

38. Hemoglobin is a protein with a:

A. site where proteolysis occurs
B. phosphate group at its active site
C. bound zinc atom
D. prosthetic group

39. Which amino acid is nonoptically active without four distinct groups bonded to the α carbon?

A. glycine
B. aspartic acid
C. glutamate
D. cysteine

40. Which statement is TRUE for the glycolytic pathway?

A. glucose produces a net of two molecules of ATP and two molecules of NADH
B. glucose produces one molecule of pyruvate
C. O_2 is a reactant for glycolysis
D. glucose is partially reduced

41. Which metabolic process takes place in the mitochondria?

I. Krebs cycle II. glycolysis III. electron transport chain

A. II only
B. I and III only
C. II and III only
D. I, II and III

42. Which statement best describes the usual relationship of the inhibitor molecule to the allosteric enzyme in feedback inhibition of enzyme activity?

A. The inhibitor is the substrate of the enzyme
B. The inhibitor is the product of the enzyme-catalyzed reaction
C. The inhibitor is the final product of the metabolic pathway
D. The inhibitor is a metabolically unrelated signal molecule

43. *Clostridium butyricum* is an obligate anaerobe that grows on glucose and converts it to butyric acid. If the ΔG for this reaction is –50 kcal, the synthesis of ATP occurs through:

A. substrate-level phosphorylation
B. oxidative phosphorylation
C. neither substrate-level nor oxidative phosphorylation
D. both substrate-level and oxidative phosphorylation

44. While covalent bonds are the strongest bonds that form protein structure, which of the following are connected by a peptide bond?

A. ammonium group and ester group
B. two amino groups
C. the α carbons
D. amino group and carboxylate group

45. All statements apply to oxidative phosphorylation, EXCEPT:

A. it can occur under anaerobic conditions
B. it produces two ATPs for each $FADH_2$
C. it involves O_2 as the final electron acceptor
D. it takes place on the inner membrane of the mitochondrion

46. Like other catalysts, enzymes:

I. increase the rate of reactions without affecting ΔG
II. shift the chemical equilibrium from reactants to products
III. do not alter the chemical equilibrium between reactants and products

A. I only
B. I and II only
C. I and III only
D. III only

47. Enzyme activity can be regulated by:

I. zymogen proteolysis
II. changes in substrate concentration
III. post-translational modifications

A. I only
B. II and III only
C. I, II and III
D. I and II only

48. Which interactions stabilize parallel and non-parallel beta-pleated sheets?

A. hydrophobic interactions
B. hydrogen bonds
C. van der Waals interactions
D. covalent bonds

49. Glycogen is:

A. degraded by glycogenesis
B. synthesized by glycogenolysis
C. the storage polymer of glucose
D. in plants and animals

50. If $[S] = 2\ K_m$, what portion of active sites of the enzyme is filled by substrate?

A. 3/4
B. 2/3
C. 1/2
D. 1/3

51. In allosteric regulation, how is enzyme activity affected by binding a small regulatory molecule?

A. It is inhibited
B. It is stimulated
C. Can be stimulated or inhibited
D. Is neither stimulated nor inhibited

52. All biological reactions:

A. are exergonic
B. have an activation energy
C. are endergonic
D. occur without a catalyst

53. In eukaryotes, energy is trapped in a high-energy phosphate group during oxidative phosphorylation in:

A. nucleus
B. mitochondrial matrix
C. inner mitochondrial membrane
D. outer mitochondrial membrane

54. All statements about enzymes are true, EXCEPT:

A. They function optimally at a particular temperature
B. They function optimally at a particular pH
C. They may interact with non-protein molecules to achieve biological activity
D. Their activity is not affected by a genetic mutation

55. The Gibbs free-energy change (ΔG) of a reaction is determined by:

I. intrinsic properties of the reactants and products
II. concentrations of the reactants and products
III. the temperature of the reactants and products

A. I only
B. I and III only
C. II and III only
D. I, II and III

56. Allosteric enzymes:

I. are regulated by metabolites that bind at sites other than the active site
II. have a quaternary structure
III. show cooperative binding of substrate

A. I only
B. I and II only
C. II and III only
D. I, II and III

57. Which symptom is characteristic of a patient exposed to monoamine oxidase inhibitors, preventing the breakdown of catecholamines (i.e., epinephrine)?

A. decreased blood flow to skeletal muscles
B. excessive digestive activity
C. dilated pupils
D. decreased heart rate

58. The ΔG for hydrolysis of ATP to ADP and P*i* is:

A. greater than +7.3 kcal/mole
B. +7.3 kcal/mole
C. –7.3 kcal/mole
D. –0.5 kcal/mole

59. The active site of an enzyme is where:

I. prosthetic group is bound
II. proteolysis occurs for zymogens
III. non-competitive inhibitors bind

A. I only
B. II only
C. I and II only
D. II and III only

60. The hydrolysis of ATP → ADP + phosphate allows glucose-6-phosphate to be synthesized from glucose and phosphate because:

A. heat produced from ATP hydrolysis drives the glucose-6-phosphate synthesis
B. enzymatic coupling of these two reactions allows the energy of ATP hydrolysis to drive the synthesis of glucose-6-phosphate
C. energy of glucose phosphorylation drives ATP splitting
D. all the above

61. Which statement is TRUE?

A. Protein function can be altered by modification after synthesis
B. Covalent bonds stabilize the secondary structure of proteins
C. A protein with a single polypeptide subunit has a quaternary structure
D. Integral membrane proteins contain high amounts of acidic amino acids

62. What does alcoholic fermentation have in common with pyruvate oxidation under aerobic conditions?

A. no commonality
B. triose sugar is a product of each reaction
C. ethyl alcohol is a product of each reaction
D. CO_2 is a product of each reaction

63. Which statement is TRUE?

A. Disaccharides must contain fructose
B. Most polysaccharides contain ribose
C. Polysaccharides are energy-generating molecules
D. Glucose and fructose have different chemical properties even with the same molecular formula

Notes for active learning

Notes for active learning

Photosynthesis

1. What mechanism is used by C_4 plants to conserve water?

A. developing deep roots
B. performing the Calvin cycle during the day
C. developing water storages in their leaves and stems
D. closing the stomata during heat and dryness

2. What mechanism is used by CAM plants to conserve water?

A. performing the Calvin cycle during the day
B. developing water storages in their leaves and stems
C. including carbon dioxide into RuBP
D. opening their stomata during the night

3. Which of the choices is an autotroph?

A. beech tree
B. octopus
C. zooplankton
D. coral

4. Which is NOT a true statement about ATP?

A. ATP provides energy for the mechanical functions of cells
B. Used ATP is discarded by the cell as waste
C. ATP consists of ribose, adenine, and three phosphate groups
D. ADP is produced when ATP releases energy

5. Photosynthesis plays a role in the metabolism of a plant by:

A. breaking down sugars into H_2O and O_2
B. converting H_2O into CO_2
C. consuming CO_2 and synthesizing sugars
D. converting O_2 into cellulose

6. From the figure, all the following are parts of an ADP molecule, EXCEPT:

A. structure A
B. structure B
C. structure C
D. structure D

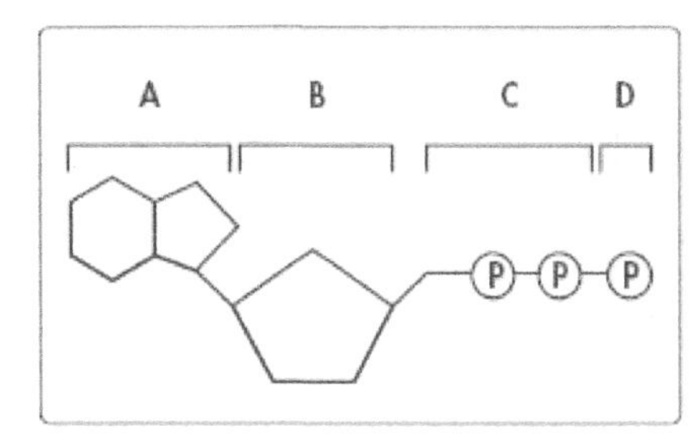

7. Within the inner membrane of a chloroplast, stacks of thylakoids are surrounded by:

A. stroma fluid
B. grana
C. chloroplast
D. thylakoids

8. What happens during photosynthesis?

A. Autotrophs consume carbohydrates
B. Autotrophs produce carbohydrates
C. Heterotrophs consume ATP
D. Heterotrophs produce ATP

9. The role of stomata is to facilitate:

A. gas exchange
B. H_2O release
C. Calvin cycle
D. H_2O uptake

10. Plants gather the sun's energy using:

A. glucose
B. chloroplasts
C. thylakoids
D. pigments

11. Which structure is used by plants to obtain most of their water?

A. Stomata
B. Flowers
C. Roots
D. Chloroplasts

12. Which structure in the image illustrates a single thylakoid?

A. Structure A
B. Structure B
C. Structure C
D. Structures A and B

13. Membranous structures in chloroplasts are:

A. organelles
B. thylakoids
C. stomata
D. plasma

14. Chlorophyll is within the chloroplast in:

A. thylakoid space
B. thylakoid membrane
C. stroma
D. ATP

15. Grana is/are:

A. stacks of membranous sacs
B. chloroplast pigments
C. fluid in the chloroplasts
D. the space between the inner and outer membrane of the chloroplasts

16. Which chemical shown in the figure is an electron carrier molecule?

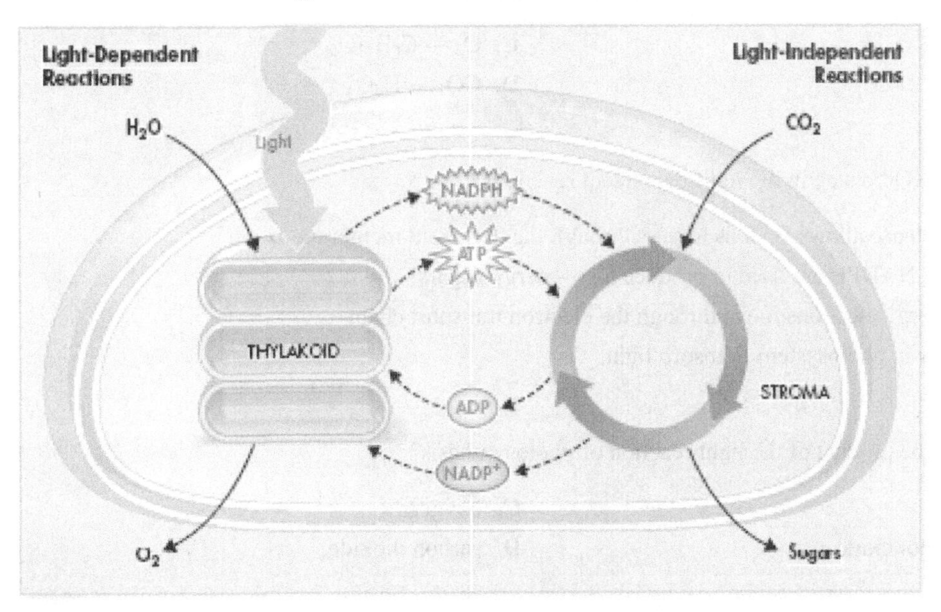

A. $NADP^+$
B. Oxygen
C. H_2O
D. CO_2

17. Which is likely to result if a shade-tolerant plant would receive a minimal amount of water while receiving its necessary amount of light?

A. Accelerated plant growth
B. Low ATP production
C. Increased output of oxygen
D. Increased consumption of carbon dioxide

18. Why are electron carriers needed for transporting electrons from one part of the chloroplast to another?

A. High-energy electrons get their energy from electron carriers
B. High-energy electrons are not soluble in the cytoplasm
C. High-energy electrons are highly reactive
D. High-energy electrons would be destroyed

19. Which equation describes the reaction of photosynthesis?

A. $6\ O_2 + 6\ CO_2 \rightarrow C_6H_{12}O_6 + 6\ H_2O$
B. $C_6H_{12}O_6 + 6\ H_2O \rightarrow 6\ CO_2 + 6\ O_2$
C. $C_6H_{12}O_6 \rightarrow 6\ CO_2 + 6\ H_2O + 6\ O_2$
D. $6\ H_2O + 6\ CO_2 \rightarrow C_6H_{12}O_6 + 6\ O_2$

20. What is the result of an increase in light intensity that a plant receives?

A. The rate of photosynthesis increases and then levels off
B. The rate of photosynthesis does not change
C. The rate of photosynthesis increases indefinitely with light intensity
D. The rate of photosynthesis decreases indefinitely with light intensity

21. In redox reactions of photosynthesis, electron transfer goes as follows:

A. $H_2O \rightarrow CO_2$
B. $C_6H_{12}O_6 \rightarrow O_2$
C. $O_2 \rightarrow C_6H_{12}O_6$
D. $CO_2 \rightarrow H_2O$

22. Which is NOT a step in the light-dependent reactions?

A. ATP synthase allows H^+ ions to pass through the thylakoid membrane
B. ATP and NADPH are used to produce high-energy sugars
C. High-energy electrons move through the electron transport chain
D. Pigments in photosystem II absorb light

23. Which is the product of the light reaction of photosynthesis?

A. sugar
B. carbon monoxide
C. oxygen
D. carbon dioxide

24. Photosystems I and II are in:

A. cell membrane
B. the Calvin cycle
C. thylakoid membrane
D. stroma

25. Which components from the light reactions are required by the C_3 cycle?

A. NADH and RuBP
B. NADPH and ATP
C. ATP and NADH
D. glucose and $NADP^+$

26. Which pathway is the correct flow of electrons during photosynthesis?

A. Photosystem I $\rightarrow$ Calvin cycle $\rightarrow$ $NADP^+$
B. $H_2O \rightarrow NADP^+ \rightarrow$ Calvin cycle
C. $H_2O \rightarrow$ Photosystem I $\rightarrow$ Photosystem II
D. $O_2 \rightarrow$ ADP $\rightarrow$ Calvin cycle

27. Light-dependent reactions of photosynthesis produce:

A. H_2O and RuBP
B. ATP and CO_2
C. NADH and ATP
D. NADPH and ATP

28. The Calvin cycle takes place in:

A. chlorophyll molecules
B. thylakoid membranes
C. photosystems
D. stroma

29. The wavelength of which a blue-colored plant reflects light?

A. violet
B. yellow
C. blue
D. lime

30. What are the three parts of an ATP molecule?

A. Adenine, ribose, and three phosphate groups
B. NADH, NADPH, and $FADH_2$
C. Adenine, thylakoid, and a phosphate group
D. Stroma, grana, and chlorophyll

31. When observing a pigmented object, visible color is:

A. wavelength emitted by the object
B. wavelength from the return of excited electrons to their ground state
C. wavelength being reflected by that object
D. wavelength absorbed by the pigment of the object

32. Energy is released from ATP when:

A. a phosphate group is removed
B. ATP is exposed to sunlight
C. adenine binds to ribose
D. a phosphate group is added

33. The wavelength energy least utilized by photosynthesis is:

A. orange
B. blue
C. green
D. cyan

34. Organisms, such as plants that make their food are:

A. symbiotic
B. parasitic
C. autotrophs
D. heterotrophs

35. During the fall foliage, which pigments are responsible for the yellow, red, and orange colors of leaves?

A. carotenoids
B. chlorophyll *b*
C. melanin
D. chlorophyll *a*

36. Which organism is a heterotroph?

A. sunflower
B. flowering plant
C. alga
D. mushroom

37. In addition to chlorophyll *a*, plants have chlorophyll *b* and carotenoids accessory pigments because:

A. there is not enough chlorophyll *a* produced for the plant's energy needs
B. plants must have leaves of distinct colors
C. these pigments absorb energy wavelengths that chlorophyll *a* does not
D. these pigments protect plants from UV radiation

38. Plants get the energy they need for photosynthesis by absorbing:

A. chlorophyll *b*
B. energy from the sun
C. high-energy sugars
D. chlorophyll *a*

39. A discrete packet of light is a:

A. photon
B. neutron
C. proton
D. wavelength

40. Most plants appear green because chlorophyll:

A. does not absorb violet light
B. does not absorb green light
C. absorbs violet light
D. absorbs green light

41. In visible light, shorter wavelengths carry:

A. more energy
B. more photons
C. more red color
D. less energy

42. Interconnected sacs of a membrane suspended in a thick fluid are:

A. stroma
B. thylakoids
C. chlorophyll
D. grana

43. When a molecule absorbs a photon, its electrons are raised to a(n):

A. higher state
B. excited state
C. lower state
D. ground state

44. What is the function of $NADP^+$ in photosynthesis?

A. Photosystem
B. Pigment
C. Electron carrier
D. High-energy sugar

45. A molecule releases energy gained from the absorption of a photon through:

I. fluorescence II. heat III. light

A. I only
B. II only
C. III only
D. I, II and III

46. Photosynthesis uses sunlight to convert water and carbon dioxide into:

A. oxygen and high-energy sugars
B. ATP and oxygen
C. high-energy sugars and proteins
D. oxygen and carbon

47. Photosystems are in:

A. grana
B. stroma
C. stomata
D. thylakoid membranes

48. The light-dependent reactions take place:

A. within the thylakoid membranes
B. in the outer membrane of the chloroplast
C. in the stroma of the chloroplast
D. within the mitochondria membranes

49. Which compound is in the photosystem's reaction center?

A. chlorophyll *a*
B. rhodopsin
C. ATP
D. ADP

50. What are the products of light-dependent reactions?

A. CO_2 gas, O_2 gas, and NADPH
B. ATP, CO_2 gas, and NADPH
C. ATP, NADPH, and O_2 gas
D. O_2 gas and glucose

51. Which is the correct matching of molecules and products in the Calvin cycle?

A. ATP + NADPH + carbon dioxide ⇒ sugar
B. light + water + carbon dioxide ⇒ sugar and oxygen
C. ATP + NADPH + carbon dioxide ⇒ sugar and oxygen
D. light + water + carbon dioxide ⇒ sugar

52. Which activities happen within the stroma?

A. Electrons move through the electron transport chain
B. The Calvin cycle produces sugars
C. ATP synthase produces ATP
D. Photosystem I absorbs light

53. Oxygen released by a photosystem comes from:

A. ATP
B. carbon dioxide
C. Chlorophyll *a*
D. water

54. The Calvin cycle is another name for:

A. photosynthesis reaction
B. electron transport chain
C. light-independent reactions
D. light-dependent reactions

55. Electrons for the light reactions originate from:

A. NADPH
B. water
C. light
D. carbon dioxide

56. Which mechanism occurs in light reactions of photosynthesis and cellular respiration?

A. Electron transport chain
B. Beta oxidation
C. Glycolysis
D. Krebs cycle

57. During photosynthesis, an H^+ ion gradient forms across:

A. mitochondrial inner membrane
B. inner chloroplast membrane
C. thylakoid membrane
D. mitochondrial outer membrane

Notes for active learning

Notes for active learning

Specialized Cells and Tissues

1. What is the role of Ca^{2+} in muscle contractions?

A. Breaking the cross-bridges as a cofactor in the hydrolysis of ATP
B. Binding to the troponin complex, which leads to exposure of the myosin-binding sites
C. Transmitting the action potential across the neuromuscular junction
D. Spreading the action potential through the T tubules

2. As sodium moves from the extracellular to intracellular space, which anion follows for electrical neutrality?

A. chloride
B. potassium
C. magnesium
D. lithium

3. Which statements about caffeine is FALSE?

A. It inhibits the signaling pathway normally stimulated by epinephrine
B. It is a signal molecule
C. It acts in different ways in specific tissues
D. It is a common ingredient in headache remedies

Use the graph to answer questions **4–8**

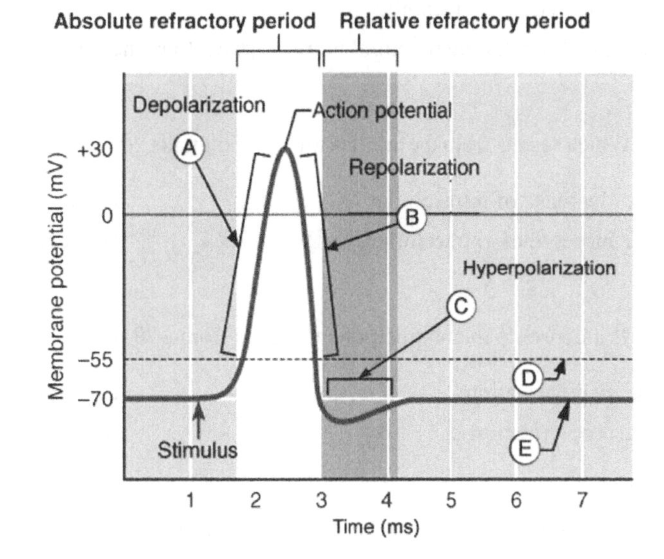

4. From the figure, arrow A points to which ion entering the axon?

A. Ca^{2+}
B. K^+
C. Cl^-
D. Na^+

5. From the figure, arrow B points to which ion leaving the axon?

A. Ca^{2+}
B. K^+
C. Cl^-
D. Na^+

6. From the figure, arrow C points to the slow close of:

A. ATPase
B. K^+ voltage-gated channels
C. Cl^- voltage-gated channels
D. Na^+ voltage-gated channels

7. From the figure, arrow D points to:

A. hyperpolarization
B. threshold
C. overshoot
D. resting potential

8. From the figure, arrow E points to:

A. hyperpolarization
B. hypopolarization
C. overshoot
D. resting potential

9. What is the effect of chemical X that denatures all enzymes in the synaptic cleft?

A. inhibition of depolarization of the presynaptic membrane
B. prolonged depolarization of the presynaptic membrane
C. prolonged depolarization of the postsynaptic membrane
D. inhibition of depolarization of the postsynaptic membrane

10. A "resting" motor neuron is expected to:

A. release elevated levels of acetylcholine
B. have high permeability to Na^+
C. have equal permeability to Na^+ and K^+
D. exhibit a resting potential more negative than the threshold potential

11. Which results from the administration of digitalis, known to block Na^+/K^+ ATPase?

A. decrease of intracellular $[K^+]$
B. increase of extracellular $[Na^+]$
C. decrease of intracellular $[Ca^{2+}]$
D. decrease of intracellular $[Na^+]$

12. If a neuron's membrane potential goes from –70 mV to –90 mV, this is an example of:

A. depolarization
B. repolarization
C. hyperpolarization
D. Na^+ channel inactivation

13. Which tissue is an example of connective tissue?

I. bone II. cartilage III. nervous

A. II only
B. I and II only
C. II and III only
D. I, II and III

14. Which factors do NOT affect the resting membrane potential?

A. The Na^+/K^+ pump
B. Active transport across the plasma membrane of the axon
C. Equal distribution of ions across the plasma membrane of the axon
D. Selective permeability for ions across the plasma membrane of the axon

15. The first event to occur when a resting axon reaches its threshold potential is:

A. closing of K^+ gates
B. activation of the Na^+/K^+ pump
C. opening of Na^+ gates
D. closing of Na^+ gates

16. Multiple sclerosis is a demyelinating disease that most severely affects the following muscle fibers?

A. C-pain – temperature and mechanoreception (velocity 0.75-3.5 m/s)
B. gamma – intrafusal muscle spindle (velocity 4-24 m/s)
C. beta – touch (velocity 25-75 m/s)
D. alpha – extrafusal muscle spindle (velocity 75-130 m/s)

17. The measure of the postsynaptic response after stimulation by the presynaptic cell is synaptic:

A. area
B. strength
C. speed
D. summation

18. What molecule must a cell have to respond to a signal?

A. paracrine
B. receptor
C. autocrine
D. responder

19. Muscle contraction takes place due to:

A. myosin filaments and actin filaments sliding past each other
B. shortening of only actin filaments
C. shortening of only myosin filaments
D. simultaneous shortening of myosin and actin filaments

20. When an organism dies, its muscles remain in the contracted state of *rigor mortis* for a brief period. Which most directly contributes to this phenomenon?

A. no ATP is available to move cross-bridges
B. no ATP is available to break bonds between the thick and thin filaments
C. no calcium to bind to troponin
D. no oxygen supplied to muscles

21. Which is expected in a cell exposed to ouabain, known to block the activity of the Na^+/K^+ ATPase?

A. increase in ATP consumption
B. spontaneous depolarization
C. increase in extracellular $[Na^+]$
D. increase in intracellular $[K^+]$

22. The region on neurons that brings the graded potential to the neuronal cell body is:

A. axon
B. dendrite
C. T-tubule
D. node of Ranvier

23. Which statement describes the role of the myelin sheath in action potential transmission?

A. Saltatory conduction dissipates current through specialized leakage channels
B. Oligodendrocytes cover the nodes of Ranvier to prevent backflow of current
C. Protein fibers cover the axon and prevent leakage of current across the membrane
D. Lipids insulate the axons, while membrane depolarization occurs within the nodes

24. Which human structure is analogous to an electrical device t allowing current to flow only in one direction?

A. dendrite
B. axon process
C. myelin sheath
D. synaptic cleft

25. In the communication link between a motor neuron and a skeletal muscle:

A. motor neuron is presynaptic, and the skeletal muscle is the postsynaptic cell
B. motor neuron is postsynaptic, and the skeletal muscle is the presynaptic cell
C. action potentials are possible on the motor neuron but not on the skeletal muscle
D. action potentials are possible on the skeletal muscle but not on the motor neuron

26. Which organelle undergoes self-replication?

A. DNA
B. mitochondria
C. nucleolus
D. ribosomes

27. The resting membrane potential of a neuron would be closest to:

A. 70 mV
B. 120 mV
C. –70 mV
D. 0 mV

28. A molecule that binds to the three-dimensional structure of another molecule's receptor is:

A. responder
B. receptor
C. ligand
D. ion channel

29. *Myasthenia gravis* is a severe autoimmune disease of neuromuscular junctions. A patient produces antibodies against acetylcholine receptors on muscle membranes (i.e., the sarcolemma), causing their removal by phagocytosis. Which process would be directly affected by this condition?

A. Acetylcholine synthesis
B. Calcium release by the endoplasmic reticulum
C. Sarcomere shortening during muscle contraction
D. Action potential conduction across the sarcolemma

30. Which of the following are shared by skeletal, cardiac, and smooth muscles?

A. A bands and I bands
B. transverse tubules
C. gap junctions
D. thick and thin filaments

31. Procaine is a local anesthetic used during many dental procedures that inhibit the propagation of an action potential along a neuron by:

A. blocking Na^+ voltage-gated channels
B. removing Schwann cells covering the axon
C. increasing Cl^- movement out of the neuron in response to an action potential
D. stimulating Ca^{2+} voltage-gated channels at the synapse

32. The type of glial cell that myelinates an axon in the CNS is:

A. astrocyte
B. oligodendrocyte
C. Schwann cell
D. choroid plexus

33. The myelin sheath around axons of the peripheral nervous system is produced by:

A. axon hillock
B. nerve cell body
C. nodes of Ranvier
D. Schwann cell

34. All statements are true for muscles, EXCEPT:

A. Resting muscle is completely relaxed
B. Tonus is the state of partial contraction which occurs in a resting muscle
C. Isometric contraction means that the length of the muscle is constant
D. Isotonic contraction means that the length of the muscle shortens

35. Tissues are composed of cells, and a group of tissues functioning together makes up:

A. organs
B. membranes
C. organ systems
D. organelles

36. If a neuronal membrane, which is slightly passively permeable to K^+, becomes impermeable, but the Na^+/K^+-ATPase remains active, the neuron's resting potential would become more:

A. negative because [K^+] increases inside the neuron
B. negative because [K^+] increases outside the neuron
C. positive because [K^+] increases inside the neuron
D. positive because [K^+] increases outside the neuron

37. The asymmetric concentration gradient of Na^+ and K^+ across the membrane is maintained by:

A. voltage-gated channels
B. Na^+/K^+ ATPase
C. mitochondria
D. constitutive ion channels

38. Which statement about the insulin receptor is FALSE?

A. Once activated, it undergoes autophosphorylation
B. It requires binding by two insulin molecules to be activated
C. It catalyzes the phosphorylation of the insulin response substrate
D. It is entirely within the cytoplasm

39. Which process results in hyperpolarization?

A. excessive outflow of K^+
B. excessive outflow of Na^+
C. excessive influx of K^+
D. excessive influx of Na^+

40. The deficiency of which vitamin is associated with neural tube defects?

A. B_6
B. calcium
C. folic acid
D. B_{12}

41. Which membrane-bound protein channel must be inhibited to cause a blockage of nerve conduction by a hydrophobic local anesthetic such as lidocaine?

A. Cl^- channel
B. Ca^{2+} channel
C. K^+ channel
D. Na^+ channel

42. Which is NOT a class of molecules used as a neurotransmitter?

A. peptides
B. catecholamines
C. amino acids
D. enzymes

43. Which is FALSE?

A. Cells are bombarded with numerous signals, but they respond to only a few
B. A cell's receptors determine whether the cell will respond to a signal
C. Receptor proteins are specific
D. There are only a few kinds of signal receptor proteins

44. Which neurons participate in the piloerection of hair standing on its end?

A. sympathetic motor neurons
B. sympathetic sensory neurons
C. parasympathetic motor neurons
D. parasympathetic sensory neurons

45. Which statement best summarizes the relationship between the cytoplasm and cytosol?

A. Cytoplasm includes the cytosol, a watery fluid inside the cell
B. Cytoplasm is within the nucleolus, while cytosol is within the cell outside the nucleus
C. Cytoplasm is within the cell outside the nucleus, while cytosol is within the nucleolus
D. Cytoplasm is within the nucleus, while cytosol is within the nucleolus

46. During depolarization of a muscle cell, Ca^{2+} is released from the sarcoplasmic reticulum and binds:

A. muscle ATPase
B. troponin C
C. myosin heads
D. actin thin filaments

47. What is TRUE about saltatory conduction?

A. Current passes through the myelin sheath
B. Voltage-gated Ca^{2+} channels are concentrated at the nodes of Ranvier
C. Myelinated axons exhibit greater conduction velocity than non-myelinated axons
D. It is much slower than conduction along non-myelinated axons

48. The specialized region of neurons that connect to axons and sum the graded inputs before the propagation of *all or none* depolarizations:

A. axon hillock
B. nerve cell body
C. node of Ranvier
D. glial cell

49. Myelin covers axons and is responsible for:

A. initiating the action potential
B. allowing pumping of Na^+ out of the cell
C. maintaining the resting potential
D. allowing faster conduction of impulses

50. Which tissue forms coverings, linings, and glands?

A. connective tissue
B. cellular matrix
C. endothelium
D. epithelial

51. What is the function of the nodes of Ranvier within the neuron?

A. To provide a binding site for acetylcholine
B. To provide a space for Schwann cells to deposit myelin
C. To regenerate the anterograde conduction of the action potential
D. To permit the axon hillock to generate a stronger action potential

52. An organ is a structure with a recognizable shape, specific functions, and composed of different:

A. tissues
B. cells
C. germ layers
D. mesoderm

53. What can be deduced about the conduction velocity of Purkinje fibers?

A. Fast, ion independent channel
B. Slow, ion independent channel
C. Fast, Na^+ dependent channel
D. Slow, Na^+ dependent channel

54. Which is NOT classified as one of the four primary (basic) tissue types?

A. connective
B. blood
C. muscle
D. nervous

55. The release of a neurotransmitter into the synaptic cleft results from the influx of:

A. Na^+ ions
B. K^+ ions
C. Ca^{2+} ions
D. Cl^- ions

56. Which connective tissue stores triglycerides and provides cushioning and support for organs?

A. glycogen
B. muscle
C. connective
D. adipose

57. Which cells do NOT utilize voltage-gated Na^+ channels?

A. cardiac cells
B. endothelial cells
C. smooth muscle cells
D. skeletal muscle cells

58. The cells lining the air sacs in the lungs are:

A. simple columnar epithelium
B. simple squamous epithelium
C. stratified squamous epithelium
D. pseudostratified ciliated columnar epithelium

Notes for active learning

Genetics

1. Which characteristic makes an organism unsuitable for genetic studies?

A. A large number of chromosomes
B. Short generation time
C. Ease of cultivation
D. Ability to control crosses

2. People with sex-linked hemophilia suffer from excessive bleeding because their blood will not clot. Tom, Mary, and their four daughters do not exhibit symptoms. However, their son has symptoms because:

A. Tom is heterozygous
B. Tom is homozygous
C. Mary is heterozygous
D. Mary is homozygous

3. Which factor would NOT favor an *r-selection* over a *K-selection* reproductive strategy?

A. Commercial predation by humans
B. Limited space
C. Shorter growing season
D. Frequent and intense seasonal flooding

4. Several eye colors are characteristic of *Drosophila melanogaster*. Red eyes are dominant over sepia or white eyes. What percent of offspring of a sepia-eyed fly will have sepia eyes if that fly mated with a red-eyed fly that was a cross of red-eyed and sepia-eyed parents?

A. 0%
B. 25%
C. 50%
D. 75%

5. Color blindness mutations in humans result from:

A. fragile X syndrome
B. chromosome nondisjunction
C. reciprocal translocation
D. unequal crossing-over

6. A small subpopulation of flies with a slightly advantageous modification in the structure was extinct after a locally isolated decimating fire. A geneticist would attribute the loss of this advantageous gene to:

A. differential reproduction
B. natural selection
C. Hardy-Weinberg principle
D. genetic drift

7. Which method was NOT used by Mendel to study the genetics of garden peas?

A. Maintenance of true-breeding lines
B. Cross-pollination
C. Microscopy
D. Production of hybrid plants

8. In a cross of AAbbCc × AaBbCc where A, B, and C are unlinked genes, what is the probability of offspring having the AaBbCc genotype?

A. 1/4
B. 1/8
C. 1/16
D. 1/32

9. What is the probability of a child being affected by a disease with an autosomal recessive inheritance if the mother and father are carriers?

A. 0%
B. 25%
C. 50%
D. 75%

10. All the following are necessary conditions for the Hardy-Weinberg equilibrium, EXCEPT:

A. forward mutation rate equals backward mutation rate
B. random emigration and immigration
C. large gene pool
D. random mating

11. For the multi-step progression of cancer, the major mutational target(s) is/are:

A. telomerase
B. X-linked traits
C. tumor suppressor gene
D. trinucleotide repeats

12. Since the gene responsible for color blindness is on the X chromosome, what probability will a son of an afflicted man and a woman-carrier be colorblind?

A. 75%
B. 100%
C. 25%
D. 50%

13. If two strains of true-breeding plants with alleles for a character are crossed, their progeny are:

A. P generation
B. F_1 generation
C. F_2 generation
D. F_1 crosses

14. The *Arabidopsis* plant has five pairs of homologous chromosomes. Suppose an *Arabidopsis* is heterozygous for five mutations, and each mutation is on a different chromosome. How many genetically distinct gametes will this plant make after meiosis?

A. 5
B. 10
C. 32
D. 64

15. An unknown inheritance pattern has the following characteristics:

- 25% probability of having a homozygous unaffected child
- 25% probability of having a homozygous affected child
- 50% probability of having a heterozygous child

Which Mendel's inheritance pattern best matches the observations?

A. autosomal recessive
B. autosomal dominant
C. X-linked recessive
D. X-linked dominant

16. What is the frequency of heterozygotes within a population in Hardy-Weinberg equilibrium if the frequency of the dominant allele D is three times that of the recessive allele d?

A. 7.25%
B. 12.75%
C. 33%
D. 37.5%

17. A recessive allele may appear in a phenotype due to:

A. gain-of-function mutation
B. acquired dominance
C. senescence
D. loss of heterozygosity

18. Which observations support the theory of maternal inheritance for the spunky phenotype?

A. Spunky female × wild-type male → progeny all spunky
B. Wild-type female × spunky male → progeny all spunky
C. Wild-type female × spunky male → progeny 1/2 spunky, 1/2 wild-type
D. Spunky female × wild-type male → progeny 1/2 spunky, 1/2 wild-type

19. Mendel (1822-1884) concluded that each pea has two units for each characteristic, and each gamete contains one unit. Mendel's "unit" is now referred to as:

A. gene
B. hnRNA
C. codon
D. transcription factor

20. Which leads to a complete loss of gene function?

A. A missense mutation that causes the nonpolar methionine to be replaced with glycine
B. GC base pair being converted to an AT base pair in the promoter
C. A mutation in the third codon of the open reading frame
D. A base pair change that does not affect the amino acid sequence

21. All the following effects are possible after a mutation, EXCEPT:

A. abnormal lipid production
B. abnormal protein production
C. gain of enzyme function
D. loss of enzyme function

22. Which cross produces all green, smooth peas if green (G) is dominant over yellow (g) and smooth (S) is dominant over wrinkled (s)?

A. GgSs × GGSS
B. GgSS × ggSS
C. Ggss × GGSs
D. GgSs × GgSs

23. Retinoblastoma is inherited as:

A. a multifactorial trait
B. X-linked recessive
C. Mendelian dominant
D. Mendelian recessive

24. Tay-Sachs disease is a rare autosomal recessive genetic disorder. If a male heterozygous carrier and a female heterozygous carrier have a first child who is homozygous wild-type, what is the probability that the second child develops Tay-Sachs?

A. 1/4
B. 1/2
C. 1/16
D. 1/8

25. Mendel's crossing of spherical-seeded pea plants with wrinkled-seeded pea plants resulted in progeny that all had spherical seeds. This indicates that the wrinkled-seed trait is:

A. codominant
B. dominant
C. recessive
D. penetrance

26. The result of mitosis is the production of:

A. two (1N) cells identical to the parent cell
B. two (2N) cells identical to the parent cell
C. four (1N) cells identical to the parent cell
D. four (2N) cells identical to the parent cell

27. What is the probability (p) of randomly rolling a pair of 4s using two six-sided dice?

A. 1/12
B. 1/16
C. 1/36
D. 1/72

28. The degree of genetic linkage is often measured by:

A. frequency of nonsense mutations
B. histone distribution
C. frequency of missense mutations
D. probability of crossing over

29. Cancers associated with defects in mismatch repair are inherited via:

A. dominant inheritance
B. maternal inheritance
C. X-linked inheritance
D. epigenetic inheritance

30. Given that color blindness is a recessive trait inherited through a sex-linked gene on the X chromosome, what is the probability that a daughter born to a colorblind father and a mother who carries the trait is a carrier?

A. 0%
B. 25%
C. 50%
D. 100%

31. What is the probability that a cross between a true-breeding pea plant with a dominant trait and a true-breeding pea plant with a recessive trait will result in all F_1 progeny having the dominant trait?

A. 1/2
B. 1/4
C. 0
D. 1

32. The tall allele is dominant to the short. True breeding tall plants were crossed with true-breeding short plants. F_1 plants were self-crossed to produce F_2 progeny. What are the phenotypes of the F_1 and F_2 progeny?

A. F_1 and 1/4 of the F_2 are short
B. F_1 are short, and 1/4 of the F_2 are tall
C. F_1 and 3/4 of the F_2 are tall
D. F_1 are tall, and 3/4 of the F_2 plants are short

33. All these DNA lesions result in a frameshift mutation, EXCEPT:

A. 1 inserted base pair
B. 2 substituted base pairs
C. 4 inserted base pairs
D. 2 deleted base pairs

34. If two species with the AaBbCc genotype reproduce, what is the probability that their progeny have the AABBCC genotype?

A. 1/2
B. 1/4
C. 1/16
D. 1/64

35. At the hypoxanthine-guanine phosphoribosyltransferase (HPRT) locus, there is an average amount of mRNA but no protein. This phenotype is caused by:

A. frameshift mutation
B. nonsense mutation affecting message translation
C. point mutation leading to an amino acid substitution necessary for enzyme function
D. gene deletion or mutation affecting the promoter

36. Hemophilia is a recessive X-linked trait. Knowing that females with Turner's syndrome have a high incidence of hemophilia, it can be concluded that these females have:

A. lost an X and gained a Y
B. lost an X
C. gained an X
D. gained a Y

37. What is the pattern of inheritance for a rare recessive allele?

A. Each affected person has an affected parent
B. Unaffected parents can produce children who are affected
C. Unaffected mothers have affected children who are carriers
D. Each affected person produces an affected offspring

38. True-breeding plants with large purple flowers were crossed with true-breeding plants with small white flowers. The F_1 progeny all had large purple flowers. The F_1 progeny were crossed to true-breeding plants with small white flowers. Among 1,000 progeny:

Number of progeny	Flower size	Flower color
250	small	white
250	small	purple
250	large	white
250	large	purple

The genes for flower size and color:

A. are unlinked
B. are sex-linked
C. are linked and separated by no more than 25 centimorgans
D. require determination of the cross of the F_2 progeny

39. Mitosis does NOT serve the purpose of:

A. replenishment of erythrocytes
B. transduction
C. organ repair
D. tissue growth

40. If tall height and brown eye color are dominant, what is the probability for a heterozygous tall, heterozygous, brown-eyed mother and a homozygous tall, homozygous blue-eyed father to have a tall child with blue eyes? Note: the genes for eye color and height are unlinked.

A. 3/4
B. 1/8
C. 1/4
D. 1/2

41. Recombination frequencies:

A. are the same for *cis-* and *trans*-heterozygotes
B. arise from completely random genetic exchanges
C. decrease with distance
D. are the same for all genes

42. How many different gametes can be produced from genotype *AaBbCc*, assuming independent assortment?

A. 4
B. 6
C. 8
D. 16

43. What is the pattern of inheritance for a rare dominant allele?

A. Each affected person has an affected parent
B. Unaffected parents can produce children who are affected
C. Unaffected mothers have affected sons and daughter carriers
D. Each affected person produces an affected offspring

44. Individuals homozygous for an autosomal recessive mutation accumulate harmful amounts of lipids. Jane and her parents are not afflicted. However, Jane's sister accumulates lipids. What is the probability that Jane is heterozygous for the mutation?

A. 1/4
B. 1/3
C. 2/3
D. 1/2

45. A genetic disease with an earlier onset and more severe symptoms with each generation is an example of:

A. codominance
B. penetrance
C. anticipation
D. gain-of-function mutations

46. For a trait with two alleles, if the recessive allele frequency is 0.6 in a population, what is the frequency of individuals expressing the dominant phenotype?

A. 0.48
B. 0.64
C. 0.16
D. 0.36

47. The maximum recombination frequency between two genes is:

A. 100%
B. 80%
C. 50%
D. 10%

48. In mice, short hair is dominant over long hair. If a short-haired individual is crossed with a long-haired individual and both long and short-haired offspring result, what can be concluded?

A. Short-haired individual is homozygous
B. Short-haired individual is heterozygous
C. Long-haired individual is homozygous
D. Long-haired individual is heterozygous

49. The result of meiosis in males is the production of:

A. two (1N) cells genetically identical to the parent cell
B. two (2N) cells genetically identical to the parent cell
C. four (1N) cells genetically identical to the parent cell
D. four (1N) unique cells genetically different from the parent cell

50. Which is an example of a transversion mutation where purine is converted to pyrimidine?

A. uracil → thymine
B. cytosine → thymine
C. guanine → cytosine
D. guanine → adenine

51. Which is a genetic mutation?

I. insertion II. frameshift III. nonsense IV. missense

A. I and II only
B. I, II and III only
C. II and IV only
D. I, II, III and IV

52. Two reciprocal crossing over events appears in the progeny at an approximate ratio of:

A. 4:1
B. 3:1
C. 2:1
D. 1:1

53. In dogs, phenotype A (erect ears and barking while following a scent) is caused by dominant alleles; recessive alleles cause phenotype B (droopy ears and silent while following a scent). A dog homozygous dominant is mated with a homozygous recessive for both traits. If the two genes are unlinked, which is the expected F_1 phenotypic ratio?

A. 9:3:3:1
B. 1:1
C. 16:0
D. 1:2:1

54. Mutations:

A. always cause severe mutant phenotypes
B. never cause severe mutant phenotypes
C. are not inherited by the progeny
D. may cause premature termination of translation

55. What is the probability of having a child affected by a disease with autosomal dominant inheritance if the mother and father have one mutant gene for that disease?

A. 0%
B. 25%
C. 50%
D. 75%

56. Given the recombinant frequencies, what is the sequence of linked genes D, E, F and G?

GE: 23%	ED: 15%	EF: 8%
GD: 8%	GF: 15%	DF: 7%

A. FGDE
B. EFGD
C. GFDE
D. GDFE

Questions **57** through **63** are based on the following:

The pedigree illustrated by the schematic shows the inheritance of albinism, a homozygous recessive condition manifested in a lack of pigment. Specify the genotypes using *A* and *a* to indicate dominant and recessive alleles.

Note: solids are albino individuals.

57. Individual A-1 in the pedigree shown is:

A. *AA*
B. *aa*
C. *Aa*
D. any of the above

58. Individual A-2 in the pedigree shown is:

A. *AA*
B. *aa*
C. *Aa*
D. any of the above

59. Individual B-1 in the pedigree shown is:

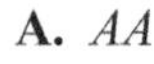

A. *AA*
B. *aa*
C. *Aa*
D. any of the above

60. Individual B-2 in the pedigree shown is:

A. *AA*
B. *aa*
C. *Aa*
D. any of the above

61. Individual C-3 in the pedigree shown is:

A. *AA*
B. *aa*
C. *Aa*
D. any of the above

62. Individual C-4 in the pedigree shown is:

A. *AA*
B. *aa*
C. *Aa*
D. any of the above

63. Individual D-4 in the pedigree shown is:

A. *AA*
B. *aa*
C. *Aa*
D. any of the above

64. In cocker spaniels, black color (B) is dominant over red (b), and solid color (S) is dominant over spotted (s). If the genes are unlinked and the offspring of BBss and bbss individuals are mated, what fraction of their offspring will be black and spotted?

A. 1/16
B. 3/4
C. 1/9
D. 3/16

65. Why do genes that cause disease often appear to skip generations in an X-linked recessive inheritance?

A. The disease is primarily transmitted through unaffected carrier females
B. Males with an affected gene are carriers but do not show the disease
C. X-linked diseases are only expressed in males
D. All X-linked diseases display incomplete penetrance

66. The "calico" coat pattern of a female cat is a result of:

A. endoreduplication
B. unequal crossing-over
C. random X chromosome inactivation
D. Turner syndrome

67. Which statement is true for an autosomal dominant inheritance?

I. A single allele of the mutant gene is needed to exhibit the phenotype
II. Transmission to the son by the father is not observed
III. Autosomal dominant traits do not skip generations

A. II only
B. I, II and III
C. I only
D. I and III only

68. What chromosomal abnormality results in some XY individuals being phenotypically females?

A. fragile X syndrome
B. deletion of the portion of the Y chromosome containing the testis-determining factor
C. dosage compensation
D. mosaicism

69. Which event would NOT disrupt the Hardy-Weinberg equilibrium?

A. An entire population is exposed to intense cosmic radiation
B. Massive volcano eruption kills one-sixth of a large homogeneous population
C. A predator selectively targets old and infirm organisms within the population
D. Population experiences emigration

70. Which event risks joining two recessive alleles, resulting in a genetic defect?

A. genetic mutation
B. transformation
C. inbreeding
D. crossing over

71. To engineer polyploid plants in plant breeding, genetic engineers use drugs that:

A. insert new DNA into plants' genome
B. damage the DNA and cause mutations
C. rearrange the sequences of codons on the DNA strand
D. alter the number of chromosomes

72. To create mules, horses are bred with donkeys by:

A. crossing over
B. genetic engineering
C. hybridization
D. inbreeding

73. Bacteria transformed by a plasmid can be distinguished from untransformed bacteria by:

A. genetic marker
B. trisomy
C. presence of DNA strands
D. absence of cytosine

74. When treated with penicillin, a bacterial culture transformed with recombinant plasmids with a gene for resistance to this antibiotic will:

A. undergo lysis
B. rapidly replicate DNA
C. die
D. survive

75. Which takes place during transformation?

A. bacterial DNA undergoes mutation
B. bacterial DNA is inserted into a plasmid
C. a bacterial cell takes in foreign DNA material
D. a prokaryotic cell becomes eukaryotic

76. Recombinant DNA experiments utilize plasmids because:

A. they contain foreign DNA
B. their genetic material cannot be cut with restriction enzymes
C. they are unable to replicate inside the bacteria
D. they are used to transform bacteria

77. The figure shown illustrates:

A. PCR making a copy of the DNA
B. enzyme cutting the DNA
C. use of hybridization in genetic engineering
D. DNA sequencing via gel electrophoresis

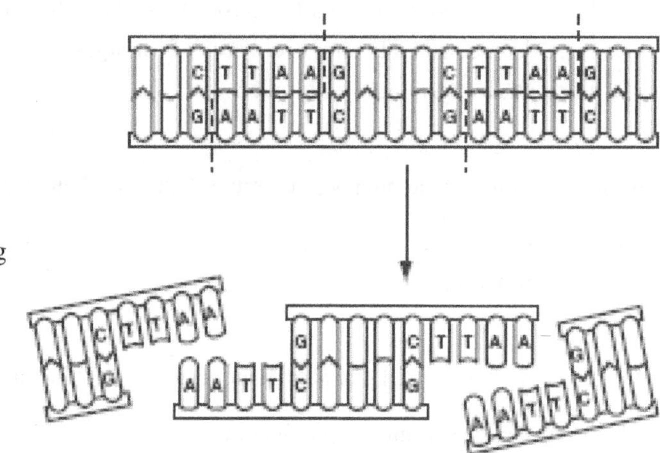

78. Between which two nucleotides are DNA cut in the figure?

A. thymine and adenine
B. adenine and guanine
C. adenine and cytosine
D. thymine and guanine

79. What is the product of combining DNA from dissimilar sources?

A. recombinant DNA
B. clone
C. hybrid DNA
D. mutant

80. Plasmids are easily inserted into bacteria but not into yeast because yeasts are:

A. mutants
B. protists
C. eukaryotes
D. prokaryotes

81. Which pairing represents two transgenic organisms?

A. Appletree hybrid and a polyploid cherry tree
B. Human growth hormone-producing bacteria and genetically modified soybeans
C. Appletree hybrid and human growth hormone-producing bacteria
D. Genetically modified soybeans and a polyploid cherry tree

82. Which task requires recombinant DNA technology?

A. Creating bacteria that produce human growth hormone
B. Creating a polyploid cherry tree
C. Crossing two types of orange trees to create new orange fruits
D. Crossing a donkey with a horse to breed a mule

83. A sheep in 1996 named Dolly was different from animals produced by sexual reproduction because:

A. her DNA is identical to the DNA of her offspring
B. she was carried by a surrogate mother, while her DNA came from two other individuals
C. all her cells' DNA is identical
D. her DNA was taken from a somatic cell of an adult individual

84. Transformation of a plant cell is successful when:

A. plasmid cannot enter the cell
B. cell produces daughter cells that subsequently produce other daughter cells
C. foreign DNA is integrated into the plant cell's chromosome
D. cell's enzymes destroy the plasmid after it enters the cell

85. Genetically modified (GM) crops produce a higher yield per plant by:

A. less food but with higher nutritional content
B. the same amount of food but with higher nutritional content
C. more food per acre
D. less food per acre

86. Gene therapy is successful when:

A. the person's cells express the newly introduced gene
B. the replacement gene is integrated into viral DNA
C. the virus with the replacement gene enters the person's cells
D. the person's cells replicate the newly introduced gene

87. Which describes establishing parental relationships through DNA fingerprinting of specific genes?

A. Mitochondrial DNA links a daughter to the mother, while plasmid DNA links to the father
B. Mitochondrial DNA links a son to the mother, while the Y chromosome links to the father
C. X chromosome links a daughter to the mother, while the Y chromosome links to the father
D. X chromosome links a son to the mother, while mitochondrial DNA links to the father

Notes for active learning

Genetics and Reproduction

1. What number of double-stranded DNA molecules are in a single mouse chromosome immediately after gametes form?

A. 0
B. 1
C. 2
D. 4

2. All the following about human gamete production is true, EXCEPT:

A. meiosis in females produces four egg cells
B. sperm develop in the seminiferous tubules within the testes
C. eggs develop in the ovarian follicles within the ovaries
D. FSH stimulates gamete production in males and females

3. Common red-green color blindness is an X-linked trait. When a woman whose father is color blind has a son with a non-afflicted man, what is the probability that their son is color blind?

A. 0
B. 1/4
C. 1/2
D. 3/4

4. At birth, a woman possesses a finite number of ova. In oogenesis, the meiotic division is arrested at which stage until she reaches menarche?

A. ovum
B. oogonium
C. primary oocytes
D. secondary oocytes

5. The likely gamete cell to be produced from meiosis in the seminiferous tubules is:

A. diploid 2° spermatocytes
B. haploid 1° spermatocytes
C. haploid spermatids
D. diploid spermatids

6. A human cell after the first meiotic division is:

A. 2N and 2 chromatids
B. 2N and 4 chromatids
C. 1N and 2 chromatids
D. 1N and 1 chromatid

7. All statements regarding the menstrual cycle are true, EXCEPT:

A. Graafian follicle, under the influence of LH, undergoes ovulation
B. follicle secretes estrogen as it develops
C. corpus luteum develops from the remains of the post-ovulatory Graafian follicle
D. posterior pituitary secretes FSH and LH

8. What distinguishes meiosis from mitosis?

I. Genetic recombination

II. Failure to synthesize DNA between successive cell divisions

III. Separation of homologous chromosomes into distinct cells

A. I only
B. II only
C. I and III only
D. II and III only

9. Oocytes within the primordial follicles of the ovary are arrested in:

A. interphase
B. prophase II of meiosis
C. prophase I of meiosis
D. prophase of mitosis

10. SRY gene encoding for the testis-determining factor is the primary sex-determining gene that resides on:

A. pseudoautosomal region of the Y chromosome
B. short arm of the Y chromosome, but not in the pseudoautosomal region
C. X chromosome
D. pseudoautosomal region of the X chromosome

11. The number of chromosomes contained in the primary human spermatocyte is:

A. 23
B. 46
C. 92
D. 184

12. Which process does NOT contribute to genetic variation?

A. Random segregation of homologous chromosomes during meiosis
B. Random segregation of chromatids during mitosis
C. Recombination
D. Mutation

13. In human females, secondary oocytes do not complete meiosis II until:

A. menarche
B. menstruation
C. fertilization
D. menopause

14. 47, XXY is a condition known as:

A. Turner syndrome
B. double Y syndrome
C. trisomy X syndrome
D. Klinefelter syndrome

15. All these cell types contain the diploid (2N) number of chromosomes, EXCEPT:

A. primary oocyte
B. spermatogonium
C. spermatid
D. zygote

16. The probability that all children in a four-children family will be males is:

A. 1/2
B. 1/4
C. 1/8
D. 1/16

17. Unequal cytoplasm division is characteristic of:

A. binary fission of bacteria
B. mitosis of a kidney cell
C. production of a sperm
D. production of an ovum

18. All the following are clinical manifestations of Kartagener's syndrome, resulting from defective dynein that causes paralysis of cilia and flagella, EXCEPT:

A. chronic respiratory disorders
B. cessation of ovulation
C. male infertility
D. ectopic pregnancy

19. Translation, transcription, and replication occur in which cell cycle phase?

A. G1
B. G2
C. metaphase
D. S

20. All statements are true for a typical human gamete, EXCEPT it:

A. originates via meiosis from a somatic cell
B. contains genetic material that has undergone recombination
C. contains a haploid number of genes
D. always contains an X or Y chromosome

21. Which inheritance has a pattern where an affected male has all affected daughters but no affected sons?

A. X-linked recessive
B. Y-linked
C. X-linked dominant
D. Autosomal recessive

22. Which cell division results in four genetically different haploid daughters?

A. interphase
B. meiosis
C. cell division
D. mitosis

23. Crossing over occurs during:

A. anaphase I
B. telophase I
C. prophase I
D. metaphase I

24. A genetically important event of crossing over occurs during:

A. metaphase II
B. telophase I
C. anaphase I
D. prophase I

25. Which does NOT describe events occurring in prophase I of meiosis?

A. chromosomal migration
B. genetic recombination
C. formation of a chiasma
D. spindle apparatus formation

26. The difference between spermatogenesis and oogenesis is:

A. spermatogenesis produces 4 1N sperms, while oogenesis produces 1 egg cell and polar bodies
B. spermatogenesis produces gametes, while oogenesis does not produce gametes
C. oogenesis is a mitotic process, while spermatogenesis is a meiotic process
D. spermatogenesis is a mitotic process, while oogenesis is a meiotic process

27. How many Barr bodies are in the white blood cells of a 48, XXYY individual?

A. 0
B. 1
C. 2
D. 3

28. Polar bodies are the products of:

A. meiosis in females
B. meiosis in males
C. mitosis in females
D. mitosis in males

29. Turner syndrome results from:

A. monosomy of X chromosome
B. absence of Y chromosome
C. presence of an extra Y chromosome
D. trisomy of X chromosome

Notes for active learning

Notes for active learning

Development

1. Which statement is true regarding respiratory exchange during fetal life?

A. Respiratory exchanges occur through the placenta
B. Since lungs develop later in gestation, a fetus does not need a mechanism for respiratory exchange
C. The respiratory exchange is made through the ductus arteriosus
D. The respiratory exchange is not necessary

2. When each cell in an early stage of embryonic development still has the ability to develop into a complete organism, it is known as:

A. gastrulation
B. blastulation
C. determinate cleavage
D. indeterminate cleavage

3. Mutations in *Drosophila*, transforming one body segment into another, effect:

A. maternal-effect genes
B. homeotic genes
C. execution genes
D. segmentation genes

4. Which structure originates from the embryonic ectoderm?

A. connective tissue
B. hair
C. rib cartilage
D. epithelium of the digestive system

5. The placenta is a vital metabolic organ made from a contribution by the mother and fetus. The portion of the placenta contributed by the fetus is:

A. amnion
B. yolk sac
C. umbilicus
D. chorion

6. What occurs when an embryo lacks the synthesis of human chorionic gonadotropin (hCG)?

A. The embryo does not support the maintenance of the corpus luteum
B. The embryo increases the production of progesterone
C. The embryo develops immunotolerance
D. The placenta forms prematurely

7. Which germ layer gives rise to smooth muscle?

A. ectoderm
B. epidermis
C. mesoderm
D. endoderm

8. In early embryogenesis, the critical morphological change in the development of cellular layers is:

A. epigenesis
B. gastrulation
C. conversion of morula to blastula
D. acrosomal reaction

9. During the first eight weeks of development, all the following events occur, EXCEPT:

A. myelination of the spinal cord
B. presence of all body systems
C. formation of a functional cardiovascular system
D. beginning of ossification

10. Which structures derive from the ectoderm germ layers?

A. epidermis and neurons
B. heart, kidneys, and blood vessels
C. nails, epidermis, and blood vessels
D. epidermis and adrenal cortex

11. A diagram of the blastoderm that identifies regions from which specific adult structures are derived is a:

A. phylogenetic tree
B. pedigree diagram
C. fate map
D. linkage map

12. Which tissue is the precursor of long bones in the embryo?

A. hyaline cartilage
B. fibrocartilage
C. dense fibrous connective tissue
D. elastic cartilage

13. What changes are observed in cells as development proceeds?

A. Cytoskeletal elements involved in forming the mitotic spindle
B. Energy requirements of each cell
C. Genetic information that was duplicated with each round of cell division
D. The composition of polypeptides within the cytoplasm

14. During fertilization, what is the earliest event in the process?

A. sperm contacts the cortical granules around the egg
B. sperm nucleic acid enters the egg's cytoplasm to form a pronucleus
C. acrosome releases hydrolytic enzymes
D. sperm contacts the vitelline membrane around the egg

15. The embryonic ectoderm layer gives rise to the following, EXCEPT:

A. eyes
B. fingernails
C. integument
D. blood vessels

16. All the following are correct matches of a fetal structure with what it becomes at birth, EXCEPT:

A. ductus venosus—ligamentum venosum
B. umbilical arteries—medial umbilical ligament
C. foramen ovale—fossa ovalis
D. ductus arteriosus—ligamentum teres

17. All statements regarding gastrulation are true, EXCEPT:

A. the primitive gut that results from gastrulation is the archenteron
B. for amphibians, gastrulation is initiated at the gray crescent
C. after gastrulation, the embryo consists of two germ layers of endoderm and ectoderm
D. amphibian blastula cells migrate during gastrulation through an invagination known as the blastopore

18. A homeobox is a:

A. protein involved in the control of meiosis
B. transcriptional activator of other genes
C. sequence that encodes for a DNA binding motif
D. DNA binding site

19. After the gastrulation's completion, the embryo undergoes:

A. cleavage
B. blastulation
C. blastocoel formation
D. neurulation

20. Shortly after implantation:

A. trophoblast forms two distinct layers
B. embryo undergoes gastrulation within 3 days
C. maternal blood sinuses bathe the inner cell mass
D. myometrial cells cover and seal off the blastocyst

21. What is the anatomical connection between the placenta and embryo?

A. chorion
B. umbilical cord
C. endometrium
D. corpus luteum

22. Which statement correctly illustrates the principle of induction during vertebrate development?

A. Neural tube develops into the brain, the spinal cord, and the nervous system
B. Secretion of TSH stimulates the release of thyroxine hormone
C. Presence of a notochord beneath the ectoderm results in the formation of a neural tube
D. Neurons synapse with other neurons via neurotransmitters

23. The acrosomal reaction by the sperm is:

A. a transient voltage change across the vitelline envelope
B. the jelly coat blocking penetration by multiple sperms
C. the consumption of yolk protein
D. hydrolytic enzymes degrading the plasma membrane

24. Which primary germ layer gives rise to the cardiovascular system, bones, and skeletal muscles?

A. endoderm
B. blastula
C. mesoderm
D. ectoderm

25. The dorsal surface cells of the inner cell mass form:

A. notochord
B. primitive streak
C. one of the fetal membranes
D. embryonic disc

26. All the following occurs in a newborn immediately after birth, EXCEPT:

A. the infant completely stops producing fetal hemoglobin
B. resistance in the pulmonary arteries decreases
C. pressure in the left atrium increases
D. pressure in the inferior vena cava and the right atrium increase

27. Homeobox sequences are in:

A. introns
B. exons
C. 3'-untranslated regions
D. 5'-untranslated regions

28. After 30 hours of incubation, the ectoderm tissue within the gastrula differentiates into different specific tissues, which supports the conclusion that:

I. cells become endoderm or mesoderm
II. cells contain a different genome from their parental cells
III. gene expression is altered

A. III only
B. I and III only
C. I only
D. I and II only

29. What is the function of the yolk sac in humans?

A. forms into the placenta
B. secretes progesterone in the fetus
C. gives rise to blood cells and gamete-forming cells
D. stores embryonic wastes

30. The trophoblast is primarily responsible for forming:

A. placental tissue
B. lining of the endometrium
C. allantois
D. archenteron

31. Certain lesions to the mesodermal embryonic primary germ layer may stimulate development of *spina bifida*, a congenital fissure in the lower vertebrae. Besides the spinal column, what structures would be affected by such lesions?

I. intestinal epithelium
II. skin and hair
III. blood vessels
IV. muscles

A. I and II only
B. II and III only
C. III and IV only
D. I, III and IV only

32. The homeotic genes encode for:

A. repressor proteins
B. transcriptional activator proteins
C. helicase proteins
D. single-strand binding proteins

33. Which cell group gives rise to muscles in a frog embryo?

A. neural tube
B. ectoderm
C. endoderm
D. mesoderm

34. Which is NOT involved in the implantation of the blastocyst?

A. Settling of the blastocyst onto the prepared uterine lining
B. Adherence of the trophoblast cells to the uterine lining
C. Inner cell mass giving rise to the primitive streak
D. Endometrium proteolytic enzymes produced by the trophoblast cells

35. During labor, which hormone stimulates contractions of uterine smooth muscle?

A. oxytocin
B. prolactin
C. luteinizing hormone
D. hCG

36. In a chick embryo, specific ectoderm cells give rise to wing feathers, while others develop into thigh feathers or feet claws. The ectodermal cells that develop into wing feathers were transplanted to an area that develops into thigh feathers or feet claws. It was observed that the transplanted cells developed into claws. Which of the following best explains the experimental results?

A. ectoderm cells possess positional information
B. destiny of the cells was already determined
C. ectoderm cells can develop into any tissue
D. the underlying mesoderm induced cells

37. The *slow block* to polyspermy is due to:

A. transient voltage changes across membrane
B. jelly coat blocking sperm penetration
C. consumption of yolk protein
D. formation of the fertilization envelope

38. Polyspermy in humans results in:

A. mitotic insufficiency
B. interruption of meiosis
C. nonviable zygote
D. multiple births

39. Mesoderm gives rise to:

A. intestinal mucosa
B. nerves
C. heart
D. lung epithelium

40. Genomic imprinting is:

A. inactivation of a gene by interruption of its coding sequence
B. organization of molecules in the cytoplasm to provide positional information
C. DNA modification in gametogenesis that affects gene expression in the zygote
D. suppression of a mutant phenotype because of a mutation in a different gene

41. Comparing a developing frog embryo and an adult, cells of which organism have a greater translation rate?

A. Adult, because ribosomal production is more efficient in a mature organism
B. Adult, because a mature organism has more complex metabolic requirements
C. Embryo, because a developing organism requires more protein production than an adult
D. Embryo, because ribosomal production is not yet under regulatory control by DNA

42. Which structure is the first to form during fertilization in humans?

A. blastula
B. morula
C. zygote
D. ectoderm

43. It is impossible for sperm to be functional (i.e., able to fertilize the egg) until after:

I. they undergo capacitation
II. the tail disappears
III. they have been in the uterus for several days
IV. they become spermatids

A. I only
B. II and IV only
C. I and IV only
D. I and III only

44. Where is the deformity if a teratogen affects endoderm development shortly after gastrulation?

A. nervous system
B. lens of the eye
C. liver
D. skeleton

45. Mutations that cause cells to undergo developmental fates of other cell types are:

A. heterochronic mutations
B. loss-of-function mutants
C. homeotic mutations
D. execution mutations

46. Each is true for the cells of an early gastrula's eye field, EXCEPT that they are:

A. terminally differentiated
B. competent
C. derived from the ectoderm layer
D. capable of becoming other ectoderm structures

47. What is the role of proteases and acrosin enzymes in reproduction?

A. They degrade the nucleus of the egg and allow the sperm to enter
B. They degrade the protective barriers around the egg and allow the sperm to penetrate
C. They direct the sperm to the egg through chemotaxis messengers
D. They neutralize the mucous secretions of the uterine mucosa

48. When does the human blastocyst implant in the uterine wall?

A. about a week past fertilization
B. at blastulation
C. a few hours past fertilization
D. at primary germ formation

49. Which primary layer develops into the retina of the eye?

I. endoderm II. ectoderm III. mesoderm

A. I only
B. II only
C. III only
D. II and III

50. What changes must occur in a newborn's cardiovascular system after the infant takes its first breath?

A. Ductus arteriosus constricts and is converted to the ligamentum arteriosum
B. The urinary system is activated at birth
C. Ductus venosus is severed from the umbilical cord, and visceral blood enters the vena cava
D. Foramen ovale between the atria of the fetal heart closes at birth

51. Early activation of the mammalian zygote nucleus may be necessary because:

A. most developmental decisions occur under the influence of the paternal genome
B. mammalian oocytes are too small to store molecules needed to support the cleavage divisions
C. in gametogenesis, specific genes undergo imprinting
D. mammals do not have maternal-effect genes

52. In reptiles, the aquatic environment necessary for the embryonic development of amphibians is replaced by:

A. amniotic fluid
B. humid atmospheric conditions
C. shells which prevent the escape of gas
D. intrauterine development

53. What would be expected to form from a portion of cells destined to become the heart if it were excised from an early gastrula and placed in a culture medium?

A. undifferentiated mesoderm
B. undifferentiated ectoderm
C. differentiated endoderm
D. undifferentiated endoderm

54. When can an ultrasound determine the sex of the fetus during gestation?

A. at the midpoint of the first trimester
B. about 18 weeks after fertilization
C. at the end of the first trimester
D. at the midpoint of the second trimester

55. How long is the egg viable and able to be fertilized after ovulation?

A. 36-72 hours
B. a full week
C. 12-24 hours
D. 24-36 hours

56. Which stage of embryonic development has a hollow ball of cells surrounding a fluid-filled center?

A. 3-layered gastrula
B. blastula
C. morula
D. zygote

57. Which statement describes the acrosome of a sperm cell?

A. It contains the nucleic acid
B. It contains hydrolytic enzymes which are released when the sperm encounters the jelly coat of the egg
C. It fuses with the egg's cortical granules
D. It functions to prevent polyspermy

58. Which statement about fertilization is correct?

A. Most sperm cells are protected and remain viable once inside the uterus
B. If estrogen is present, the pathway through the cervical opening is blocked from sperm entry
C. The vagina's acidic environment destroys millions of sperm cells
D. Spermatozoa remain viable for about 72 hours in the female reproductive tract

59. All statements are correct regarding cleavage in human embryos, EXCEPT:

A. blastomeres are genetically identical to the zygote
B. holoblastic cleavage occurs in one portion of the egg
C. morula is a solid mass of cells produced via cleavage of the zygote
D. size of the embryo remains constant throughout the initial cleavage of the zygote

Notes for active learning

Molecular Biology of Eukaryotes

1. Which primers should be used to amplify the DNA shown via PCR?

5' AAAA ——— GGGG 3'
3' TTTT ——— CCCC 5'

A. 5'-CCCC-3' and 5'-AAAA-3'
B. 5'-GGGG-3' and 5'-TTTT-3'
C. 5'-AAAA-3' and 5'-GGGG-3'
D. 5'-TTTT-3' and 5'-CCCC-3'

2. The major phenotypic expression of a genotype is in:

A. proteins
B. tRNA
C. mRNA
D. nucleic acids

3. Which molecule is used in DNA sequencing to cause termination when the template strand is G?

I. HO-P(O)(O⁻)-O-P(O)(O⁻)-O-P(O)(O⁻)-O-CH_2 Guanine (fluorescent labeled); H H

II. HO-P(O)(O⁻)-O-P(O)(O⁻)-O-P(O)(O⁻)-O-CH_2 Cytosine (fluorescent labeled); H H

III. HO-P(O)(O⁻)-O-P(O)(O⁻)-O-P(O)(O⁻)-O-CH_2 Cytosine (fluorescent labeled); OH OH

IV. HO-P(O)(O⁻)-O-CH_2 Cytosine (fluorescent labeled); H H

A. molecule I & III
B. molecule III & IV
C. molecule II
D. molecule IV

4. Which is NOT a part of post-translational protein modifications?

A. addition of a 3' poly-A tail
B. phosphorylation
C. methylation
D. glycosylation

5. A chromosome with its centromere in the middle is:

A. acrocentric
B. telocentric
C. metacentric
D. holocentric

6. Which is NOT an example of an environmental factor affecting how a gene is expressed?

A. Heat shock proteins are synthesized in cells after a temperature increase
B. *Drosophila* with specific genes develop bent wings when incubated at low temperatures and straight wings when incubated at elevated temperatures
C. Himalayan hares change hair color after cooling of the naturally warm regions
D. Shivering occurs after a decrease in body temperature

7. cDNA libraries contain:

A. promoters
B. intron portions of expressed genes
C. exon portions of expressed genes
D. non-expressed retrotransposons

8. Individual genes often encode for:

I. enzymes with tertiary structure
II. enzymes with quaternary structure
III. complex polysaccharides

A. I only
B. II only
C. I and II only
D. I, II and III

9. What enzyme is often used to make a genomic library?

A. restriction endonuclease
B. reverse transcriptase
C. deoxyribonuclease
D. DNA polymerase

10. Attachment of glycoprotein side chains and amino acid hydroxylation are post-translational modificátions. What is the site for protein glycosylation?

I. Lysosomes
II. Golgi apparatus
III. Rough endoplasmic reticulum

A. II only
B. III only
C. I and II only
D. II and III only

11. The enzyme used for restoring the ends of the DNA in a chromosome is:

A. telomerase
B. helicase
C. polymerase
D. gyrase

12. A cDNA library is generated using:

A. DNA from the region where the gene of interest is expressed
B. mRNA from the region where the gene of interest is expressed
C. mRNA from the region where the gene of interest is not expressed
D. rRNA from the region where the gene of interest is expressed

13. Which statement is the *central dogma* of molecular biology?

A. Information flow between DNA, RNA, and protein is reversible
B. Information flow in the cell is unidirectional, from protein to RNA to DNA
C. Information flow in the cell is unidirectional, from DNA to RNA to protein
D. The DNA sequence of a gene can be predicted from the amino acid sequence of the protein

14. What is alternative splicing?

A. Cleavage of peptide bonds to create different proteins
B. Cleavage of DNA to make different genes
C. Cleavage of hnRNA to make different mRNAs
D. A new method of splicing that does not involve snRNPs

15. This compound is synthesized by the nucleolus and is necessary for ribosomal function.

A. ribozyme
B. riboflavin
C. liposome
D. rRNA

16. *E. coli* RNA polymerase:

I. synthesizes RNA in the 5' to 3' direction
II. synthesizes RNA in the 3' to 5' direction
III. copies a DNA template
IV. copies an RNA template

A. I and III only
B. II and III only
C. I and IV only
D. II and IV only

17. Within primary eukaryotic transcripts, introns are:

A. often functioning as exons in other genes
B. different in size and number among different genes
C. joined to form mature mRNA
D. highly conserved in nucleotide sequence

18. Which statement(s) is/are TRUE for eukaryotic protein synthesis?

I. exons of mRNA are spliced together before translation
II. proteins must be spliced soon after translation
III. prokaryotic ribosomes are smaller than eukaryotic ribosomes

A. I only
B. II only
C. I and III only
D. I, II and III only

19. Which would decrease the transcription of retrotransposons?

I. Acetylation of histones associated with the retrotransposon
II. Deacetylation of histones associated with the retrotransposon
III. Methylation of retrotransposon DNA
IV. Loss of methylation of retrotransposon DNA

A. I and II only
B. I and III only
C. II and III only
D. III and IV only

20. Which is an exception to the principle of the *central dogma of molecular biology*?

A. yeast
B. retroviruses
C. bread mold
D. skin cells

21. miRNA is generated from the cleavage of:

A. double-stranded RNA
B. single-stranded RNA
C. double-stranded DNA
D. single-stranded DNA

22. The DNA polymerase cannot fully replicate the 3' DNA end, resulting in shorter DNA with each division. The new strand synthesis mechanism prevents the loss of the DNA coding region.

Which structure is at the location of new strand synthesis?

A. kinetochore
B. centrosome
C. telomere
D. centromere

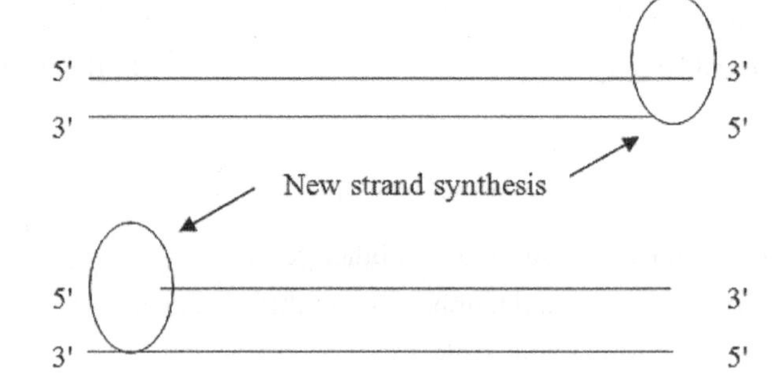

23. The cell structure composed of a core particle of 8 histones is:

A. telomere
B. nucleosome
C. kinetochore
D. centrosome

24. Which statement is correct about miRNA? (i.e., interference RNA):

I. It is a backup system for tRNA in the regulation of translation
II. It base-pairs with mRNA and causes it to be cleaved
III. It base-pairs with mRNA and prevents its translation

A. II only
B. I and II only
C. II and III only
D. I, II and III

25. The region of DNA in prokaryotes to which RNA polymerase binds most tightly is the:

A. promoter
B. poly C center
C. enhancer
D. operator site

26. Genomic libraries contain:

I. promoters
II. intron portions of genes
III. exon portions of genes
IV. retrotransposons

A. I and II only
B. I and III only
C. I, II and III only
D. I, II, III and IV

27. Which RNA molecule has a typical secondary structure of clover leaves and is relatively small?

A. hnRNA
B. mRNA
C. rRNA
D. tRNA

28. A chromosome when the sequence of grouped genes is reverse of the typical sequence has undergone:

A. translocation
B. inversion
C. duplication
D. deletion

29. If a drug inhibits ribosomal RNA synthesis, which eukaryotic organelle is most affected by this drug?

A. Golgi apparatus
B. lysosome
C. mitochondria
D. nucleolus

30. What evidence shows the AG gene is essential for forming reproductive organs in *Arabidopsis* flowers?

A. The AG gene encodes a miRNA
B. RNA blot experiments show that the AG gene is strongly expressed in flowers, leaves, and roots
C. The AG gene is in all flowering Arabidopsis plants
D. AG mutant flowers do not have reproductive organs

31. Which statement about the glycocalyx is FALSE?

A. May be composed of polysaccharide
B. May be composed of polypeptide
C. Protects from osmotic lysis
D. Is used to adhere to surfaces

32. Which does NOT affect chromatin structure?

A. tandem repeats
B. DNA acetylation
C. histone acetylation
D. chromatin remodeling proteins

33. Which enzyme maintains and regulates normal DNA coiling?

A. topoisomerase
B. helicase
C. DNA polymerase I
D. DNA polymerase III

34. RNA polymerase uses the two ribonucleotide triphosphates shown to make 5'-CG-3'. Which of the indicated phosphorous atoms participates in phosphodiester bond formation?

A. phosphorous atom A
B. phosphorous atom B
C. phosphorous atom C
D. phosphorous atom D

HO-P-O-P-O-P-O-CH_2 (Guanine) — O⁻ O⁻ O⁻ — A B — OH OH

HO-P-O-P-O-P-O-CH_2 (cytosine) — O⁻ O⁻ O⁻ — C D E — OH OH

35. When eukaryotic mRNA hybridizes with its corresponding DNA coding strand (i.e., heteroduplex analysis) and is visualized by electron microscopy, the looping strands of nucleic acid which are seen represent:

A. introns
B. exons
C. lariat structures
D. inverted repeats

36. Which statement does NOT accurately describe an aspect of the nucleosome?

A. an octet of proteins
B. a histone H1
C. first step in compacting the DNA in the nucleus
D. has DNA wrapped on the outside

37. Which is NOT a chemical component of a bacterial cell wall?

A. cellulose
B. peptidoglycan
C. teichoic acids
D. peptide chains

38. Combinatorial control of gene transcription in eukaryotes is when:

I. each transcription factor regulates only one gene
II. a single transcription factor regulates a combination of genes
III. presence or absence of a combination of transcription factors is required

A. I only
B. II only
C. II and III only
D. III only

39. Which post-transcriptional modifications have mature eukaryotic mRNAs undergone before being transported into the cytoplasm?

A. addition of 3' G-cap and 5' poly-A-tail, removal of introns, and splicing of exons
B. RNA splicing exons and removal of introns
C. RNA addition of 5' cap and 3' poly-A-tail
D. addition of 5' G-cap and 3' poly-A-tail, removal of introns, and splicing of exons

40. Which statement about gene expression is correct?

A. The ribosome binding site lies at the 3' end of mRNA
B. A second round of transcription can begin before the preceding transcript is completed
C. Only one gene can be within a given DNA sequence
D. Mistakes in transcription are corrected by RNA polymerase

41. Considering that in vitro, the transcription factor SP1 binds nucleic acids with high affinity, where would the radiolabeled SP1 likely NOT be found?

A. Golgi apparatus
B. mitochondria
C. nucleolus
D. ribosomes

42. During splicing, snRNA base pairs with:

A. hnRNA sequences in the intron
B. hnRNA sequences in the exon
C. DNA sequences in the intron
D. DNA sequences in the exon

43. Which macromolecule would be repaired rather than degraded?

A. triglyceride
B. polynucleotide
C. polypeptide
D. polysaccharide

44. The poly-A tail of RNA is:

A. encoded in the DNA sequence of the gene
B. added by the ribosome during translation
C. base paired with tRNA during translation initiation
D. enzymatically added soon after transcription is finished

45. Which histone is not part of the nucleosome core particle?

A. H3
B. H2B
C. H2A
D. H1

46. During splicing, the phosphodiester bond at the upstream exon/intron boundary is hydrolyzed by:

A. protein within the snRNP complex
B. 2'-OH of a base within the intron
C. 3'-OH of a base within the intron
D. RNA polymerase III

47. What is the expected charge, if any, on a histone that binds to DNA?

A. neutral
B. depends on the DNA conformation
C. positive
D. negative

48. RNA polymerase uses the two ribonucleotide triphosphates shown to make 5'-CG-3'. Which of the indicated oxygen atoms participates in phosphodiester bond formation?

A. oxygen atom A
B. oxygen atom B
C. oxygen atom C
D. oxygen atom D

HO-P-O-P-O-P-O-CH_2 Guanine; OH (A), OH (B)
HO-P-O-P-O-P-O-CH_2 Cytosine; OH (C), OH (D)

49. Chromosome regions with few functional genes are:

A. heterochromatin
B. mid-repetitive sequences
C. euchromatin
D. chromatids

50. Which is characteristic of prokaryotes only?

A. primary transcripts of RNA have introns
B. the processed RNA has a polyA tail
C. the processed RNA has a 5'-cap
D. transcription of the RNA occurs simultaneously with translation for the RNA

Notes for active learning

Notes for active learning

DNA and Protein Synthesis

1. DNA and RNA differ because:

A. only DNA contains phosphodiester bonds
B. only RNA contains pyrimidines
C. DNA is in the nucleus, and RNA is in the cytosol
D. RNA is associated with ribosomes, and DNA is associated with histones

2. In the 1920s, circumstantial evidence indicated that DNA was the genetic material. Which experiments led to the acceptance of this hypothesis?

A. Griffith's experiments with *Streptococcus pneumoniae*
B. Avery, MacLeod, and McCarty's work with isolating the transforming principle
C. Hershey and Chase's experiments with viruses and radioisotopes
D. A, B, and C were used to support this hypothesis

3. The N-glycosidic bond is relatively unstable within a guanine molecule and can be hydrolyzed through depurination. Which molecule is likely to undergo depurination?

A. sterols
B. lipids
C. phospholipids
D. DNA

4. What process duplicates a single gene?

A. Unequal recombination at repeated sequences that flank the gene
B. Equal recombination at repeated sequences that flank the gene
C. Unequal recombination within the single gene
D. Equal recombination within the single gene

5. Which element is NOT within nucleic acids?

A. nitrogen
B. oxygen
C. phosphorus
D. sulfur

6. Which RNA molecule is translated?

A. miRNA
B. tRNA
C. rRNA
D. mRNA

7. The aging of normal cells is associated with:

A. loss of telomerase activity
B. a decrease in contact inhibition
C. an increase in mutation rate
D. activation of the maturation promoting factor

8. Protein synthesis in eukaryotic cells initiates the following structure?

A. nucleus
B. Golgi
C. cytoplasm
D. rough endoplasmic reticulum

9. When a gene is duplicated on one chromatid, the gene on the other chromatid is:

A. duplicated
B. inverted
C. transposed to another site
D. deleted

10. Experiments by Avery, MacLeod and McCarty (1944) to identify the transforming principle were based on:

I. purifying each of the macromolecule types from a cell-free extract
II. removing each of the macromolecules from a cell, then testing its type
III. selectively destroying the different macromolecules in a cell-free extract

A. I only
B. II only
C. III only
D. I, II and III

11. What is the term for a blotting method where proteins are transferred from a gel to membranes and probed by antibodies to specific proteins?

A. Eastern blotting
B. Western blotting
C. Northern blotting
D. Southern blotting

12. The figure shows a nucleotide. At what position will the incoming nucleotide be attached?

A. position A
B. position B
C. position C
D. position D

13. All the following are correct about DNA, EXCEPT:

A. the strands are anti-parallel
B. the basic unit is a nucleotide
C. adenine and guanine are pyrimidines
D. guanine binds to cytosine via three hydrogen bonds

14. Tumor-suppressor genes normally control:

A. cell differentiation
B. necrosis
C. cell proliferation or activation of apoptosis
D. sister chromatid separation

15. Select the correct statement for aminoacyl tRNA synthetase.

A. It binds several different amino acids
B. It is an enzyme that uses energy from ATP to attach a specific amino acid to a tRNA
C. It is a tRNA that covalently binds amino acids
D. It synthesizes tRNA

16. Griffith's experiment in 1928 with pneumococcus demonstrated that:

A. smooth bacteria can survive heating
B. DNA, not protein, is the genetic molecule
C. materials from dead organisms can affect and change organisms
D. nonliving viruses can change living cells

17. The genetic code deciphered by Noble laureate Marshall W. Nirenberg (1927-2010) in 1964 encodes each amino acid by three nucleotides (codons). How many codons exist in nature to encode 20 amino acids in polypeptides?

A. 4
B. 20
C. 27
D. 64

18. What mechanism targets proteins to organelles (e.g., chloroplast, mitochondrion)?

A. Addition of phosphate groups to the protein
B. Synthesizing the proteins as zymogens
C. A signal sequence at the N-terminus of the polypeptide
D. Cysteine bond formation

19. When DNA is treated with 2-aminopurine, adenine is replaced by guanine on one strand. During replication, the complementary strand will have a substitution of:

A. guanine for adenine
B. adenine for guanine
C. cytosine for thymine
D. thymine for cytosine

20. Before Nobel laureate Marshall W. Nirenberg *et al.* determined the genetic code experimentally in 1964, why was it hypothesized that each codon would contain at least three bases?

A. Three bases are needed to produce a stable codon structure
B. There were three known nucleotide bases
C. There were more proteins than nucleotide bases
D. Three bases can form $4^3 = 64$ pairs, which is enough to encode 20 amino acids

21. DNA of bacteria grown in a heavy (^{15}N) medium was isolated and added to an *in vitro* synthesis system. The bacteria were grown in a light (^{14}N) medium. After several hours, a sample of DNA was taken and analyzed for differing densities. How many DNA densities were in the sample after 2 generations?

A. 1
B. 2
C. 4
D. 8

22. Which experimental procedure simultaneously measures the level of all mRNAs in a tissue?

I. Northern blot   II. *In situ* hybridization   III. Microarray experiment

A. I only
B. II only
C. III only
D. I, II and III

23. To demonstrate that DNA is the "transforming principle," Avery, MacLeod, and McCarty (1944) showed that DNA could transform nonvirulent strains of pneumococcus. Their hypothesis was strengthened by their demonstration that:

A. enzymes that destroyed proteins also destroyed transforming activity
B. enzymes that destroyed nucleic acids also destroyed transforming activity
C. enzymes that destroyed complex carbohydrates also destroyed transforming activity
D. the transforming activity was destroyed by boiling

24. Which component of the codon-anticodon hybridization on ribosomes determines the fidelity of protein synthesis?

A. mRNA & tRNA
B. mRNA & rRNA
C. tRNA & rRNA
D. DNA & RNA polymerase

25. Which procedure measures mRNA levels from only a single gene?

I. Northern blot   II. *In situ* hybridization   III. Microarray analysis

A. II only
B. I and II only
C. II and III only
D. I, II and III

26. Which stage of cell division is the stage when chromosomes replicate?

A. prophase
B. interphase
C. anaphase
D. metaphase

27. If the transcript's sequence is 5'-CUAAGGGCUAC-3', what is the sequence of the DNA template?

A. 3'-GUAGCCCUUAG-5'
B. 5'-GTAGCCCTTAG-3'
C. 5'-GTAACCCTTAG-3'
D. 5'-GUTACCUGUAG-3'

28. Duplicated genes:

A. are more common in prokaryote genomes than in eukaryote genomes
B. are closely related but diverged in sequence and function over evolutionary time
C. never encode for essential proteins, such as transcription factors
D. encode for proteins that catalyze different steps of a biochemical pathway

29. The Hershey–Chase experiment:

A. proved that DNA replication is semiconservative
B. used ^{32}P to label protein
C. used ^{35}S to label DNA
D. supported the hypothesis that DNA is the transforming molecule

30. Which statement is NOT correct about DNA replication?

A. DNA polymerase synthesizes and proofreads the DNA
B. RNA primers are necessary for the hybridization of the polymerase
C. Ligase relaxes positive supercoils that accumulate as the replication fork opens
D. DNA polymerase adds Okazaki fragments in a 5' → 3' direction

31. Which structure represents a peptide bond between adjacent amino acids?

A. structure A
B. structure B
C. structure C
D. structure D

A. H–N–C–C–N–C–C–O–H

C. H–N–C–C–O–N–C–C–O–H

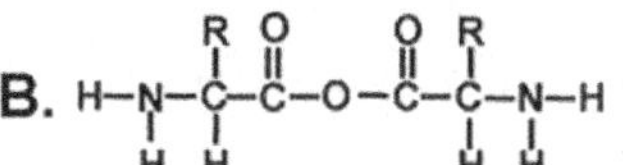
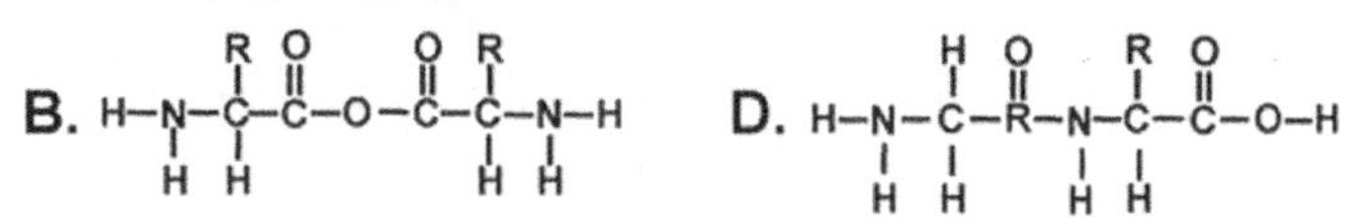

32. All statements apply to proteins, EXCEPT:

A. they regulate cell membrane trafficking
B. they catalyze chemical reactions
C. they can be hormones
D. they undergo self-replication

33. Eukaryote RNA polymerase usually:

A. binds to the TATAA promoter sequence and initiates transcription
B. needs general transcription factors to bind to the promoter and initiate basal-level transcription
C. needs specific regulatory transcription factors to bind to the promoter and initiate basal-level transcription
D. transcribes tRNA genes

34. If an RNA sequence has a cytosine content of 25%, what is its adenine content?

A. 50%
B. cannot be determined
C. 12.5%
D. 25%

35. If a portion of prokaryotic mRNA has the base sequence 5′-ACUACUA<u>U</u>GCGUCGA-3′, what could result from a mutation where the underlined base is changed to A?

I. truncation of the polypeptide
II. inhibition of initiation of translation
III. no effect on protein synthesis

A. I and II only
B. I and III only
C. II and III only
D. III only

36. Which statement is INCORRECT about the genetic code?

A. Many amino acids are specified by more than one codon
B. Most codons specify more than one amino acid
C. There are multiple stop codons
D. Codons are three bases in length

37. In bacteria, the enzyme that removes the RNA primers is:

A. DNA ligase
B. primase
C. reverse transcriptase
D. DNA polymerase I

38. Okazaki fragments are:

A. synthesized in a 5'→ 3' direction by DNA polymerase I
B. covalently linked by DNA polymerase I
C. synthesized in a 5'→ 3' direction by DNA polymerase III
D. components of DNA synthesized to fill in gaps after excision of the RNA primer

39. Peptide bond synthesis is catalyzed by:

A. tRNA in the cytoplasm
B. ribosomal proteins
C. ribosomal RNA
D. mRNA in the ribosome

40. Which statement does NOT apply to protein synthesis?

A. The process does not require energy
B. rRNA is required for proper binding of the mRNA message
C. tRNA molecules shuttle amino acids assembled into the polypeptide
D. The amino acid is bound to the 3' end of the tRNA

41. All statements about PCR are correct, EXCEPT:

A. PCR can be used to obtain large quantities of a particular DNA sequence
B. PCR does not require knowledge of the terminal DNA sequences of the region to be amplified
C. PCR uses a DNA polymerase to synthesize DNA
D. PCR uses short synthetic oligonucleotide primers

42. The shape of a tRNA is determined primarily by:

A. its number of bases
B. proteins that bind it
C. tRNA and aminoacyl tRNA synthetase interactions
D. intramolecular base pairing

43. In prokaryotic cells, methylated guanine contributes to:

A. increased rate of DNA replication
B. correcting mismatched pairs of bases
C. correcting the separation of DNA strands
D. proofreading the replicated strands

44. In the polymerization reaction by DNA polymerase, what is the function of magnesium?

$$\text{Primer (free 3' OH)} + \text{5' PPP} \xrightarrow[\text{Mg}^{+2}\text{, 4 dNTPs, DNA polymerase}]{} \text{Primer 3'O-P-5'} + \text{PPi}$$

A. cofactor
B. monovalent metal ion
C. substrate
D. enzyme

45. The structure of the ribosome is created by:

I. internal base-pairing of rRNA
II. ribosomal proteins
III. internal base-pairing of mRNA
IV. internal base-pairing of tRNA

A. I only
B. II only
C. I and II only
D. I, II and IV only

46. Which statement is true for tRNA?

A. It has some short double-stranded segments
B. It has a poly-A tail
C. It is produced in the nucleolus
D. It is a long molecule of RNA

47. Which chemical group is at the 5' end of a single polynucleotide strand?

A. diester group
B. purine base
C. hydroxyl group
D. phosphate group

48. The drug aminoacyl-tRNA is an analog of Puromycin. Both have an amino group capable of forming a peptide bond, but Puromycin lacks a carboxyl group to form another peptide bond. What is the effect of adding Puromycin to bacteria undergoing protein synthesis?

A. Inhibition of initiation of protein synthesis
B. Inhibition of entry of aminoacyl-tRNA into the P site during elongation
C. Termination of protein synthesis via covalent attachment of Puromycin
D. Substitution of Puromycin for another amino acid in the protein, yielding a normal length protein

49. In *E. coli* cells, DNA polymerase I:

I. synthesizes most of the Okazaki fragments
II. simultaneously copies both strands of DNA
III. degrades the RNA primer portion of Okazaki fragments

A. I only
B. II only
C. III only
D. I and III only

50. During DNA synthesis, the error rate is about one mismatched nucleotide per:

A. 100
B. 1,000
C. 10,000
D. 1,000,000

51. All the following are in a molecule of DNA, EXCEPT:

A. nitrogenous bases
B. phosphodiester bonds
C. polypeptide bonds
D. deoxyribose sugars

52. In *E. coli* cells, DNA polymerase III:

A. synthesizes most of the Okazaki fragments
B. removes the RNA primer
C. is the only DNA polymerase used by *E. coli* during replication
D. degrades the RNA portion of an Okazaki fragment

53. Which molecule belongs to a different chemical category than the others?

A. cysteine
B. guanine
C. adenine
D. thymine

54. An enzyme that cleaves DNA at the sequence-specific site is:

A. restriction endonuclease
B. exonuclease
C. DNA polymerase
D. ligase

55. *E. coli* RNA polymerase-initiated transcription and synthesized one phosphodiester bond. Which molecule shown is RNA polymerase made from?

A.
HO-P(=O)(O⁻)-O-P(=O)(O⁻)-O-P(=O)(O⁻)-O-CH_2 Base
O H
O=P-O-CH_2 Base
O^-
OH H

B.
HO-P(=O)(O⁻)-O-CH_2 Base
O OH
O=P-O-CH_2 Base
O^-
OH OH

C.
HO-P(=O)(O⁻)-O-P(=O)(O⁻)-O-P(=O)(O⁻)-O-CH_2 Base
O OH
O=P-O-CH_2 Base
O^-
OH OH

D.
HO-P(=O)(O⁻)-O-P(=O)(O⁻)-O-P(=O)(O⁻)-O-CH_2 Base
OH O
O=P-O-CH_2 Base
O^-
OH OH

56. What rate does PCR increase the amount of DNA during each additional cycle?

A. additively
B. exponentially
C. linearly
D. systematically

57. Which is in RNA but absent in DNA?

A. additional hydroxyl group
B. hydrogen bonds
C. thymine
D. double helix

58. After the new DNA strands are synthesized, which enzyme completes the process of DNA replication?

A. primase
B. ligase
C. helicase
D. reverse transcriptase

59. When a base pairs with its complementary strand, which strand would have the highest melting point?

A. TTAGTCTC
B. GCCAGTCG
C. AGCTTCGT
D. CGCGTATA

60. A technique that investigates gene functions by mutating wildtype genes is:

A. contig building
B. transgenetics
C. reverse genetics
D. gene therapy

61. How many high-energy phosphate bonds are needed to translate a 50-amino acid polypeptide (starting with mRNA, tRNA, amino acids, and the necessary enzymes)?

A. 49
B. 50
C. 101
D. 199

62. The mRNA in *E. coli* cells is composed primarily of:

A. four bases – A, T, C, G
B. phosphodiester linkages connecting deoxyribonucleotide molecules
C. two strands that base pair in an anti-parallel orientation
D. phosphodiester linkages connecting ribonucleotide molecules

63. Which statement about mismatch repair of DNA is correct?

A. DNA is scanned for any base-pairing mismatches after methyl groups are added to guanines
B. Errors in replication made by DNA polymerase are corrected on the unmethylated strand
C. The proofreading mechanism removes all abnormal bases
D. Repairs from high-energy radiation damage are made

64. What is the first amino acid of each protein of eukaryotic cells?

A. methionine
B. glutamate
C. valine
D. proline

65. DNA in *E. coli* is composed of:

I. four bases – A, T, C, G
II. phosphodiester linkages that connect deoxyribonucleotide molecules
III. two strands that base pair in an anti-parallel orientation
IV. phosphodiester linkages that utilize the 3'-OH

A. I and II only
B. I and III only
C. I, II and III only
D. I, II, III and IV

66. If a peptide has the sequence val-ser-met-pro and the tRNA molecules used in its synthesis have the corresponding sequence of anticodons 3'-CAG-5', 3'-UCG-5', 3'-UAC-5', 3'-UUU-5', what sequence of the DNA codes for this peptide?

A. 5'–CAGTCGTACTTT–3'
B. 5'–TTTCATGCTGAC–3'
C. 5'–GACGCTCATTTT–3'
D. 5'–UUUCAUGCUGAC–3'

67. The site of the DNA template that RNA polymerase binds during transcription is:

A. promoter
B. leader sequence
C. enhancer
D. domain

68. Which dipeptide is synthesized by a ribosome?

A. isoleucine-glycine
B. cytosine-guanine
C. proline-thymine
D. uracil-glutamic acid

69. Which is the correct order of events in delivering a protein to its cellular destination?

A. Signal sequence binds to docking protein → membrane channel forms → chaperonins unfold protein → protein enters the organelle → protein refolds
B. Membrane channel forms → signal sequence binds to docking protein → chaperonins unfold protein → protein enters the organelle → protein refolds
C. Chaperonins unfold protein → signal sequence binds to docking protein → membrane channel forms → protein enters the organelle → protein refolds
D. Membrane channel forms → chaperonins unfold protein → signal sequence binds to docking protein → protein enters the organelle → protein refolds

70. Select the correct mRNA sequences depending on the direction RNA polymerase transcribes.

	RNA sequence if RNA polymerase goes left:	RNA sequence if RNA polymerase goes right:
A.	5'-GGG-3'	5'-AAA-3'
B.	5'-GGG-3'	5'-UUU-3'
C.	5'-CCC-3'	5'-AAA-3'
D.	5'-CCC-3'	5'-UUU-3'

Left ← → Right
3' C C C A A A 5'
5' G G G T T T 3'
RNA polymerase

71. Which statement is TRUE for the base composition of DNA?

A. In double-stranded DNA, the number of G bases equals the number of T bases
B. In double-stranded DNA, the number of A bases equals the number of T bases
C. In double-stranded DNA, the number of C bases equals the number of T bases
D. In every single strand, the number of A bases equals the number of T bases

72. The figure shows a replication fork in *E. coli*. Which of the indicated sites is the 3' of the lagging strand?

A. site A
B. site B
C. site C
D. site D

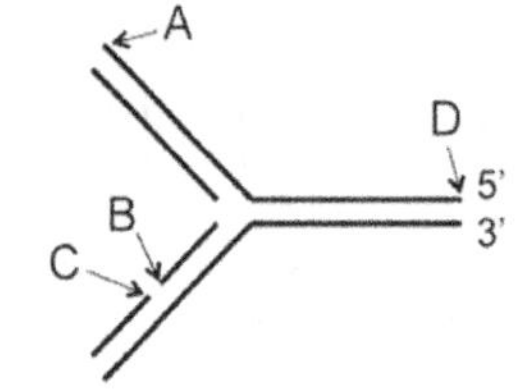

73. Ribosomal subunits are isolated from bacteria grown in a "heavy" ^{13}C and ^{15}N medium and added to an *in vitro* system that actively synthesizes protein. Following translation, a sample is removed and centrifuged. Which would be the best illustration of centrifugation results?

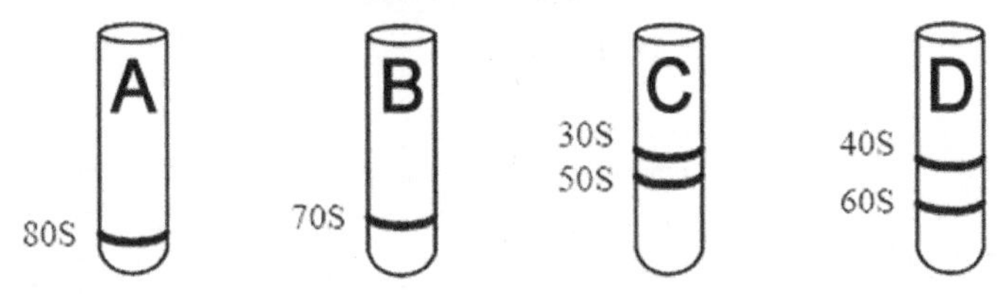

A. Test tube A
B. Test tube B
C. Test tube C
D. Test tube D

74. Which statement is TRUE?

A. polypeptides are synthesized by the addition of amino acids to the amino terminus
B. prokaryotic RNA usually undergoes nuclear processing
C. RNA polymerase has a proof-reading activity
D. 3' end of mRNA corresponds to the carboxyl terminus of the protein

75. A codon for histidine is 5'-CAU-3'. The anticodon in the tRNA that brings histidine to the ribosome is:

A. 5'-CAU-3'
B. 5'-GUA-3'
C. 5'-UAC-3'
D. 5'-AUG-3'

76. During translation elongation, the existing polypeptide chain is transferred to which site as the ribosome moves in the 3' direction?

A. tRNA occupying the A site
B. tRNA occupying the P site
C. ribosomal rRNA
D. signal recognition particle

77. Which is the primer to amplify the DNA fragments *via* PCR?

5′-ATCGGTATGTAACGCTCACCTGT-3′

A. 5′-ACAG-3′
B. 5′-AGAC-3′
C. 5′-TAGC-3′
D. 5′-GACT-3′

78. Which statement about the genetic code is FALSE?

A. It is mostly the same for *E. coli* and humans
B. It is redundant
C. It is ambiguous
D. It has one codon for starting translation

79. What portion of the polypeptide chain is responsible for establishing and maintaining the force that stabilizes the secondary structure?

A. C-terminus
B. N-terminus
C. carbonyl oxygen
D. R-groups

80. A ribosome has made a tripeptide, MET-ARG-SER, attached to the tRNA in the P site. Using the genetic code table, what codon is in the E site of the ribosome?

A. AUG
B. CGU
C. UCA
D. UGA

81. A ribosome has made a tripeptide, MET-ARG-SER, attached to the tRNA in the P site. Using the genetic code table, what codon is in the A site of the ribosome?

A. AUG
B. CGU
C. UCA
D. It cannot be determined

First base (5' end)	Second base: U	C	A	G	Third base (3' end)
U	UUU Phe	UCU Ser	UAU Tyr	UGU Cys	U
	UUC	UCC	UAC	UGC	C
	UUA Leu	UCA	UAA Stop	UGA Stop	A
	UUG	UCG	UAG Stop	UGG Trp	G
C	CUU Leu	CCU Pro	CAU His	CGU Arg	U
	CUC	CCC	CAC	CGC	C
	CUA	CCA	CAA Gln	CGA	A
	CUG	CCG	CAG	CGG	G
A	AUU Ile	ACU Thr	AAU Asn	AGU Ser	U
	AUC	ACC	AAC	AGC	C
	AUA	ACA	AAA Lys	AGA Arg	A
	AUG Met start	ACG	AAG	AGG	G
G	GUU Val	GCU Ala	GAU Asp	GGU Gly	U
	GUC	GCC	GAC	GGC	C
	GUA	GCA	GAA Glu	GGA	A
	GUG	GCG	GAG	GGG	G

Notes for active learning

Notes for active learning

Evolution and Natural Selection

1. During his trip to the Galapagos Islands in 1835, Charles Darwin observed that:

A. local fossils were not related to contemporary organisms of that region
B. all organisms were related
C. organisms in tropical regions were closely related independent of the region
D. several species of finches varied from island to island

2. In evolutionary terms, organisms belonging to which category would be the most similar?

A. genus
B. family
C. order
D. kingdom

3. What is the source of genetic variation for natural selection?

A. gene duplication
B. mitosis
C. meiosis
D. mutation

4. In modern evolutionary theory, chloroplasts descended from:

A. free-living cyanobacteria
B. red algae
C. mitochondria
D. aerobic prokaryote

5. Speciation is the evolution of new, genetically distinct populations from a common ancestral stock by:

I. random mutation II. geographic isolation III. reduction of gene flow

A. I and III only
B. II and III only
C. I and II only
D. I, II, and III

6. Darwin (1809-1882) hypothesized that the mechanism of evolution involves:

A. selective pressure
B. epigenetics
C. natural selection
D. selective breeding

7. The complexity of the organisms that exist on earth today is the result of:

I. multicellularity II. photosynthesis III. eukaryotic cell development

A. I only
B. II only
C. I and II only
D. I, II and III

8. The Archaean Eon contains the oldest known fossil record dating to about:

A. 1.5 billion years
B. 2.0 million years
C. 7,000 years
D. 3.5 billion years

9. The Urey-Miller experiment at the University of Chicago in 1952 demonstrates that:

A. life may have evolved from inorganic precursors
B. humans have evolved from photosynthetic cyanobacteria
C. life existed on prehistoric earth
D. small biological molecules cannot be synthesized from inorganic material

10. To ensure the survival of their species, animals that do not care for their young:

A. have protective coloring
B. produce many offspring
C. lay eggs
D. can live in water and on land

11. Which describes the relationship between nitrogen-fixing bacteria that derive nutrition from plants and plants that benefit from the nitrogen supplied by the bacteria?

A. parasitism
B. commensalism
C. mutualism
D. mimicry

12. Which selection type leads to speciation?

A. sexual selection
B. stabilizing selection
C. directional selection
D. disruptive selection

13. The similarity among the embryos of fish, amphibians, reptiles, and humans is evidence of:

A. genetic drift
B. sexual selection
C. analogous traits
D. common ancestry

14. Selective breeding of soybeans by humans has genetically altered the soybean so that it could not survive in the wild without human intervention. The soybean population is controlled, and most soybean seeds are eaten or spoiled. The relationship between humans and soybeans is best described as:

A. mutualism, because both species benefit
B. parasitism, because humans benefit, and soybeans are harmed
C. commensalism, because there is no benefit to either species
D. commensalism, because humans benefit, and soybeans are neither benefited nor harmed

15. Natural selection leads to:

A. larger population
B. population most adapted to its environment
C. phenotypic diversity
D. broad genetic variation

16. From an evolutionary perspective, which cell property is paramount?

A. passing genetic information to progeny
B. containing a nucleus
C. containing mitochondria
D. interacting with other cells

17. Inherited traits determined by elements of heredity are:

A. crossing over
B. homologous chromosomes
C. locus
D. genes

18. Which statement is correct about the evolutionary process?

A. Organisms develop traits that they need for survival
B. Mutations decrease the rate of evolution
C. Natural selection works on traits that cannot be inherited
D. Natural selection works on existing genetic variation within a population

19. Genetic drift results from:

A. environmental change
B. genetic diversity
C. probability
D. sexual selection

20. The likely result of polygenic inheritance is:

A. human height
B. blood type
C. freckles
D. polydactyly (extra digits)

21. Which of the following is the earliest form of life to evolve on Earth?

A. plants
B. eukaryotes
C. prokaryotes
D. protists

22. If two animals produce viable, fertile offspring under natural conditions, it can be concluded that:

A. for any given allele, they have the same gene
B. their blood types are compatible
C. they have haploid somatic cells
D. they are from the same species

23. The population's total collection of alleles at any one time makes up its:

A. phenotype
B. biodiversity
C. gene pool
D. genotype

24. A pivotal point in Darwin's explanation of evolution is that:

A. biological structures inherited are those better suited to the environment through constant use
B. mutations that occur are those that help future generations fit into their environments
C. any trait that confers even a slight increase in the probability that its possessor will survive and reproduce will be strongly favored and spread through the population
D. genes change to help organisms cope with problems encountered within their environments

25. If one allele frequency in a population is 0.7, what is the alternate allele frequency?

A. 0.14
B. 0.21
C. 0.30
D. 0.4

26. Which statement about evolution is CORRECT?

A. Darwin's theory of natural selection relies solely on environmental conditions
B. Natural selection is when random mutations are selected for survival by the environment
C. Darwin's theory of natural selection relies solely on genetic mutation
D. Lamarck's theory of use and disuse adequately describes why giraffes have long necks

27. A significant genetic drift may be prevented by:

A. random mutations
B. large population size
C. small population size
D. genetic variation

28. Which statement applies to a population that survived a bottleneck and recovered to its original size?

A. It is subject to genetic drift
B. It is less likely to get extinct than before the bottleneck
C. It has more genetic variation than before the bottleneck
D. It has less genetic variation than before the bottleneck

29. The difference between the founder effect and a population bottleneck is that the founder effect:

A. only occurs in island populations
B. requires the isolation of a small group from a larger population
C. requires a large gene pool
D. involves sexual selection

30. Which compound was unnecessary for the origin of life on Earth?

A. carbon
B. O_2
C. hydrogen
D. H_2O

31. In a community of humans, there is a higher rate of polydactyly (extra fingers or toes) than in the human population. The likely explanation is:

A. bottleneck effect
B. founder effect
C. sexual selection
D. natural selection

32. Gene flow occurs through:

A. random mutations
B. bottleneck effect
C. migration
D. directional selection

33. The first living organisms on Earth derived their energy from:

A. eating dead organisms
B. eating organic molecules
C. the sun
D. eating each other

34. Evolutionary fitness measures:

A. population size
B. reproductive success
C. gene pool size
D. genetic load

35. Which scientist would explain the hawk's lost flying ability with a theory that "Since the hawk stopped using its wings, the wings became smaller, and this acquired trait was passed on to the offspring"?

A. Lamarck
B. de Vries
C. Mendel
D. Darwin

36. Which example is a result of directional selection?

A. Increased number of cat breeds
B. Python snakes with distinct color patterns exhibit different behavior when threatened
C. Female *Drosophila* select usual yellowish-grey colored males over less common, yellow-colored males
D. Non-poisonous butterflies evolving color changes to look like poisonous butterflies

37. A genetic variation would be decreased by:

A. stabilizing selection
B. balancing selection
C. directional selection
D. sexual selection

38. Asexually reproducing species have a selective disadvantage over sexually reproducing species because sexual reproduction:

A. always decreases an offspring's survival ability
B. decreases the likelihood of mutations
C. creates novel genetic recombination
D. is more energy efficient

39. Which example is a result of stabilizing selection?

A. Female *Drosophila* select typical yellowish-grey colored males to mate over less common yellow colored males
B. Increased number of different breeds within one species
C. Non-poisonous butterflies evolving color changes to look like poisonous butterflies
D. Female birds that lay an intermediate number of eggs have the highest reproductive success

40. According to one theory about the origins of life, these molecules were formed by purines, pyrimidines, sugars, and phosphates combining:

A. lipids
B. carbohydrates
C. nucleosides
D. nucleotides

41. Which example is a result of sexual selection?

A. Female deer choosing to mate with males with the biggest antlers
B. Python snakes with assorted color patterns exhibit different behavior when threatened
C. Non-poisonous butterflies evolving color changes that make them look like poisonous butterflies
D. Increased number of different breeds within one species

42. Some fossils from before the Cambrian Explosion are embryos, suggesting that the organisms belong to:

A. reproduce sexually
B. exhibit cephalization
C. reproduce asexually
D. have bilateral symmetry

43. The Cambrian Explosion resulted in the evolution of the first:

A. bacteria
B. land animals
C. dinosaurs and mammals
D. representatives of most animal phyla

44. A primate's ability to hold objects in its hands or feet is an evolutionary development necessary for it to:

A. create elaborate social systems
B. consume food
C. use simple tools
D. walk upright

45. Suppose a paleontologist discovers a fossil skull that he believes might be distantly related to primates. Unlike true primates, the face is not flat, and the eyes do not face entirely forward. The paleontologist would likely conclude that the animal lacked the ability to:

A. manipulate tools
B. judge the location of tree branches
C. form extended family groups
D. grip branches precisely

46. When an animal's environment changes, sexual reproduction improves a species' ability to:

A. increase its numbers rapidly
B. produce genetically identical offspring
C. react to new stimuli
D. adapt to new living conditions

47. Researchers have concluded that Dikika Baby was a better climber than modern humans. This evidence suggests that Dikika Baby's relatives may have spent part of their time:

A. hunting in groups
B. waging war on other troops
C. using tools
D. in trees

48. Fossil evidence indicates that *Australopithecus afarensis:*

A. was bipedal
B. appeared later than *Homo ergaster*
C. was primarily a meat-eater
D. had a large brain

49. One way in which reptiles are adapted to fully terrestrial life is:

A. endothermy
B. viviparous development
C. external fertilization
D. amniotic egg

50. Researchers concluded from the leg bones of the fossil Lucy (discovered in 1974) that it was bipedal. Which would indicate that this hominine was bipedal?

A. bowl-shaped pelvis
B. opposable thumbs
C. skull with a flat face
D. broad rib cage

51. Which statement is true of *Homo sapiens?*

A. They replaced *Homo habilis* in the Middle East
B. They became extinct about 1 million years ago
C. They have been Earth's only hominine for the last 24,000 years
D. They evolved after the Cro-Magnons

52. Which of the following was a unique characteristic of Neanderthals?

A. Producing tools from bones and antlers
B. Burying their dead with simple rituals
C. Making sophisticated stone blades
D. Producing cave paintings

Notes for active learning

Notes for active learning

Animal Behavior and Evolution

1. Which behavior must be learned from another animal?

A. potato washing in macaques
B. suckling of newborn mammals
C. web building in spiders
D. nest building in birds

2. A cat hears a rustling in the leaves that sounds like a mouse digging for food. The cat crouched, becoming still, and focused on the leaves as it waited to pounce. This combination of movements is an example of:

A. behavior
B. stimulus
C. imprinting
D. circadian rhythm

3. For a behavior to evolve under the influence of natural selection, that behavior must be:

A. acquired through learning
B. influenced by genes
C. related to predator avoidance
D. neither adaptive nor harmful

4. If a dog that barks indoors is always let outside immediately, it learns to bark whenever it wants to go outside. This change in the dog's behavior is an example of:

A. imprinting
B. insight learning
C. operant conditioning
D. classical conditioning

5. A behavior is innate, rather than learned, when:

A. all individuals perform the behavior the same way each time
B. individuals become better at performing the behavior the more they practice it
C. some individuals perform the behavior, and some do not
D. the behavior is different in individuals with different experiences

6. The terms "inborn behavior" and "instinct" have the same meaning as:

A. courtship behavior
B. imprinting
C. learned behavior
D. innate behavior

7. When disturbed, certain moths lift their front wings to expose eyelike markings on their hind wings. This behavior would be most effective against predators that hunt by:

A. touch
B. sight
C. smell
D. sound

8. Which learning occurs when a stimulus produces a particular response because it is associated with a positive or negative experience:

A. trial-and-error learning
B. habituation
C. operant conditioning
D. classical conditioning

9. Certain behaviors are innate in animals because they are essential for:

A. acquiring other behaviors
B. developing a circadian rhythm
C. survival immediately after birth
D. guarding territory

10. Imprinting is a form of behavior that:

A. occurs during a specific time in young animals
B. always involves the sense of sight
C. is restricted to birds
D. is often used in the training of adult animals

11. When people first move into an apartment near railroad tracks, they are awakened when they hear a train. Which response to the sound of the train would result from habituation?

A. People begin to sleep through the sound of the train over the next few nights
B. People learn that they can cover the sound of the train by sleeping with the radio on
C. People associate the sound of the train with the arrival of the morning newspaper
D. People learn they can sleep between the times that the train travels by their home

12. Aquarium fish swim to the water's surface when a person approaches. Their behavior has formed through:

A. imprinting
B. insight learning
C. instinct
D. classical conditioning

13. Which chemical signals do insects use to affect the behavior or development of others of the same species?

A. cilia
B. spiracles
C. pheromones
D. peptidoglycans

14. The ability of salmon to recognize their home stream at spawning time is an example of:

A. communication
B. imprinting
C. competition
D. insight learning

15. Learning occurs whenever:

A. a stimulus does not affect an animal the first time the animal encounters the stimulus
B. an animal leaves a chemical scent on its territory
C. a stimulus causes an animal to change its behavior
D. an animal performs a task perfectly without prior experience

16. The appearance of fireflies at dusk is an example of a circadian rhythm because it:

A. happens daily
B. happens seasonally
C. is related to the phase of the moon
D. is related to the temperature of the air

17. During migration, animals:

A. search for new permanent habitats
B. enter a sleep-like state
C. repeat their daily cycle of behavior
D. conduct seasonal movement

18. The theory stating that helping family members survive increases the probability one's genes will be passed to offspring is:

A. competition
B. classical conditioning
C. kin selection
D. imprinting

19. In winter, bears settle into dens and enter a sleep-like state until spring. This state is:

A. imprinting
B. aggression
C. hibernation
D. migration

20. When a bird learns to press a button to get food, it has learned by:

A. insight learning
B. operant conditioning
C. classical conditioning
D. habituation

21. To survive during winter, when resources are scarce, some animals enter a sleep-like state of:

A. reproductive rhythm
B. territoriality
C. ritual
D. circadian rhythm

22. In some species of balloon flies, males spin balloons of silk and carry them while flying. If a female approaches a male and accepts his balloon, the two will fly off to mate. This behavior is an example of:

A. courtship
B. language
C. aggression
D. territorial defense

23. Members of a society:

A. act independently for each's benefit
B. are usually unrelated to one another
C. belong to at least two species
D. belong to the same species and interact closely with each other

24. Animals that use language are likely those with the greatest capacity for:

A. habituation
B. insight learning
C. behavioral cycles
D. innate behavior

25. An animal can benefit most by defending a territory if:

A. the animals it defends against do not use the same resources
B. there are more than enough resources in that territory for all competitors
C. that territory has more resources than surrounding areas
D. that territory has many predators

26. An innate behavior:

A. requires reasoning
B. occurs with trial and error
C. requires habituation
D. appears in fully functional form the first time it is performed

27. It is advantageous for grazing mammals to gather in groups because groups:

A. offer greater protection from predation
B. are more difficult for predators to locate than are individuals
C. can migrate more easily than individuals can
D. can make the available food resources last longer

28. Nocturnal animals with a poorly developed sense of smell are likely to communicate by:

A. pheromones
B. chemical signals
C. auditory signals
D. visual displays

29. Many cat species mark their territory by rubbing glands on their faces against surfaces such as tree trunks. This form of communication relies on:

A. chemical messenger
B. defensive display
C. visual signal
D. sound signal

30. When an animal associates a stimulus with a reward or a punishment, it has learned by:

A. imprinting
B. operant conditioning
C. habituation
D. classical conditioning

31. Cephalopods (i.e., squid and octopi) can communicate by changing skin colors and patterns. This communication is an example of:

A. visual signal
B. language
C. sound signal
D. chemical signal

32. Dolphins communicate with one another mainly through:

A. chemical signals
B. pheromones
C. auditory signals
D. visual displays

33. When newly hatched ducklings separated from their mother, follow a person swimming in a pond is:

A. imprinting
B. instrumental conditioning
C. discrimination
D. response to pheromones

Notes for active learning

Classification and Diversity

1. *Canis lupus* is a wolf in the Canidae family. Which statement is accurate about its members?

   A. They may be classified as *lupus* but not *Canis*
   B. They may be classified as *Canis* but not Canidae
   C. More are classified as *lupus* than *Canis*
   D. More are classified as Canidae than *Canis*

2. Two species of the same order must be members of the same:

   A. class
   B. habitat
   C. genus
   D. family

3. Homology serves as the evidence of:

   A. balancing selection
   B. common ancestry
   C. genetic mutation
   D. sexual selection

4. Which statement is correct about orthologous genes?

   A. They are related through speciation
   B. They are house-keeping genes
   C. They are repetitive
   D. They are related via gene duplication within species

5. Which given pair represents homologous structures?

   A. Mouth of a fly and beak of a hummingbird
   B. Wings of a dragonfly and a blue jay
   C. Forelimb of a human and of a dog
   D. Wings of a pigeon and a bat

6. Humans belong to the order:

   A. hominidae
   B. primata
   C. chordata
   D. vertebrata

7. All the following are members of the phylum Chordata, EXCEPT:

   A. birds
   B. ants
   C. tunicates
   D. apes

8. All statements regarding the phylum Echinodermata are true, EXCEPT:

A. echinoderms are heterotrophs
B. phylum includes crayfish
C. echinoderms reproduce sexually
D. phylum includes starfish and sea urchins

9. Two species of the same phylum must be members of the same:

A. order
B. kingdom
C. genus
D. class

10. *Homo sapiens* belong to the phylum:

A. Vertebrata
B. Homo
C. Mammalia
D. Chordata

11. Which organism is a chordate but not a vertebrate?

A. lizard
B. lancelet
C. shark
D. lamprey eel

12. Which represents the levels of complexity at which life is studied, from simplest to complex?

A. cell, tissue, organ, organism, population, community
B. community, population, organism, organ, tissue, cell
C. cell, organ, tissue, organism, population, community
D. cell, tissue, organ, population, organism, community

13. Which statement is TRUE for the notochord?

A. It is present in chordates during embryological development
B. It is always a vestigial organ in chordates
C. It is present in all adult chordates
D. It is present in all echinoderms

14. All are present in members of the phylum Chordata at some point in their life cycle, EXCEPT:

A. pharyngeal slits
B. tail
C. notochord
D. backbone

15. Which are two organisms of the same species?

A. Two South American iguanas which mate in different seasons
B. Two migratory birds nesting on the different Hawaiian Islands
C. Cabbage in South Carolina and Texas mate and produce fertile progeny only in seasons of extreme climate conditions
D. Two fruit flies on the island of Bali with distinct courtship behaviors

16. What is one reason sponges are classified as animals?

A. Sponges form partnerships with photosynthetic organisms
B. Sponges are autotrophic
C. Their cells have cell walls
D. Sponges are heterotrophic

17. What is a protostome?

A. outermost germ layer
B. animal whose mouth is formed from the blastopore
C. animal whose anus is formed from the blastopore
D. embryo just after fertilization

18. Arthropods have:

A. spiny skin and an internal skeleton
B. flattened body with an external shell
C. segmented body and an exoskeleton
D. soft body and an internal shell

19. A medical student looks at a slice of tissue on an unlabeled microscope slide. The student concludes that the tissue is not from an animal because the cells in the tissue have:

A. cell walls
B. cell membranes
C. nuclei
D. membrane-bound organelles

20. Which is true about annelids?

A. Each body segment contains several pairs of antennae
B. Annelids rely on diffusion to transport oxygen and nutrients to their tissues
C. Annelids have segmented bodies and a true coelom
D. Annelids are acoelomates

21. Ancient chordates are thought to be most closely related to:

A. octopi
B. sea anemones
C. spiders
D. earthworms

22. Which is true about echinoderms?

A. Echinoderms have one pair of antennae and unbranched appendages
B. Adult echinoderms have an exoskeleton
C. Most adult echinoderms exhibit radial symmetry
D. Echinoderm body is divided into a head, a thorax, and an abdomen

23. The simplest animals to have body symmetry are:

A. cnidarians
B. echinoderms
C. sponges
D. algae

24. In chordates with pharyngeal pouches that develop slits leading outside the body for breathing, adults use:

A. pharynx
B. nose
C. gills
D. lungs

25. In a chordate embryo, nerves branch in intervals from:

A. hollow nerve cord
B. notochord
C. pharyngeal pouches
D. tail

26. Each is an essential function performed by animals, EXCEPT:

A. circulation
B. cephalization
C. excretion
D. respiration

27. Which animals are deuterostomes?

A. mollusks and arthropods
B. echinoderms and chordates
C. annelids and arthropods
D. cnidarians and mollusks

28. In fishes, pharyngeal pouches may develop into:

A. gills
B. tails
C. lungs
D. fins

29. Which is true about corals?

A. The polyp form of corals is restricted to a small larval stage
B. Corals only reproduce by asexual means
C. Corals have only the medusa stage in their life cycles
D. Coral polyps secrete an underlying skeleton of calcium carbonate

30. Amphibians evolved from:

A. jawless fishes
B. lobe-finned fishes
C. ray-finned fishes
D. cartilaginous fishes

31. The notochord is responsible for which function in an embryo?

A. respiration
B. processing nerve signals
C. processing wastes
D. structural support

32. A flexible, supporting structure found only in chordates is the:

A. pharyngeal slits
B. dorsal fin
C. nerve net
D. notochord

33. Which is NOT true about earthworms?

A. Earthworms are hermaphrodites that reproduce sexually
B. Earthworms have a digestive tract that includes a mouth and an anus
C. Earthworms have a pseudocoelom
D. Their tunnels allow for the growth of oxygen-requiring soil bacteria

34. Skeletons of early vertebrates were composed of cartilage instead of bone. Which characteristic does cartilage share with notochords?

A. Oxygen can diffuse through it
B. It contracts
C. It is soft and flexible
D. It is hard and rigid

35. Which does NOT exhibit bilateral symmetry?

A. arthropods
B. cnidarians
C. mollusks
D. annelids

36. Which chordate characteristic is visible on the outside of an adult cat?

A. a tail that extends beyond the anus
B. pharyngeal pouches
C. hollow nerve cord
D. notochord

37. Fewer than 5 percent of animal species have:

A. cell membranes
B. vertebral columns
C. a protostome development pattern
D. eukaryotic cells

38. The eggs of ovoviviparous fish are:

A. released from the female before they are fertilized
B. held inside the female's body as they develop
C. released from the female immediately after being fertilized
D. retained and nourished by the female

39. Which statement about chordates is true?

A. All chordates are vertebrates
B. All chordates have paired appendages
C. All chordates have a notochord
D. All chordates have backbones

40. Which pairs of modern chordate groups are most closely related?

A. birds and crocodilians
B. sharks and the coelacanth
C. hagfishes and lungfishes
D. lampreys and ray-finned fishes

41. The hominoid group of primates includes:

A. anthropoids only
B. apes and hominines
C. New World monkeys and Old-World monkeys
D. lemurs, lorises and anthropoids

42. Which statement is supported by fossil evidence of how three vertebrates evolved: bony fish with a jaw, jawless fish, and fish with leglike fins?

A. The jawless fish was the last to evolve
B. The fish with leglike fins evolved before the jawless fish
C. The bony fish evolved before the jawless fish
D. The fish with leglike fins was the last to evolve

43. Jaws and limbs are characteristic of:

A. reptiles only
B. vertebrates only
C. all chordates
D. worms

44. Which structure in the amniotic egg provides nutrients for the embryo as it grows?

A. yolk
B. allantois
C. chorion
D. amnion

45. Which trend in reproduction is evident when following the vertebrate groups?

A. progressively fewer openings in the digestive tract
B. closed circulatory system becomes open
C. external fertilization evolves into internal fertilization
D. endothermy evolves into ectothermy

46. A tail adapted for grasping and holding objects is:

A. prehensile
B. radial
C. bipedal
D. binocular

47. Which is NOT a characteristic of mammals?

A. hair
B. endothermy
C. ability to nourish their young with milk
D. lack of pharyngeal pouches during development

48. The group that includes gibbons and humans but does not include tarsiers is:

A. hominoids
B. hominines
C. primates
D. anthropoids

49. All are examples of cartilaginous fishes, EXCEPT:

A. rays
B. sharks
C. hagfishes
D. skates

50. Old World monkeys can be distinguished from New World monkeys by observing:

A. how the monkeys use their tails
B. when the monkeys are most active
C. what the monkeys eat
D. how the monkeys interact with their troop

51. Compared with that of a reptile, a bird's body temperature is:

A. lower and more constant
B. lower and more variable
C. higher and more constant
D. higher and more variable

52. Which internal characteristics would be expected for an earthworm?

A. prostomium
B. notochord
C. pseudocoelom
D. paired organs

53. Mammals that lay eggs are:

A. reptiles
B. placentals
C. marsupials
D. monotremes

54. The presence of legs or other limbs indicates that the animal is:

A. protostome
B. segmented
C. acoelomate
D. radially symmetrical

55. A primatologist finds a new primate species in a Madagascar forest. The primate has a long snout and is active at night. The primatologist would classify this primate as a:

A. bush baby
B. hominoid
C. anthropoid
D. lemur

56. The vertebrate group with the most complex respiratory system is:

A. birds
B. amphibians
C. mammals
D. reptiles

57. Having a thumb that can move against the other fingers makes it possible for a primate to:

A. judge the locations of tree branches
B. display elaborate social behaviors
C. merge visual images
D. hold objects firmly

58. Which is NOT a characteristic of chordates?

A. pharyngeal pouches
B. vertebrae
C. tail that extends past the anus
D. dorsal, hollow nerve cord

59. An animal that has body parts that extend outward from its center shows:

A. bilateral symmetry
B. radial symmetry
C. segmentation
D. several planes of symmetry

60. Which node is expected on the cladogram for animals?

A. leg length
B. feather arrangement
C. deuterostome development
D. fur texture

61. Which variation is expected for land vertebrates?

A. Shapes of forelimbs
B. Numbers of germ layers
C. Numbers of limbs
D. Types of symmetry

62. The earliest hominine that belonged to the same genus as modern humans were probably:

A. *Australopithecus afarensis*
B. *Homo ergaster*
C. *Homo habilis*
D. *Homo neanderthalensis*

63. The important characteristic that separates birds from other chordates is:

A. amniotic egg
B. feathers
C. wings
D. four-chambered heart

64. A double-loop circulatory system is in animals with:

A. two-chambered heart
B. lungs
C. jaws
D. vertebrae

65. Which statement about the cladogram of animals is true?

A. Segmentation evolved more than once in different branches of the cladogram
B. All deuterostomes have cephalization
C. Backbones evolved before segmentation
D. Radial symmetry appears only once in the cladogram

66. All the following are reasons why green algae are classified as plants, EXCEPT:

A. They have genes similar to genes in land plants
B. They have chlorophyll *a*
C. They have cellulose in their cell walls
D. They are single-celled organisms

67. Which statement about green algae is true?

A. Like other plants, they have specialized structures
B. They are multicellular plants
C. Evidence suggests they were the first plants
D. They are found in dry areas on land

Notes for active learning

Energy Flow, Nutrient Cycles, Ecosystems and Biomes

1. The lowest level of environmental complexity that includes living and nonliving factors is:

A. ecosystem
B. biosphere
C. biome
D. community

2. How does an area's weather differ from the area's climate?

A. Weather does not change much, and an area's climate may change many times
B. Weather is the area's daily conditions, while climate is the area's average conditions
C. Weather involves temperature and precipitation, while climate involves only temperature
D. Weather depends on where it is located on Earth, while the area's climate does not

3. One type of symbiosis is:

A. parasitism
B. predation
C. competition
D. succession

4. Climate zones are the result of differences in:

A. thickness of the ozone layer
B. greenhouse gases
C. angle of the sun's rays
D. heat transport

5. The greenhouse effect is:

A. a natural phenomenon that maintains Earth's temperature range
B. the result of the differences in the angle of the sun's rays
C. primarily related to the levels of ozone in the atmosphere
D. a phenomenon that has only occurred in the last 50 years

6. The tendency for warm air to rise and cool air to sink results in:

A. regional precipitation
B. the seasons
C. ocean upwelling
D. global wind patterns

7. An ecosystem where water covers the soil or near the soil surface for at least part of the year is:

A. estuary
B. salt marsh
C. mangrove swamp
D. wetland

8. Which is a biological aspect of an organism's niche?

A. composition of soil
B. amount of sunlight
C. predators
D. the water in the area

9. An organism's niche is:

A. the range of temperatures that the organism needs to survive
B. a complete description of the place an organism lives
C. the range of physical and biological conditions in which an organism lives and the way it obtains what it needs to survive and reproduce
D. all the physical factors in the organism's environment

10. No two species can occupy the same niche in the same habitat at the same time:

A. unless the species require different biotic factors
B. because of the competitive exclusion principle
C. unless the species require different abiotic factors
D. because of the interactions that shape the ecosystem

11. Plants are:

A. omnivores
B. herbivores
C. primary consumers
D. primary producers

12. How do most primary producers make their food?

A. By breaking down remains into carbon dioxide
B. By converting water into carbon dioxide
C. By using chemical energy to make carbohydrates
D. By using light energy to make carbohydrates

13. Compared to land, the open oceans:

A. are nutrient-poor environments
B. are rich in silica, and iron
C. have less zooplankton
D. contain abundant oxygen

14. Several species of warblers can live in the same spruce tree ONLY because they:

A. can find different temperatures within the tree
B. occupy different niches within the tree
C. have different habitats within the tree
D. do not eat food from the tree

15. All the interconnected feeding relationships in an ecosystem make up a food:

A. web
B. network
C. chain
D. framework

16. A symbiotic relationship in which both species benefit is:

A. mutualism
B. parasitism
C. commensalism
D. omnivorism

17. A wolf pack hunts, kills, and feeds on a moose. In this interaction, the wolves are:

A. predators
B. mutualists
C. prey
D. hosts

18. The total amount of living tissue within a given trophic level is:

A. energy mass
B. biomass
C. organic mass
D. trophic mass

19. An interaction in which an animal feeds on plants is:

A. symbiosis
B. predation
C. herbivory
D. carnivory

20. A symbiotic relationship is when one organism is harmed, and another benefit is:

A. synnecrosis
B. predation
C. mutualism
D. parasitism

21. What animals eat producers and consumers?

A. autotrophs
B. chemotrophs
C. omnivores
D. herbivores

22. Ecosystem services include:

A. food production
B. production of oxygen
C. solar energy
D. all the above

23. Organisms that can capture the energy and produce food are:

A. omnivores
B. heterotrophs
C. autotrophs
D. consumers

24. What is one difference between primary and secondary succession?

A. Secondary succession begins with lichens, and primary succession begins with trees
B. Primary succession modifies the environment while secondary succession does not
C. Secondary succession begins on the soil, while primary succession begins on newly exposed surfaces
D. Primary succession is rapid and secondary succession is slow

25. A term that means the same thing as a *consumer* is:

A. carbohydrate
B. heterotroph
C. autotroph
D. producer

26. Primary succession would likely occur after:

A. severe storm
B. lava flow
C. earthquake
D. forest fire

27. Which organism is a detritivore?

A. fungus
B. snail
C. crow
D. caterpillar

28. Matter can recycle through the biosphere because:

A. biological systems do not deplete matter but transform it
B. biological systems use only carbon, oxygen, hydrogen, and nitrogen
C. matter does not change into new compounds
D. matter is assembled into chemical compounds

29. A tropical rain forest may not return to its original climax community after which type of disturbances?

A. volcanic eruption
B. flooding after a hurricane
C. burning of a forest fire
D. clearing and farming

30. A collection of the organisms living in a place, together with their nonliving environment, is a(n):

A. ecosystem
B. biome
C. population
D. community

31. Which biome is characterized by low temperatures, little precipitation, and permafrost?

A. tropical dry forest
B. tundra
C. temperate forest
D. desert

32. A bird stalks, kills, and then eats an insect. Based on behavior, which ecological terms describe the bird?

A. herbivore ↔ decomposer
B. autotroph ↔ herbivore
C. carnivore ↔ consumer
D. producer ↔ heterotroph

33. Which two biomes have the least precipitation?

A. boreal forest and temperate woodland
B. tundra and desert
C. tropical savanna and tropical dry forest
D. tundra and temperate shrubland

34. Which represents box 5 of the food web in the figure?

A. decomposers
B. carnivores
C. scavengers
D. herbivores

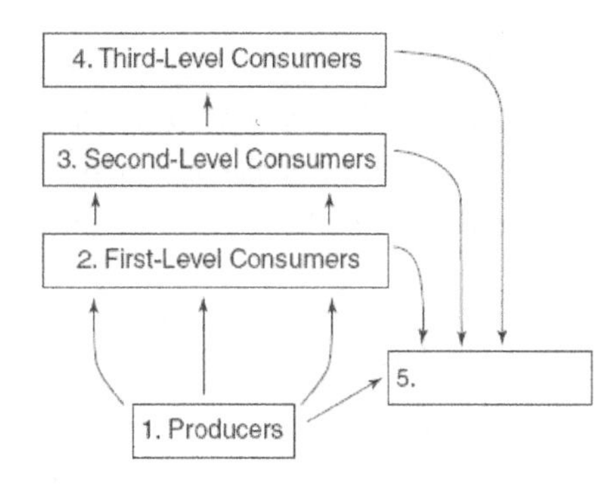

35. The average, year-after-year conditions of temperature and precipitation in a region are:

A. zonation
B. microclimate
C. weather
D. climate

36. Nitrogen fixation is carried out primarily by:

A. producers
B. consumers
C. bacteria
D. plants

37. The rate at which producers create organic matter is:

A. primary succession
B. nitrogen fixation
C. primary productivity
D. nutrient limit

38. Which landforms are NOT classified into a major biome?

A. coastlines
B. islands
C. prairies
D. mountain ranges

39. The North Pole and the South Poles are:

A. not classified into major biomes
B. part of aquatic ecosystems
C. classified as tundra biomes
D. not home to any animals

40. The type of interaction in which one organism captures and feeds on another is:

A. mutualism
B. predation
C. competition
D. parasitism

41. Is it likely to find zooplankton in the aphotic, benthic zone of an ocean?

A. No, zooplankton cannot undergo chemosynthesis in the dark without oxygen in the water
B. No, zooplankton feed on phytoplankton that cannot photosynthesize without light
C. No, zooplankton cannot photosynthesize in the dark without oxygen in the water
D. Yes, zooplankton is chemosynthetic autotrophs

42. Carbon cycles through the biosphere in all the following processes, EXCEPT:

A. decomposition of plants
B. burning of fossil fuels
C. transpiration
D. photosynthesis

43. The nutrient availability of aquatic ecosystems is:

A. number of different animal species living in the water
B. amount of rainfall the water receives
C. number of other organisms in the water
D. amount of nitrogen, oxygen, and other elements dissolved in the water

44. What type of organism forms the base of many aquatic food webs?

A. phytoplankton
B. mangrove trees
C. secondary consumers
D. plants

45. The movements of energy and nutrients through living systems are different because:

A. nutrients flow in two directions while energy recycles
B. energy forms chemical compounds while nutrients are lost as heat
C. energy flows in one direction while nutrients recycle
D. energy is limited in the biosphere while nutrients are always available

46. Boreal Forest biomes are:

A. found near the equator
B. also known as taiga
C. home to more species than all other biomes combined
D. hot and wet year-round

47. Freshwater ecosystems that often originate from underground sources in mountains or hills are:

A. lakes
B. wetlands
C. rivers and streams
D. ponds

48. Which is one way a wetland differs from a lake or pond?

A. Water does not always cover a wetland as it does a lake or pond
B. Wetlands are salty, while lakes and ponds are freshwater
C. Water flows in a lake or pond but never flows in a wetland
D. Wetlands are nesting areas for birds, while lakes and ponds are not nesting areas

49. A wetland with a mixture of fresh water and saltwater is:

A. pond
B. river
C. stream
D. estuary

50. The permanently dark zone of the ocean is:

A. aphotic zone
B. intertidal zone
C. photic zone
D. coastal zone

51. Each is an abiotic factor in the environment, EXCEPT:

A. temperature
B. rainfall
C. plant life
D. soil type

52. Estuaries are commercially important because:

A. fossil fuels are found in estuaries
B. lumber trees grow in estuaries
C. hotels are often built-in estuaries
D. abundant fish species live in estuaries

53. Animals that get energy by eating the carcasses of animals killed by predators or died by natural causes are:

A. detritivores
B. heterotrophs
C. omnivores
D. scavengers

54. Which statement is NOT true about the open ocean?

A. The open ocean begins at the low-tide mark and extends to the end of the continental shelf
B. Most of the photosynthetic activity on Earth occurs in the open ocean within the photic zone
C. The open ocean has low levels of nutrients
D. Organisms in the deep ocean are exposed to frigid temperatures

55. The branch of biology focused on interactions among and between organisms and their environment is:

A. paleontology
B. ecology
C. microbiology
D. entomology

56. Which description about the organization of an ecosystem is correct?

A. Species make up communities that comprise populations
B. Species make up populations that comprise communities
C. Communities make up species that comprise populations
D. Populations make up species that comprise communities

57. The photic zone:

A. is deep, cold, and permanently dark
B. extends to where the light intensity is reduced to 50% compared to the surface
C. extends to the bottom of the open ocean
D. extends to a depth of about 600 feet

58. Which is an example of mutualism?

A. nematodes
B. bread mold
C. tapeworms
D. lichens

59. Organisms that must obtain nutrients and energy by eating other organisms are:

A. heterotrophic
B. eukaryotic
C. herbivores
D. autotrophic

60. Complex animals break down food through the process of:

A. cephalization
B. intracellular digestion
C. complete metamorphosis
D. extracellular digestion

Notes for active learning

Populations, Communities and Conservation Biology

1. A developer wants to build a new housing development in or around a large city. Which plans would be LEAST harmful to the environment?

A. Building a neighborhood in a meadow at the edge of the city
B. Filling a wetland area and building oceanfront condominiums
C. Clearing a forested area outside of the city to build houses
D. Building apartments at the site of an abandoned factory in the city

2. Assemblages of different populations that live together in a defined area are:

A. communities
B. species
C. ecosystems
D. habitats

3. There are more than 165 cactus plants per square kilometer in an area of the Arizona desert. To which population characteristic does this information refer?

A. age structure
B. population density
C. growth rate
D. geographic range

4. Using resources in a way that does not cause long-term environmental harm is:

A. subsistence hunting
B. biological magnification
C. monoculture
D. sustainable development

5. What does the range of a population teach the observer that density does not?

A. The deaths per unit area
B. The births per unit area
C. The areas inhabited by a population
D. The number that lives in an area

6. Which ecological inquiry method is an ecologist using when she enters an area periodically to count the population numbers of a particular species?

A. modeling
B. experimenting
C. observing
D. questioning

7. Which is NOT a factor in the population growth rate?

A. demography
B. emigration
C. death rate
D. Immigration

8. Which is an example of population density?

A. number of deaths per year
B. number of bacteria per square millimeter
C. number of births per year
D. number of frogs in a pond

9. An example of a biotic factor is:

A. sunlight
B. soil type
C. competing species
D. average temperature

10. An example of a non-renewable resource is:

A. coal
B. fish
C. sunlight
D. wind

11. A mathematical formula designed to predict population fluctuations in a community is:

A. ecological model
B. ecological observation
C. biological experiment
D. biological system

12. The 1930s Dust Bowl in the Great Plains was caused by:

A. using renewable resources
B. poor farming practices
C. deforestation
D. contour plowing

13. The movement of organisms into a range is:

A. population shift
B. carrying capacity
C. immigration
D. emigration

14. Which is NOT a basic method ecologists use to study the living world?

A. modeling
B. observing
C. experimenting
D. animal training

15. If immigration and emigration remain equal, what contributes to a slowed growth rate?

A. decreased birth rate
B. constant birth rate
C. increased birth rate
D. constant death rate

16. When farming, overgrazing, climate change, or seasonal drought change farmland into land that cannot support plant life, it is:

A. deforestation
B. monoculture
C. desertification
D. depletion

17. Which factor might NOT contribute to an exponential growth rate in a given population?

A. reduced resources
B. less competition
C. higher birth rates
D. lower death rates

18. Which is NOT a sustainable development strategy for managing Earth's resources?

A. selective harvesting of trees
B. crop rotation
C. desertification
D. contour plowing

19. Which are two ways a population can decrease in size?

A. Emigration and increased birth rate
B. Decreased birth rate and emigration
C. Increased death rate and immigration
D. Immigration and emigration

20. Farmers can reduce soil erosion by:

A. plowing up roots
B. grazing cattle on the land
C. contour plowing
D. increasing irrigation

21. Which age structure is likely for a population that has not completed the demographic transition?

A. 10 percent of people aged 50–54
B. 5 percent of people aged 10–14
C. 15 percent of people under age 15
D. 50 percent of people under age 15

22. Which two factors increase population size?

A. births and immigration
B. deaths and emigration
C. births and emigration
D. deaths and immigration

23. In a logistic growth curve, exponential growth is the phase when the population:

A. growth begins to slow down
B. growth stops
C. reaches carrying capacity
D. grows quickly

24. An example of sustainable resource use is the use of predators and parasites to:

A. control pest insects
B. eat unwanted plants
C. harm natural resources
D. pollinate plants

25. The graph shows the growth of a bacterial population. Which describes the growth curve?

Growth of Bacterial Population

Number of Bacteria: 0, 100,000, 200,000, 300,000

Time (hours): 0, 2, 4, 6

A. demographic
B. exponential
C. logistic
D. limiting

26. DDT was used to:

A. form ozone
B. feed animals
C. kill insects
D. fertilize the soil

27. All renewable resources:

A. are living
B. can be recycled or reused
C. are unlimited in supply
D. can regenerate or be replenished

28. Density-dependent limiting factors include:

A. blizzards
B. damming of rivers
C. disease
D. earthquakes

29. If a population grows larger than the carrying capacity of the environment:

A. birth rate must fall
B. death rate must fall
C. birth rate may rise
D. death rate may rise

30. One property that makes DDT hazardous is that it is:

A. deadly to herbivores
B. subject to biological magnification
C. volatile pesticide
D. insecticide

31. As the population gets larger, it grows more quickly because the size of each generation of offspring is larger than the generation before, resulting in:

A. multiple growth
B. exponential growth
C. growth density
D. logistic growth

32. The gray-brown haze often found over large cities is:

A. smog
B. particulates
C. greenhouse gases
D. ozone layer

33. Compounds that contribute to the formation of acid rain contain:

A. nitrogen and sulfur
B. ammonia and nitrates
C. carbon dioxide and oxygen
D. calcium and phosphorus

34. The growth phases through which most populations go are represented on:

A. normal curve
B. population curve
C. logistic growth curve
D. exponential growth curve

35. Water lilies do not grow in desert sand because water availability to these plants in a desert is:

A. competition factor
B. logistic growth curve
C. limiting factor
D. carrying capacity

36. The sulfur and nitrogen compounds in smog combine with water to form:

A. acid rain
B. chlorofluorocarbons
C. ozone
D. ammonia

37. Air and water pollution have been reduced by:

A. raising more cattle for food
B. increasing biological magnification
C. using fossil fuels in factories
D. using only unleaded gasoline

38. Which would be least likely to be affected by a density-dependent limiting factor?

A. population with a high immigration rate
B. large, dense population
C. population with a high birth rate
D. small, scattered population

39. Raising cattle and farming rice contribute to air pollution by:

A. releasing the greenhouse gas methane into the atmosphere
B. producing smog which reacts to form dangerous ozone gas
C. producing particulates into the air
D. releasing sulfur compounds that form acid rain

40. For most populations that are growing, as resources become less available, the population:

A. enters a phase of exponential growth
B. reaches carrying capacity
C. increases more rapidly
D. declines rapidly

41. Which term best describes the number of distinct species in the biosphere or area?

A. species diversity
B. genetic diversity
C. ecosystem diversity
D. biodiversity

42. Which density-dependent factor other than predator/prey relationships affect the populations of moose and wolves on an island?

A. A hurricane for moose and wolves
B. Food availability for the moose and disease for the wolf
C. Extreme temperatures for the moose and flooding for the wolves
D. Parasitic wasps for the wolves and clear-cut forest for the moose

43. How are species diversity and genetic diversity different?

A. Species diversity measures the number of individuals, while genetic diversity is the total variety of species
B. Conservation biology is concerned with species diversity but not with genetic diversity
C. Species diversity is evaluated in ecosystems, while genetic diversity is evaluated in the entire biosphere
D. Species diversity measures the number of species in the biosphere, while genetic diversity measures the variety of genes in the biosphere, including genetic variation within species

44. Which is NOT likely to be a limiting factor on the sea otter population living in the ocean?

A. drought
B. predation
C. disease
D. competition

45. Introduced species can threaten biodiversity because they can:

A. crowd out native species
B. reduce the fertility of native species
C. cause desertification of land
D. cause biological magnification

46. Which is a density-independent limiting factor?

A. parasitism and disease
B. eruption of a volcano
C. predator/prey relationships
D. struggle for food

47. What would reduce competition within a species' population?

A. higher population density
B. fewer resources
C. higher birth rate
D. fewer individuals

48. A major factor that negatively affects biodiversity is:

A. non-renewable resources
B. contour plowing
C. habitat fragmentation
D. biological magnification

49. All the following are threats to biodiversity, EXCEPT:

A. habitat fragmentation
B. desertification
C. habitat preservation
D. biological magnification of toxic compounds

50. The graph shows the changes in a mosquito population. What caused the changes seen?

A. density-independent limiting factor
B. density-dependent limiting factor
C. reduction in resources
D. increase in predation

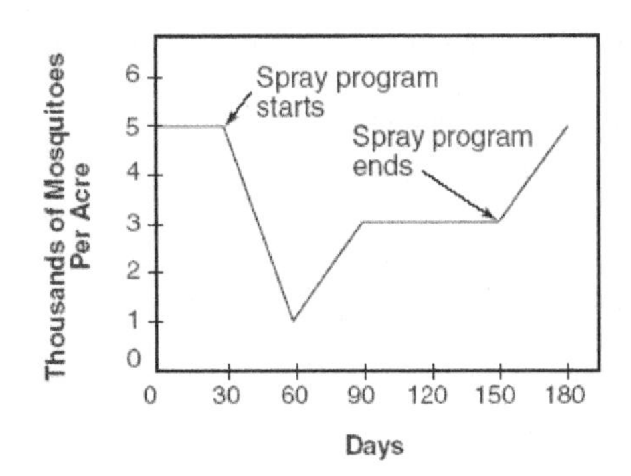

51. Each is a density-dependent limiting factor, EXCEPT:

A. crowding
B. disease
C. competition
D. temperature

52. The "hot spot" strategy seeks to protect species in danger of extinction due to:

A. human activity
B. biological magnification
C. captive breeding programs
D. expanding national parks

53. About 500 years ago, the world's population started to:

A. level off
B. grow more rapidly
C. reach carrying capacity
D. decrease

54. Protecting an entire ecosystem ensures that:

A. interactions among many species are preserved
B. governments will set aside land
C. existing parks and reserves will expand
D. captive breeding programs will succeed

55. The goals of biodiversity conservation include all the following, EXCEPT:

A. Ensuring that local people benefit from conservation efforts
B. Preserving habitats and ecosystems
C. Introducing exotic species into new environments
D. Protecting individual species

56. Countries in the first stage of demographic transition have:

A. slowly growing population
B. more older people than young people
C. high death rate and a high birth rate
D. high death rate and a low birth rate

57. Demography is the scientific study of:

A. disease
B. human populations
C. parasitism
D. modernized countries

58. The amount of land and water necessary to provide the resources for a person's living and to neutralize that person's waste is that person's:

A. habitat
B. ecological sustainability
C. biodiversity
D. ecological footprint

59. Population density refers to the:

A. number of people in each age group
B. carrying capacity
C. number of individuals per unit area
D. area inhabited by a population

60. The anticipated human population by the year 2050 is about:

A. 780 million
B. 11 trillion
C. 9.8 billion
D. 3.6 billion

61. Demographic transition changes from high birth rates and high death rates to:

A. indefinite growth
B. low birth rates and high death rates
C. low birth rates and low death rates
D. exponential growth

62. Imported plants and animals in Hawaii have:

A. increased crop yields
B. improved soil fertility
C. increased the native bird species
D. caused native species to die out

63. A benefit of monoculture farming practices is:

A. pest resistance of the crops
B. the ability to grow a lot of food
C. the ability to spend less money on fertilizer
D. the use of less water for irrigation

64. An example of a density-independent limiting factor is:

A. disease
B. predation
C. unusual weather
D. competition

65. In countries like India, the human population is growing:

A. logistically
B. linearly
C. exponentially
D. transitionally

66. Most of the worldwide human population is growing exponentially because:

A. human population does not conform to the logistic model
B. the food supply is limitless
C. human populations have not reached their exponential curve
D. most countries have not yet completed the demographic transition

67. Solving an environmental problem is likely when researchers follow basic principles of ecology because:

A. ecology uses scientific research to identify the cause and best practices to solve problems
B. ecologists are good at influencing government officials into changing laws to improve the environment
C. ecological solutions are typically easy to implement and can be done quickly
D. most people worldwide are more interested in saving the environment than in their convenience

68. Which environmental problem can be identified by ecologists through the data in the graph?

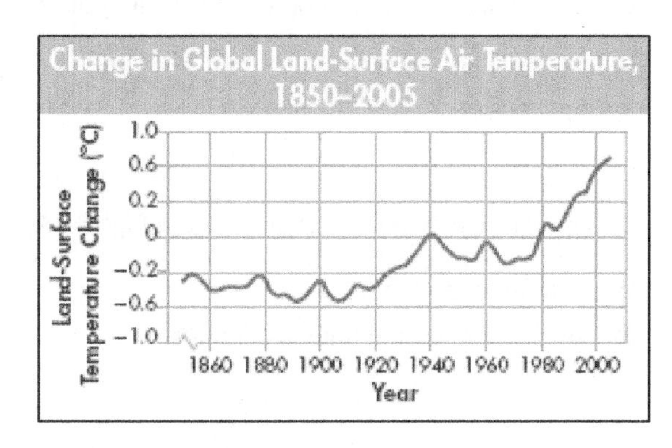

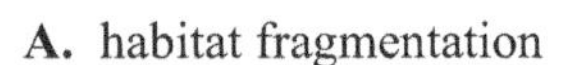

A. habitat fragmentation
B. desertification
C. the hole in the ozone layer
D. global warming

69. The total genetically based variety of organisms in the biosphere is:

A. ecosystem diversity
B. biodiversity
C. genetic diversity
D. species diversity

70. An ecological hot spot is an area where:

A. many habitats and species are at high risk of extinction
B. species diversity is too high
C. habitats show a high amount of biodiversity
D. hunting is encouraged

71. In a climax community, which would be a dominant species?

A. shrubs
B. annual grasses
C. mosses
D. deciduous trees

72. Which statement is TRUE for a climax community?

A. It is stable within a given climate
B. It is independent of the environment
C. It consists of only one species of life
D. It is populated mainly by pioneer organisms

Notes for active learning

Notes for active learning

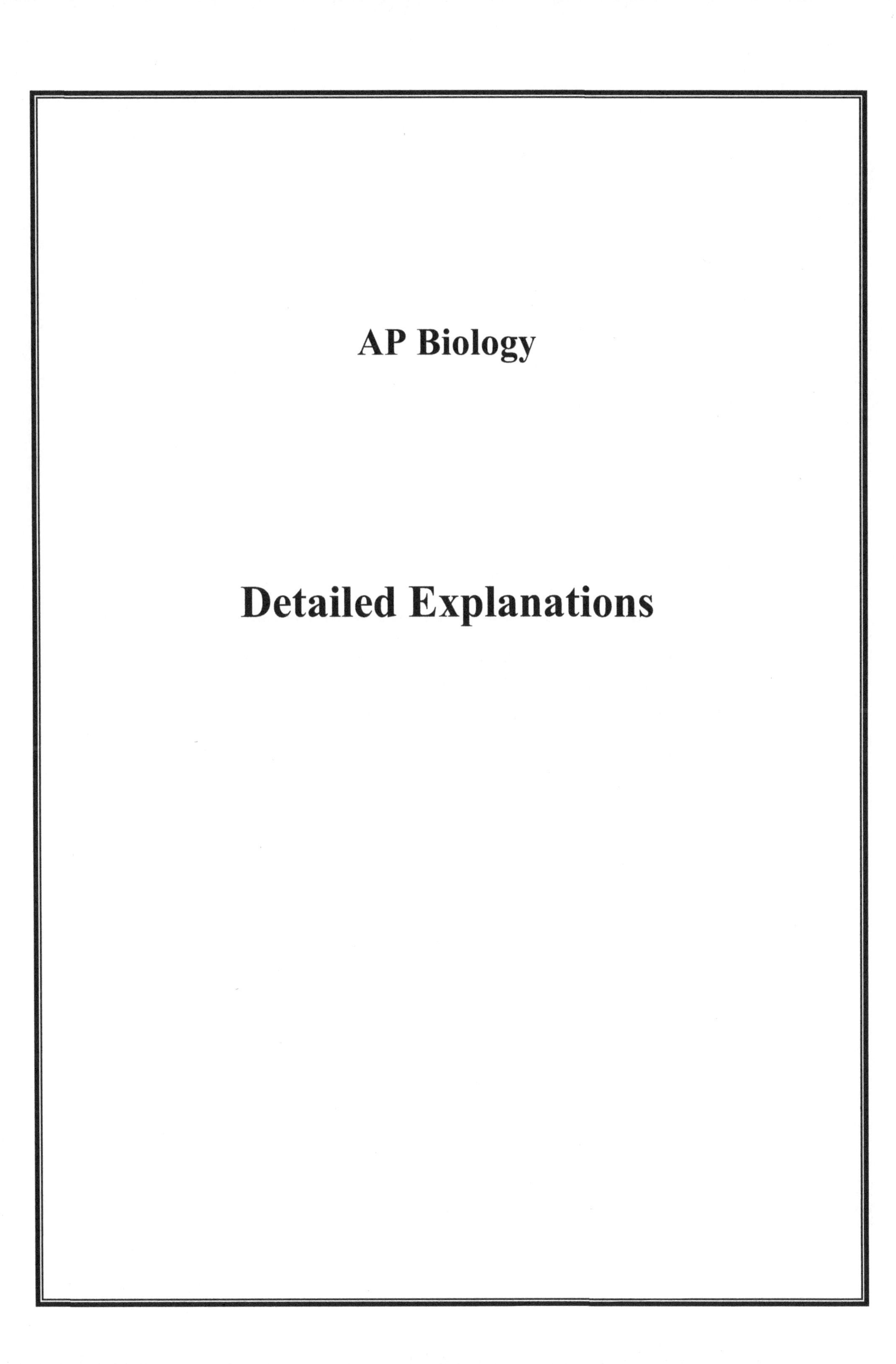

AP Biology

Detailed Explanations

If you benefited from this book, we would appreciate if you left a review on Amazon, so others can learn from your input. Reviews help us understand our customers' needs and experiences while keeping our commitment to quality.

Answer Keys

Chapter 1. Macromolecules

1: A	21: B	41: D	61: D	81: D
2: B	22: B	42: A	62: B	82: B
3: A	23: D	43: C	63: D	83: D
4: A	24: C	44: D	64: B	84: C
5: B	25: C	45: D	65: A	85: D
6: C	26: D	46: C	66: D	86: A
7: B	27: D	47: B	67: D	87: B
8: B	28: B	48: A	68: C	88: A
9: C	29: B	49: A	69: D	89: B
10: C	30: D	50: C	70: D	90: C
11: D	31: C	51: D	71: A	91: C
12: D	32: B	52: D	72: D	92: C
13: B	33: A	53: D	73: A	93: C
14: C	34: B	54: C	74: D	94: C
15: B	35: C	55: D	75: B	95: D
16: B	36: A	56: C	76: B	96: A
17: B	37: B	57: A	77: C	97: C
18: D	38: D	58: B	78: A	
19: D	39: D	59: A	79: A	
20: D	40: C	60: A	80: B	

Chapter 2. Eukaryotic Cell: Structure and Function

1: D	11: C	21: C	31: B	41: D	51: B	61: B
2: A	12: C	22: B	32: D	42: C	52: A	62: D
3: C	13: B	23: B	33: C	43: C	53: B	63: A
4: C	14: C	24: A	34: B	44: A	54: D	64: B
5: B	15: C	25: B	35: C	45: B	55: C	65: B
6: C	16: C	26: B	36: D	46: D	56: A	66: A
7: A	17: D	27: C	37: C	47: D	57: A	67: D
8: A	18: A	28: D	38: C	48: D	58: C	68: D
9: B	19: B	29: A	39: D	49: B	59: A	
10: B	20: A	30: B	40: B	50: D	60: A	

Chapter 3. Microbiology

1: B	11: A	21: A	31: C	41: C	51: B
2: B	12: B	22: D	32: A	42: B	52: B
3: D	13: A	23: D	33: D	43: C	53: C
4: D	14: C	24: B	34: B	44: A	54: C
5: B	15: A	25: C	35: D	45: C	55: A
6: C	16: D	26: D	36: B	46: A	56: D
7: D	17: B	27: C	37: A	47: A	57: C
8: A	18: C	28: B	38: B	48: B	
9: C	19: A	29: A	39: A	49: B	
10: B	20: C	30: C	40: C	50: B	

Chapter 4. Cellular Metabolism and Enzymes

1: D	11: A	21: A	31: C	41: B	51: C	61: A
2: A	12: D	22: B	32: C	42: C	52: B	62: D
3: C	13: A	23: A	33: D	43: A	53: C	63: D
4: B	14: D	24: C	34: B	44: D	54: D	
5: B	15: B	25: C	35: D	45: A	55: D	
6: C	16: D	26: D	36: B	46: C	56: D	
7: D	17: C	27: C	37: A	47: C	57: C	
8: A	18: B	28: A	38: D	48: B	58: C	
9: B	19: C	29: B	39: A	49: C	59: C	
10: D	20: B	30: B	40: A	50: B	60: B	

Chapter 5. Photosynthesis

1: D	11: C	21: A	31: C	41: A	51: A
2: D	12: C	22: B	32: A	42: B	52: B
3: A	13: B	23: C	33: C	43: B	53: D
4: B	14: B	24: C	34: C	44: C	54: C
5: C	15: A	25: B	35: A	45: D	55: B
6: D	16: A	26: B	36: D	46: A	56: A
7: A	17: B	27: D	37: C	47: D	57: C
8: B	18: C	28: D	38: B	48: A	
9: A	19: D	29: C	39: A	49: A	
10: D	20: A	30: A	40: B	50: C	

Chapter 6. Specialized Cells and Tissues

1: B	11: A	21: B	31: A	41: D	51: C
2: A	12: C	22: B	32: B	42: D	52: A
3: A	13: B	23: D	33: D	43: D	53: C
4: D	14: C	24: D	34: A	44: A	54: B
5: B	15: C	25: A	35: A	45: A	55: C
6: B	16: D	26: B	36: C	46: B	56: D
7: B	17: D	27: C	37: B	47: C	57: B
8: D	18: B	28: C	38: D	48: A	58: B
9: C	19: A	29: D	39: A	49: D	
10: D	20: B	30: D	40: C	50: D	

Chapter 7. Genetics

1: A	11: C	21: A	31: D	41: A	51: D	61: C	71: D	81: B
2: C	12: D	22: A	32: C	42: C	52: D	62: B	72: C	82: A
3: B	13: B	23: C	33: B	43: A	53: C	63: B	73: A	83: D
4: C	14: C	24: A	34: D	44: C	54: D	64: B	74: D	84: C
5: D	15: A	25: C	35: B	45: C	55: D	65: A	75: C	85: C
6: D	16: D	26: B	36: B	46: B	56: D	66: C	76: D	86: A
7: C	17: D	27: C	37: B	47: C	57: C	67: D	77: B	87: B
8: B	18: A	28: D	38: A	48: B	58: C	68: B	78: B	
9: B	19: A	29: A	39: B	49: D	59: C	69: B	79: A	
10: B	20: B	30: C	40: D	50: C	60: B	70: C	80: C	

Chapter 8. Genetics and Reproduction

1: B	11: B	21: C
2: A	12: B	22: B
3: C	13: C	23: C
4: C	14: D	24: D
5: C	15: C	25: A
6: C	16: D	26: A
7: D	17: D	27: B
8: D	18: B	28: A
9: C	19: D	29: A
10: B	20: A	

Chapter 9. Development

1: A	11: C	21: B	31: C	41: C	51: C
2: D	12: A	22: C	32: B	42: C	52: A
3: B	13: D	23: D	33: D	43: A	53: A
4: B	14: C	24: C	34: C	44: C	54: C
5: D	15: D	25: B	35: A	45: C	55: C
6: A	16: D	26: D	36: D	46: A	56: B
7: C	17: C	27: B	37: D	47: B	57: B
8: B	18: C	28: A	38: C	48: A	58: C
9: A	19: D	29: C	39: C	49: B	59: B
10: A	20: A	30: A	40: C	50: A	

Chapter 10. Molecular Biology of Eukaryotes

1: A	11: A	21: A	31: C	41: A
2: A	12: B	22: C	32: A	42: A
3: C	13: C	23: B	33: A	43: B
4: A	14: C	24: C	34: B	44: D
5: C	15: D	25: A	35: A	45: D
6: D	16: A	26: D	36: B	46: B
7: C	17: B	27: D	37: A	47: C
8: A	18: C	28: B	38: D	48: C
9: A	19: C	29: D	39: D	49: A
10: D	20: B	30: D	40: B	50: D

Chapter 11. DNA and Protein Synthesis

1: D	11: B	21: B	31: A	41: B	51: C	61: D	71: B
2: D	12: C	22: C	32: D	42: D	52: A	62: D	72: B
3: D	13: C	23: B	33: B	43: B	53: A	63: B	73: C
4: A	14: C	24: A	34: B	44: A	54: A	64: A	74: D
5: D	15: B	25: B	35: A	45: C	55: C	65: D	75: D
6: D	16: C	26: B	36: B	46: A	56: B	66: B	76: B
7: A	17: D	27: B	37: D	47: D	57: A	67: A	77: A
8: C	18: C	28: B	38: C	48: C	58: B	68: A	78: C
9: D	19: C	29: D	39: C	49: C	59: B	69: A	79: C
10: C	20: D	30: C	40: A	50: D	60: C	70: D	80: B
							81: D

Chapter 12. Evolution and Natural Selection

1: D	11: C	21: C	31: B	41: A	51: C
2: A	12: D	22: D	32: C	42: A	52: B
3: D	13: D	23: C	33: C	43: D	
4: A	14: A	24: C	34: B	44: C	
5: D	15: B	25: C	35: A	45: B	
6: C	16: A	26: B	36: D	46: D	
7: D	17: D	27: B	37: A	47: D	
8: D	18: D	28: D	38: C	48: A	
9: A	19: C	29: B	39: D	49: D	
10: B	20: A	30: B	40: D	50: A	

Chapter 13. Animal Behavior and Evolution

1: A	11: A	21: A	31: A
2: A	12: D	22: A	32: C
3: B	13: C	23: D	33: A
4: C	14: B	24: B	
5: A	15: C	25: C	
6: D	16: A	26: D	
7: B	17: D	27: A	
8: D	18: C	28: C	
9: C	19: C	29: A	
10: A	20: B	30: B	

Chapter 14. Classification and Diversity

1: D	11: B	21: B	31: D	41: B	51: C	61: A
2: A	12: A	22: C	32: D	42: D	52: D	62: C
3: B	13: A	23: A	33: C	43: B	53: D	63: B
4: A	14: D	24: C	34: C	44: A	54: B	64: B
5: C	15: B	25: A	35: B	45: C	55: D	65: A
6: B	16: D	26: B	36: A	46: A	56: A	66: D
7: B	17: B	27: B	37: B	47: D	57: D	67: C
8: B	18: C	28: A	38: B	48: A	58: B	
9: B	19: A	29: D	39: C	49: C	59: B	
10: D	20: C	30: B	40: A	50: A	60: C	

Chapter 15. Energy Flow, Nutrient Cycles, Ecosystems and Biomes

1: A	11: D	21: C	31: B	41: B	51: C
2: B	12: D	22: D	32: C	42: C	52: D
3: A	13: A	23: C	33: B	43: D	53: D
4: C	14: B	24: C	34: A	44: A	54: A
5: A	15: A	25: B	35: D	45: C	55: B
6: D	16: A	26: B	36: C	46: B	56: B
7: D	17: A	27: B	37: C	47: C	57: D
8: C	18: B	28: A	38: B	48: A	58: D
9: C	19: C	29: D	39: A	49: D	59: A
10: B	20: D	30: A	40: B	50: A	60: D

Chapter 16. Populations, Communities and Conservation Biology

1: D	11: A	21: D	31: B	41: A	51: D	61: C
2: A	12: B	22: A	32: A	42: B	52: A	62: D
3: B	13: C	23: D	33: A	43: D	53: B	63: B
4: D	14: D	24: A	34: C	44: A	54: A	64: C
5: C	15: A	25: B	35: C	45: A	55: C	65: C
6: C	16: C	26: C	36: A	46: B	56: C	66: D
7: A	17: A	27: D	37: D	47: D	57: B	67: A
8: B	18: C	28: C	38: D	48: C	58: D	68: D
9: C	19: B	29: D	39: A	49: C	59: C	69: B
10: A	20: D	30: B	40: B	50: A	60: C	70: A
						71: D
						72: A

Macromolecules – Detailed Explanations

1. A is correct.

Primary structure of a protein is the *linear sequence* of amino acids.

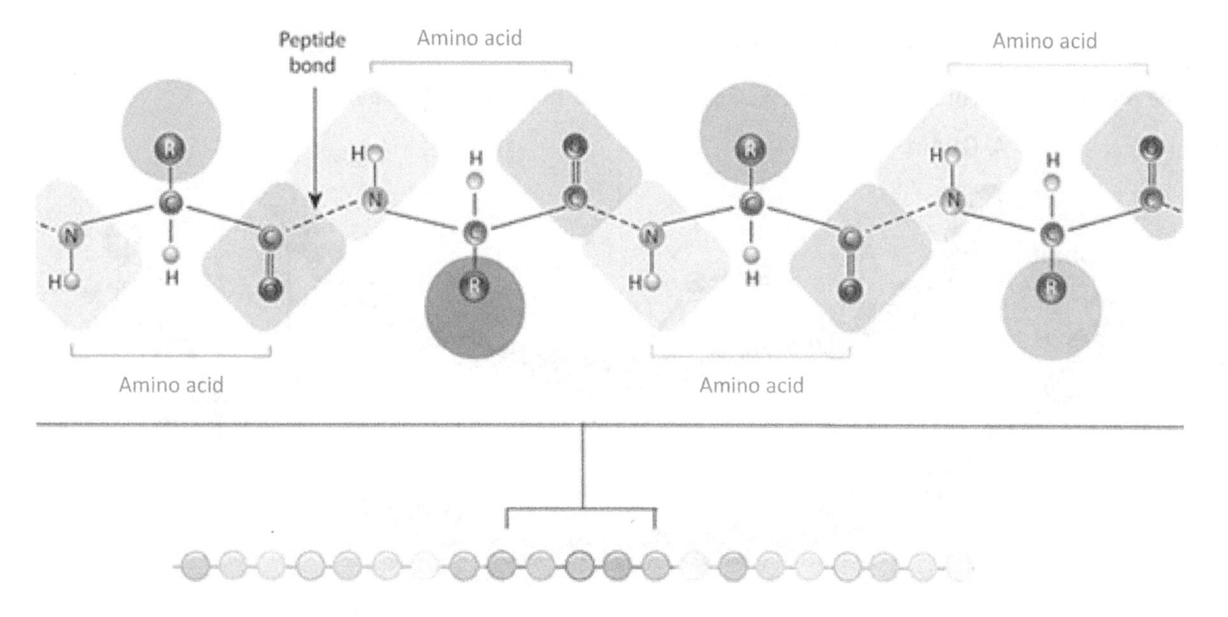

Peptide bonds link amino acids in the primary structure of proteins (circles) with amino acid side chains (R groups) facing opposite directions to reduce steric hindrance

2. B is correct.

Biomolecules are divided into four macromolecules: *carbohydrates*, *lipids*, *nucleic acids*, and *proteins.*

3. A is correct.

Amino acids are linked as peptides by *amide bonds.*

Peptide (amide) bond is anti-periplanar and includes four atoms, as shown in the box.

Peptide bonds form in a *condensation reaction via dehydration* (loss of water) when the lone pair on the nitrogen of an amino group of one amino acid makes a nucleophilic attack on the carbonyl carbon of another.

$$H{-}NH{-}CHR_1{-}C(=O){-}OH + H{-}NH{-}CHR_2{-}C(=O){-}OH \xrightarrow{-H_2O} H{-}NH{-}CHR_1{-}C(=O){-}NH{-}CHR_2{-}C(=O){-}OH$$

Peptide bond

Peptide bonds form by a condensation (dehydration) reaction of 2 amino acids

4. A is correct.

Hormones are substances secreted by a gland and released into the blood to affect a target tissue/organ.

Insulin is a hormone composed of amino acids (i.e., peptide hormones) and is a protein with two peptide chains (A chain and B chain).

Two disulfide bonds link the chains, and an additional disulfide is formed within the A chain.

The A chain consists of 21 amino acids, and the B chain has 30 amino acids in most species.

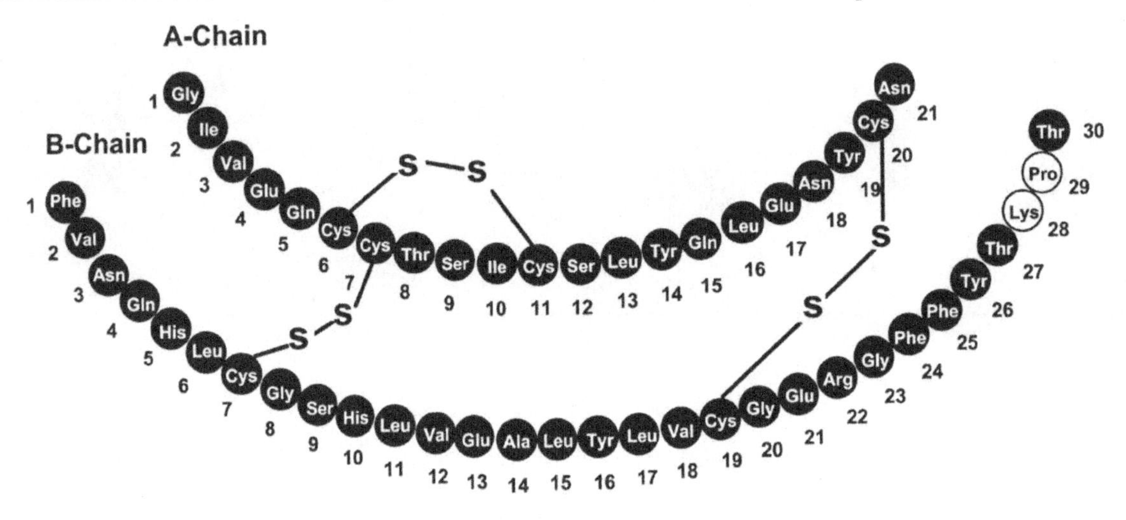

Insulin has an A chain and B chain linked by disulfide bonds

Hormones can be lipids, such as steroid derivatives (e.g., testosterone, progesterone, estrogen).

5. B is correct.

Alpha helix structure is one of two common secondary protein structures.

Hydrogen bonds hold the alpha-helix between every N–H (amino group) and the oxygen of C=O (carbonyl) in the next turn of the helix; four amino acids along the chain.

Alpha helix is typically about 11 amino acids long.

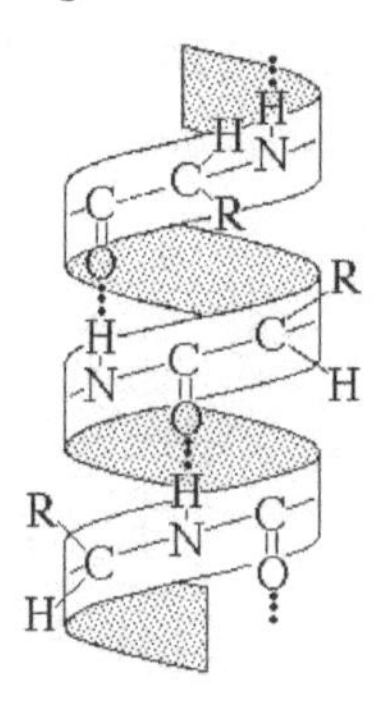

Hydrogen bonds hold the secondary structure of the alpha helix

Beta-pleated sheet is the other *secondary structure.*

Beta pleated sheets are parallel or anti-parallel (a reference to the amino terminus)

6. C is correct.

Primary structure of a protein is the amino acid sequence, formed by covalent peptide linkages.

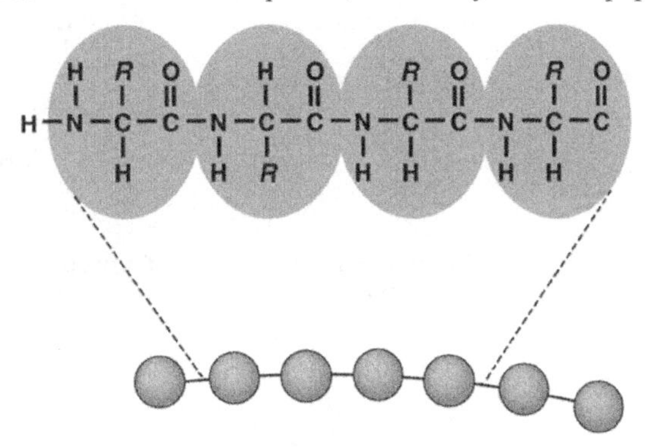

The amino acids (circles) are joined by covalent peptide bonds (lines). Peptide bonds link amino acids in the primary structure of proteins (circles) with amino acid side chains (R groups) facing opposite directions to reduce steric hindrance

A: only proteins containing more than one peptide subunit have a quaternary structure.

B: proteins are denatured by heating, and they lose their conformation above 35-40 °C.

D: many proteins contain more than one peptide chain (i.e., have a quaternary structure).

7. B is correct.

Amino acids are the building blocks of proteins.

Humans need 20 amino acids (see diagram), some are synthesized by the body (i.e., nonessential), and others must be obtained from the diet (i.e., essential).

continued...

Amino Group
Carboxylic Acid Group
Variable Side Chain
α - carbon

Amino acids contain an amine group, a carboxylic acid, an α-carbon, and an R group

Note: The 20 naturally occurring amino acids shown are not for memorization but for identifying characteristics (e.g., polar, nonpolar) for the side chains.

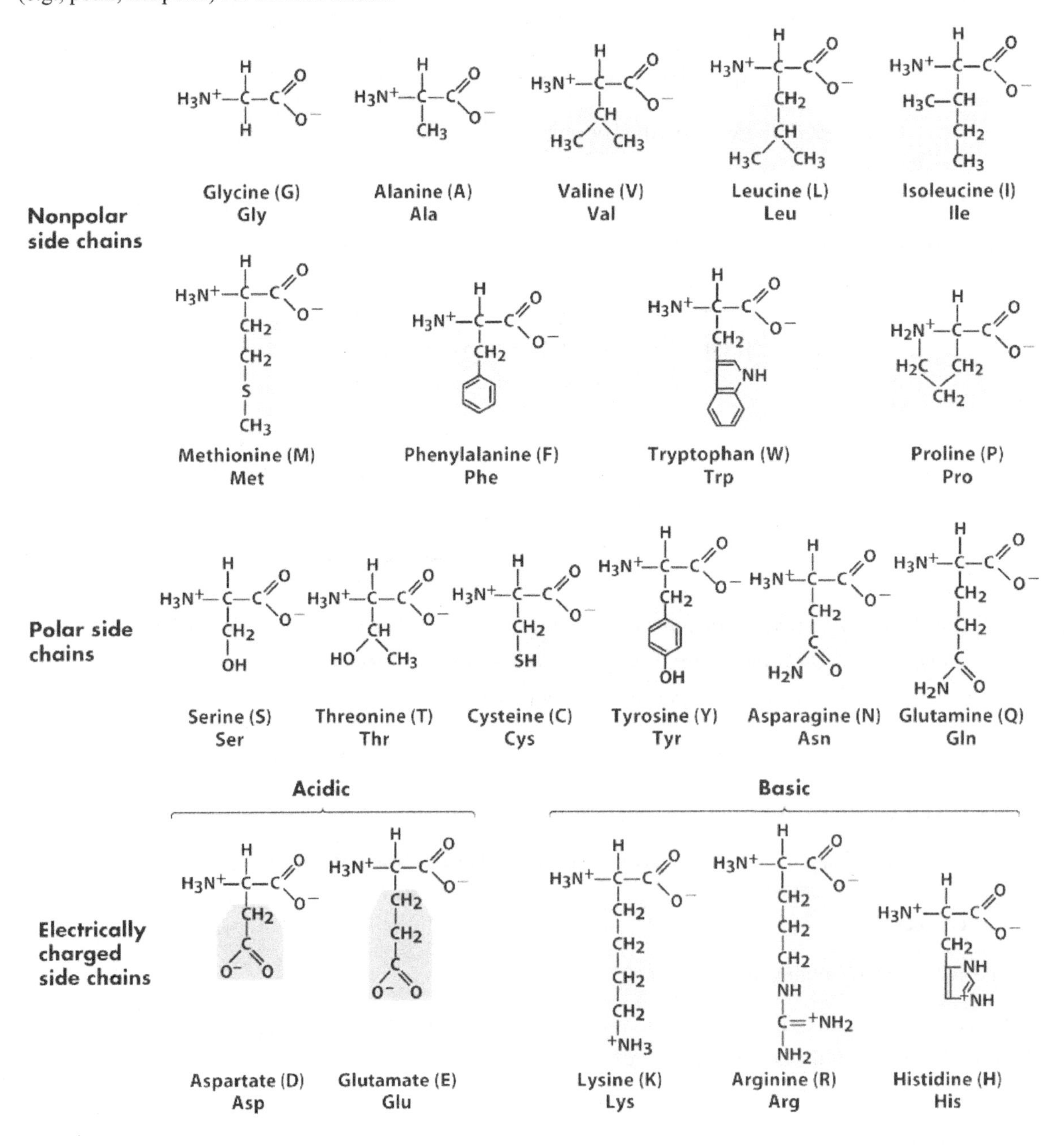

8. B is correct.

Peptide bonds link the primary sequence of amino acids in a protein between individual amino acids that form a peptide (*polypeptide*) chain.

Peptide bonds are not altered when a polypeptide bends or folds to form secondary structures (e.g., alpha helix).

Peptide bonds do *not* form when the polypeptide folds into a three-dimensional shape (tertiary structure).

A: interactions between charged groups (*electrostatic interactions*) can arise, especially in the tertiary structure.

C: *hydrogen bonds* participate in the secondary and tertiary structures.

In the secondary structure, the polypeptide chain folds to allow the carbonyl oxygen and amine hydrogen to lie nearby. As a result, hydrogen bonding occurs to form sheets, helices, or turns.

Likewise, hydrogen bonding may stabilize the secondary or tertiary structure.

D: *hydrophobic interactions* also play a vital role in the *tertiary structure*.

For example, in an aqueous environment, hydrophobic side chains of the amino acids may interact to arrange themselves towards the inside of the protein.

9. C is correct.

Amino acids are the basic building blocks for proteins.

Two amino acids (dimer) with peptide bonds are indicated by arrows

Peptide bonds are rigid with double bond character by lone pair nucleophilic attack on the adjacent carbonyl

Peptide bond is rigid due to *resonance hybrids* involving the lone pair of electrons on nitrogen, forming a double bond to the carbonyl carbon (oxygen develops a negative formal charge).

10. C is correct.

Protonation (or deprotonation) of an amino acid residue changes its *ionization state:* it may become positively charged, negatively charged, or neutral.

The process may lead to changes in the interactions among amino acid side chains, as some ionic bonds may be compromised from the lack of opposite charge pairing.

Specific hydrogen bonding interactions may be modulated if Lewis bases are protonated with Brønsted acids, impairing their ability to accept hydrogen bonds from nearby amino acid residues.

11. D is correct.

The *primary structure* of proteins refers to the *linear sequence* of amino acids.

Hydrogen bonding is essential for the secondary (alpha-helix and beta-pleated sheet) and tertiary (i.e., overall, 3-dimensional shape) structure of proteins.

Hydrophobic interactions involved in tertiary and quaternary (i.e., two or more polypeptide chains) structures arise from the hydrophobic side chains of the amino acid residues.

12. D is correct.

Collagen is a protein that supports hair, nails, and skin. It is composed of a triple helix, and the abundant amino acids in collagen include glycine, proline, alanine, and glutamic acid.

Much excess protein consumed in an animal's diet is used to synthesize collagen.

13. B is correct.

Secondary structure for proteins involves localized bonding.

Hydrogen bonding is critical intermolecular interaction for secondary structure, which maintains the alpha helix and beta pleated (parallel and antiparallel) sheet structures.

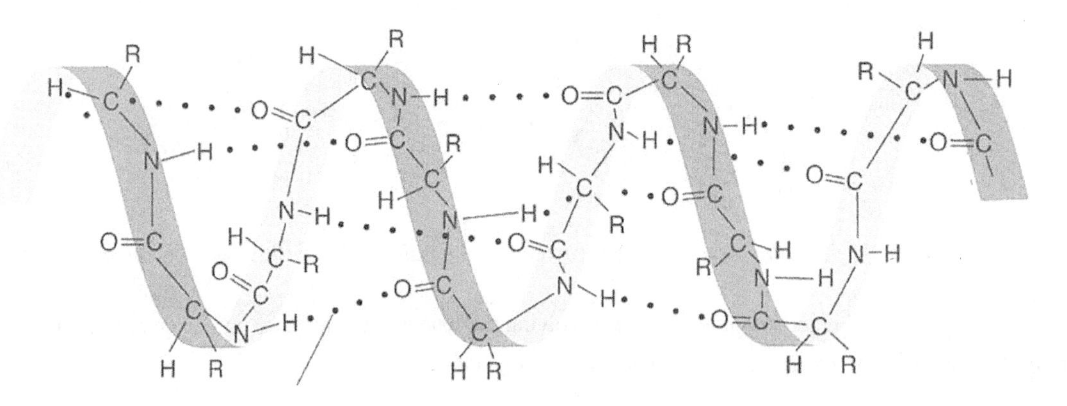

Alpha helix structure with hydrogen bonding shown as dotted lines

continued...

Beta pleated sheets (parallel and antiparallel) with hydrogen bonding shown

14. C is correct.

Standard conditions for breaking covalent bonds during peptide hydrolysis are concentrated HCl and several hours of reflux. The reaction time depends on partial or complete hydrolysis of the peptide.

15. B is correct.

Essential amino acids are those obtained from the diet.

Nonessential amino acids are synthesized by the body and do not need to be consumed.

Semi-essential (conditionally essential) amino acids are synthesized under special physiological conditions (e.g., in premature infants and under severe catabolic distress).

Nine essential amino acids for humans are histidine, isoleucine, leucine, lysine, methionine, phenylalanine, threonine, tryptophan, and valine.

Six conditionally essential amino acids are arginine, cysteine, glycine, glutamine, proline, and tyrosine.

Five nonessential amino acids are alanine, aspartic acid, asparagine, glutamic acid, and serine.

16. B is correct.

Polypeptide chains can undergo short-range bending and folding to form *β sheets* or *α helices*. These structures arise as the peptide bonds can assume a partial double-bond character and adopt different conformations.

The arrangement of groups around the rigid amide bond can cause *R* groups to alternate from side to side and interact with one another.

Carbonyl oxygen in one region of the polypeptide chain could become hydrogen-bonded to the amide hydrogen in another region of the polypeptide chain. This interaction often results in forming a *beta-pleated sheet* or an *alpha helix*.

Localized bending and folding of a polypeptide do not constitute a protein's primary structure.

A: *primary structure* of a protein is the amino acid sequence; individual amino acids are linked through peptide (i.e., amide) linkages.

C: *tertiary structure* is the 3-D shape that arises by further folding the polypeptide chain. Usually, these nonrandom folds give the protein a particular conformation and associated function.

D: *quaternary structure* is the spatial arrangement between *two or more* polypeptide chains (often linked by *disulfide bridges* between *cysteine* residues).

17. B is correct.

Proteins are biological macromolecules of amino acids bonded with *peptide (amide) bonds*.

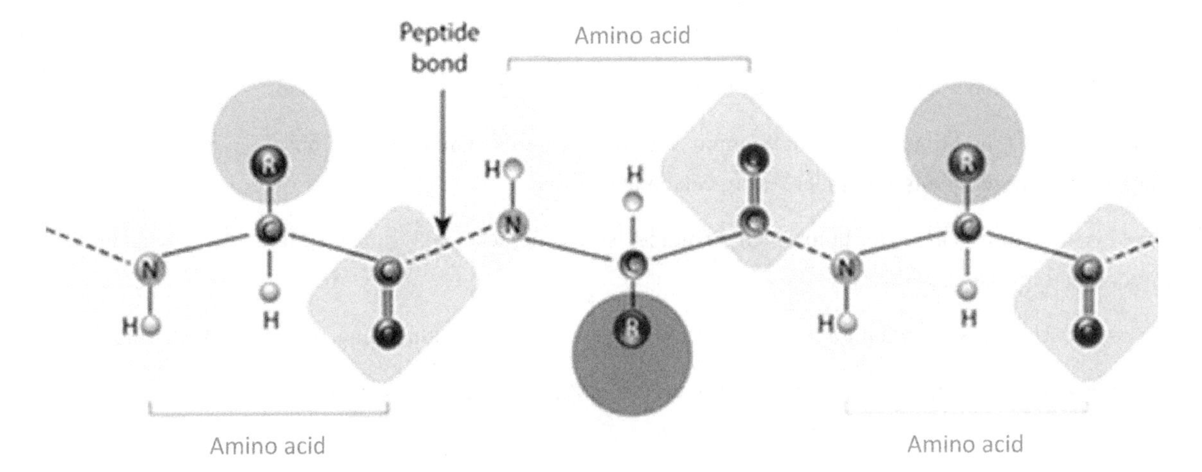

Three amino acid residues of a nascent (i.e., growing) polypeptide. Peptide bonds link amino acids in the primary structure of proteins (circles) with amino acid side chains (R groups) facing opposite directions to reduce steric hindrance.

18. D is correct.

The plasma membrane is made of lipids known as *phospholipids*. These molecules mainly possess nonpolar characteristics due to the long hydrocarbon chains, making the membrane permeable to nonpolar materials and semipermeable to polar or charged molecules.

19. D is correct.

Palmitic acid is a saturated acid, meaning that the molecule does not contain a double bond. Because this molecule lacks a double bond, the molecules stack better to form solids, and the fat has a higher melting point.

Unsaturated fats are frequently liquids at room temperature.

Linolenic acid (shown) is polyunsaturated with three *cis* double bonds.

Alkenes (i.e., unsaturation) introduce "kinks" in the chain that give the unsaturated fat an overall bent structure. This molecular geometry limits these fats from clustering closely to form solids.

Therefore, (relative to chain length), polyunsaturated molecules have the lowest melting point.

Position *omega* (ω) of the double bond(s) is the number of carbon atoms from the *terminal methyl group*.

Number of *carbon atoms* is noted from the carboxyl end

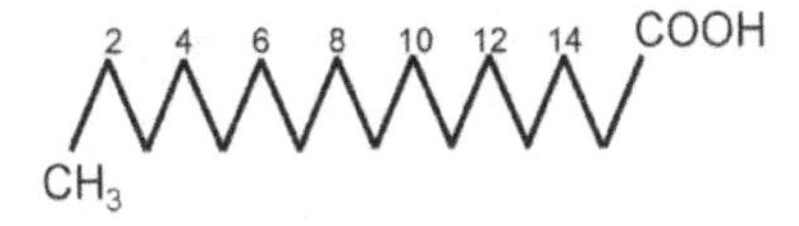

Oleic Acid

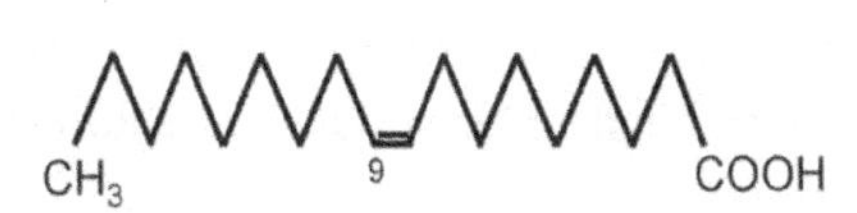

Saturated and unsaturated fatty acids – note the omega (ω) position 9 of the oleic acid double bond

Linoleic Acid

Arachidonic Acid

Omega-6 polyunsaturated fatty acids. Linoleic is ω-6,9, and arachidonic acid is ω-6,9,12,15 fatty acids.

α-Linolenic Acid

Eicosapentaenoic Acid

Docosahexaenoic Acid

Omega-6 polyunsaturated fatty acids. α-linoleic acid is ω-3,6,9, eicosapentaenoic acid is ω-3,6,9,12,15 and docosahexaenoic acid is ω-3,6,9,12,15,18.

20. D is correct.

Unsaturated fats become hydrogenated to form saturated fats, increasing the melting point.

An equivalent of hydrogen (H_2) is added across the double bonds of unsaturated fats during hydrogenation (i.e., increased hydrogen content), increasing the compound's molecular weight.

Saturation enhances the stacking ability of these compounds as solids.

More saturated (*double bonds*) compounds have *higher* melting points.

21. B is correct.

Ends of fatty acids are *hydrophobic*, nonpolar ends composed of hydrogen and carbon atoms.

The *hydrophilic*, polar end is composed of oxygen atoms and can hydrogen bond with water molecules.

22. B is correct.

Cholesterol plays a pivotal role in the synthesis of steroids and the integrity of cell membranes, but too much cholesterol in the blood results in plaque deposits in blood vessels.

23. D is correct.

Steroid molecules are one of two kinds of fat molecules with fused rings.

Triacylglycerides (or *triglycerides*) are long hydrocarbon chains with functionalized head groups.

24. C is correct.

Saponification is the base-promoted hydrolysis of esters.

This type of hydrolysis (i.e., saponification) is typically used to form soaps.

$$R{-}C({=}O){-}O{-}R' \quad + \quad NaOH \quad \rightarrow \quad R{-}C({=}O){-}O^{-}Na^{+} \quad + \quad HO{-}R'$$

carboxylate ester *sodium hydroxide* *sodium carboxylate* *alcohol*

Base hydrolysis (saponification) of an ester to form a carboxylate salt and an alcohol

Soap is hard or soft depending on the counter-ion of the carboxylate salt.

Hard soap is produced when *sodium hydroxide* is used for the base hydrolysis reaction.

Soft soap is produced when *potassium hydroxide* is used for the base hydrolysis reaction.

Other bases can give rise to soaps.

25. C is correct.

Cholesterol is a lipid molecule known as a steroid compound.

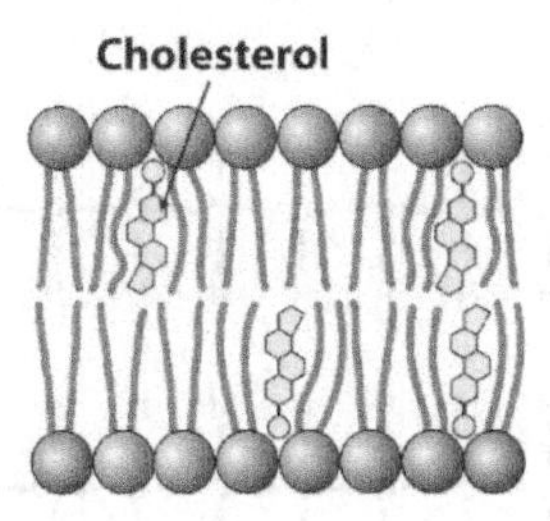

Cholesterol is embedded in the fluid mosaic phospholipid bilayer of membranes

Fused ring structure of steroid molecules makes them rigid with fewer degrees of motion due to the limited conformations available for cyclic molecules *vs.* acyclic molecules.

Molecules such as phospholipids lack fused-ring structures and exist as straight-chained molecules.

Cholesterol in the cell membrane acts as a *bidirectional regulator* of membrane fluidity: at elevated temperatures, it stabilizes the membrane and raises its melting point, whereas, at low temperatures, it intercalates between the phospholipids and prevents them from clustering and stiffening.

26. D is correct.

Saturated fats lack alkene double bonds.

Unsaturated fats convert to saturated through the process of hydrogenation. In this process, hydrogen gas is catalytically added to the alkene groups of the fatty acids to convert them to alkane groups.

27. D is correct.

Hydrogenation (i.e., adding H_2) of unsaturated fats adds hydrogen across the double bonds of the fat, causing the fats to be saturated and increasing their melting points.

Unsaturated Fat

Hydrogenation

Saturated Fat

Hydrogenation adds H_2 across double bonds to form saturated fatty acid chains

Because they form solids easily, the consumption of hydrogenated fats should be limited for health concerns.

28. B is correct.

Triglycerides (or *triacylglycerides*) are used for storage and exist in the adipose tissue of animals.

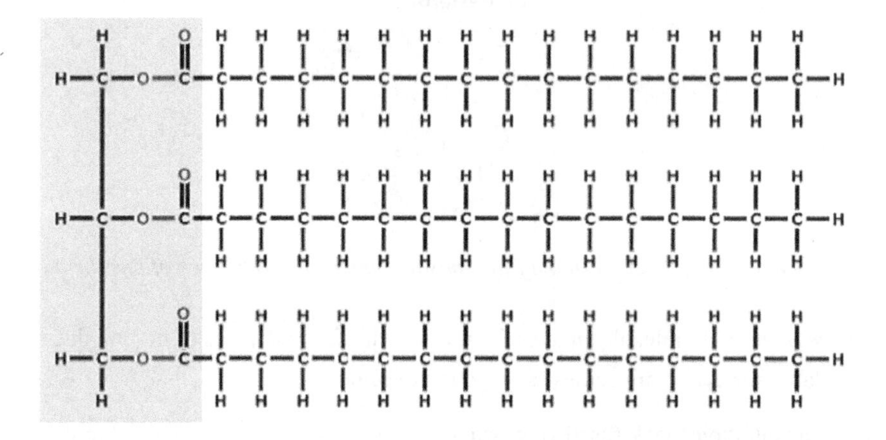

Triglyceride is glycerol backbone and three saturated fatty acid chains

Phospholipids are the largest component of semi-permeable cell membranes

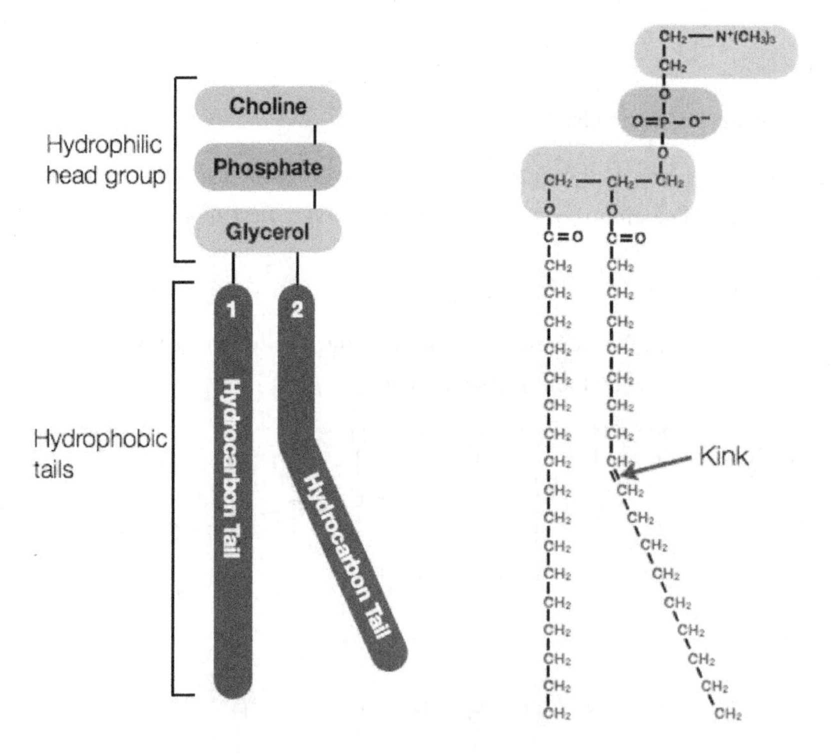

Phospholipids differ mainly in the composition of the polar head region. Hydrophobic region is the fatty acid chains (hydrocarbons) that are saturated (no double bonds) or unsaturated.

continued...

Steroids (see below) are lipids used for cell signaling.

Cholesterol

Testosterone

Estradiol

Cholesterol is the precursor molecule for several steroid hormones such as testosterone, estradiol, progesterone, and aldosterone

29. B is correct.

An omega-3 is when the alkene (E/Z) double bond is three carbon atoms from the methyl end.

Linoleic acid (top)is ω-6,9 and linolenic acid (bottom) is ω-3,6,9. Note the positions of the double bonds and cis/trans (Z / E) relationships for double bonds

Linolenic acids are omega-3 fatty acids.

Linoleic acids are omega-6 fatty acids.

These molecules contain double bonds and are *unsaturated fats*.

30. D is correct.

Estradiol (shown) is a steroid hormone derived from cholesterol.

Estradiol is a derivative of cholesterol

Cholesterol is a lipid of four fused rings; three fused rings are six-membered, and the fourth is five-membered.

Cholesterol is a four-fused ring structure

Cholesterol is a steroid that makes up one of two types of lipid molecules.

Triglyceride (i.e., glycerol backbone with three fatty acid chains) is the other lipid (shown below).

Triglyceride is glycerol backbone with three fatty acid chains

The carbon chain is numbered (example above) from the carboxyl end. Chemists number the double bonds as shown. Nutritionists specify the ω position from the terminal methyl group.

Position *omega* (ω) of the double bond(s) is the number of carbon atoms from the *terminal methyl group*.

31. C is correct.

Micelles form in aqueous environments with hydrophobic tails clusters.

Polar head regions are exposed on the surface of the micelle and exposed to the aqueous environment.

32. B is correct.

Not all lipids are entirely hydrophobic.

Ionic and polar heads of soaps and phospholipids enable the molecules to interact with aqueous (or polar) environments. These molecules are mainly hydrophobic because they primarily consist of hydrocarbon chains or rings.

33. A is correct.

The molecules are likely to exist as oils (i.e., liquids) for unsaturated fats at room temperature.

Saturated fats are solid at room temperature because reduced forms have stacking properties, forming solids.

34. B is correct.

Alkene molecules in fatty acids tend to be *Z* alkenes.

Saturated fatty acid lacks a double bond and is likely a solid at room temperature

Unsaturated fatty acid has double bonds and is likely a liquid at room temperature

Alkene double bonds (i.e., unsaturated) prevent fatty acid molecules from stacking closely, lowering the melting point for fat molecules.

The presence of double bonds may influence the state of matter of the oil, as unsaturated fats tend to be liquid at room temperature, and saturated fats tend to be solids.

continued...

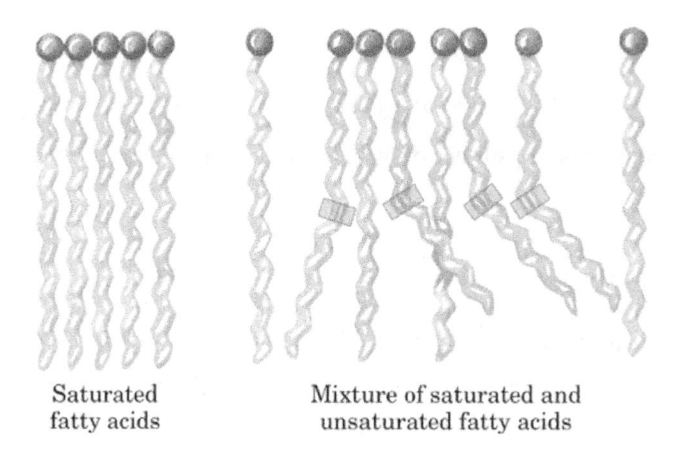

35. C is correct.

Triacylglycerols comprise a *glycerol* substructure and *three fatty acids* condensed to form a triester.

36. A is correct.

Oils are isolated from plant sources and may contain different several fatty acids.

These oils may contain saturated fat, but other fats in the mixture are unsaturated fat molecules.

Saturated fats include palmitic and stearic acid.

Unsaturated fats include oleic, palmitoleic, and linoleic acids.

37. B is correct.

There are two overall categories of lipids: long-chain lipids (e.g., triglycerides) and smaller, polycyclic lipids, such as steroids (e.g., cholesterol and its derivatives, such as estrogen and testosterone).

Lipid molecules are *fat-soluble* and are mainly *soluble in organic* (or hydrophobic) *solutions*.

38. D is correct.

In hydrogenation reactions, *Z* and *E* alkenes are reduced (adding H_2 across double bonds) to alkanes, and this process is catalyzed by transition metals, such as nickel or palladium.

In this reaction, hydrogen (H_2) is added across the double bond of the alkene.

39. D is correct.

Saturated fats tend to be solid at room temperature because they lack alkene groups.

The presence of alkene groups in fat molecules *lowers the melting point.*

For example, butter is a dairy product made from the fat of cow's milk. It is solid at room temperature and is mainly composed of saturated fat molecules.

40. C is correct.

Although waxes are lipid molecules containing esters, waxes contain a single ester functional group.

Monoalcohols form waxes, whereas glycerol forms triglycerides and phospholipids.

41. D is correct.

Fatty acids make fat molecules known as *triglycerides*.

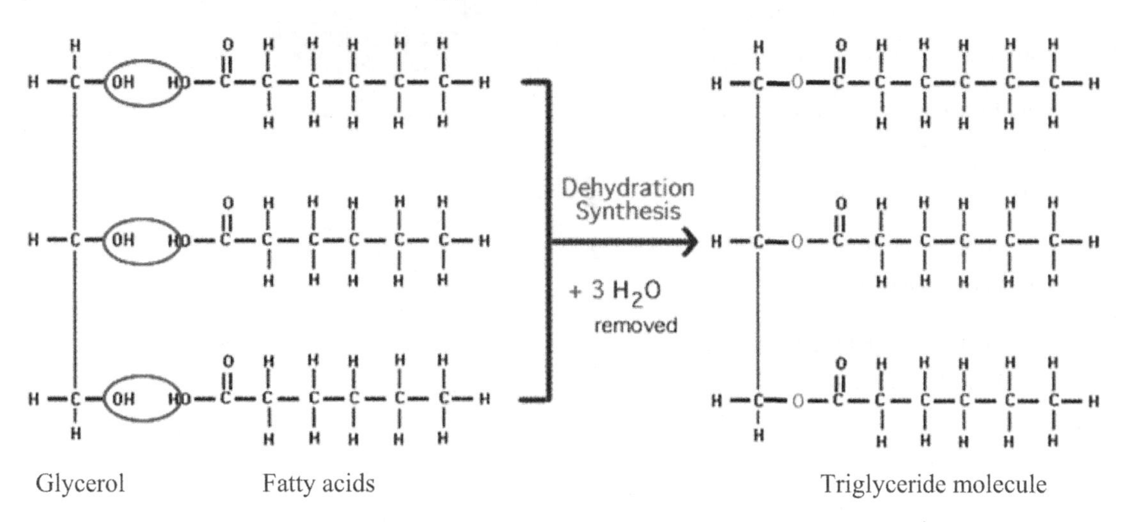

Dehydration (removal of H_2O) of glycerol and three fatty acids form triglycerides

Fatty acids are synthesized from one equivalent of a triol (glycerol and three equivalents of acid-containing groups) known as fatty acids.

42. A is correct.

Dietary triglycerides are composed of glycerol and three fatty acids.

Hydrolysis of triglycerides yields glycerol and three fatty acid chains.

$$\text{triglyceride } (R_a, R_b, R_c) + 3\,H_2O \longrightarrow \text{glycerol} + HO{-}C(=O){-}R_a + HO{-}C(=O){-}R_b + HO{-}C(=O){-}R_c$$

Hydrolysis of a triglyceride with three equivalents of water yields glycerol and three fatty acids

43. C is correct.

Phospholipids are essential lipids composing the bilayer structure of cell membranes, organelles, and other enclosed cellular structures.

Phospholipids are two (same or different) fatty acid molecules, a phosphate group, and a 3-carbon glycerol backbone.

The phospholipid contains a hydrophobic (i.e., fatty acid tail) region and a hydrophilic (polar head) region.

Hydrophobic regions point toward each other in the membrane bilayer.

Hydrophilic polar heads point towards the inside (i.e., cytosolic) or outside (i.e., extracellular).

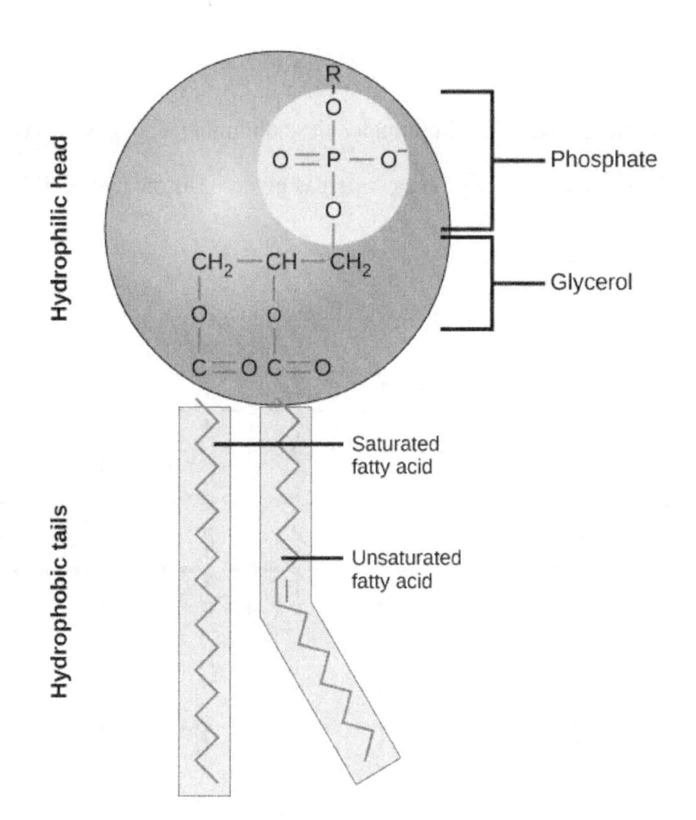

Phospholipids differ mainly in the composition of the polar head region. The hydrophobic region is the fatty acid chains (hydrocarbons) that are saturated (no double bonds) or unsaturated.

44. D is correct.

Fat can be synthesized from glucose, but glucose is *not* produced from animal fat.

Excess glucose consumption can lead to increased levels of fat in the body.

45. D is correct.

The two lipids categories are long-chain lipids (e.g., triglycerides) and smaller, polycyclic lipids, such as steroids (e.g., cholesterol and its derivatives such as estrogen and testosterone).

Terpenes are small alkene-containing hydrocarbon building blocks that can combine and cyclize to form steroids. Terpenes are simple lipids.

Examples of terpenes are shown:

limonene menthol camphor

continued...

Limonene is in citrus fruit skins, menthol in peppermint, and camphor from camphor trees.

vitamin A

citral
(lemon grass)

β carotene is a photopigment in carrots and vegetables converted to vitamin A

46. C is correct.

An exception to the tendency for sugars to have oxygen atoms linked to each carbon atom is deoxyribose (e.g., DNA). It is like a ribose (e.g., RNA) with one alcohol replaced with a carbon-hydrogen bond.

47. B is correct.

The ratio of atoms for sugars is typically 1:2:1 (carbon : hydrogen : oxygen).

Fisher projections of an example D-ribose sugar with horizontal bonds projecting forward

48. A is correct.

Monosaccharides cannot be catabolized (i.e., broken down) into simpler sugar subunits.

Monosaccharides undergo oxidative degradation when treated with nitric acid to form carbon dioxide (CO_2) and carbon monoxide (CO).

49. A is correct.

Lactose is a disaccharide of glucose and galactose.

Lactose is a disaccharide of galactose and glucose

Lactose is a disaccharide formed by a β(1→4) linkage between galactose and glucose.

50. C is correct.

Glycogen is a polymer of glucose serving as an energy store of carbohydrates in animal cells (plants use starch), common in the liver, muscle, and red blood cells.

Glycogen is a large biomolecule consisting of repeating glucose subunits. The anomeric position is carbon one and can be pointing upward (α) or down (β).

51. D is correct.

Disaccharides contain a glycosidic linkage that is an ether group.

The ether can be protonated with Brønsted acids and hydrolyzed in the presence of water.

Polysaccharides can be hydrolyzed to produce monosaccharides (i.e., individual monomers of the polymer).

52. D is correct.

Monosaccharides are the basic unit of carbohydrates.

Subjecting monosaccharides to acids or bases will not hydrolyze them; however, they undergo oxidative decomposition by treatment with periodic acid to form formaldehyde and formic acid.

53. D is correct.

Carbohydrates are organic compounds containing carbon, hydrogen, and oxygen.

The general molecular formula depends on carbohydrates, but many examples have the formula of $C_nH_{2n}O_n$.

54. C is correct.

The “di” prefix in the name indicates two smaller subunits.

Monosaccharides are linked by *glycosidic* (i.e., oxygen bonded to two ethers) functional groups.

Lactose is a disaccharide of galactose and glucose

Lactose is a disaccharide formed by a β(1→4) linkage between galactose and glucose.

55. D is correct.

Proteins are denser than lipids, and lipoproteins with higher protein content are dense.

Lipoproteins with low-density transport mainly lipids and contain little protein (i.e., VLDL transport more lipids / less protein than LDL).

Chylomicrons are formed by the small intestine and have the lowest density and the highest lipid/lowest protein content of lipoproteins.

56. C is correct.

Lipids are the primary food storage molecule, and lipids release more energy per gram (9 kcal/gram) than carbohydrates (4 kcal/gram) or proteins (4 kcal/gram).

Lipids provide insulation and protection against injury as the major component of adipose (fat) tissue.

A: *proteins* are mainly composed of amino acids with C, H, O, and N but may contain S (i.e., cysteine).

B: α *helices* and β *pleated sheets* are secondary structures of proteins.

D: C:H:O ratio of carbohydrates is 1:2:1 ($C_nH_{2n}O_n$).

57. A is correct.

Carbohydrates (e.g., glucose, fructose, lactose, maltose) and proteins provide 4 calories per gram.

Fats (lipids) are energy-dense and provide 9 calories per gram.

58. B is correct.

The proper digestion of macromolecules is required to absorb nutrients from the *small intestine*.

Carbohydrates must be degraded into monosaccharides like glucose, fructose, and galactose.

Lactose is a disaccharide of glucose and galactose.

Sucrose is glucose and fructose.

Maltose is a disaccharide of two glucose units.

Disaccharide digestion into monomers occurs at the intestinal brush border of the small intestine via enzymes like lactase, sucrase, and maltase.

A: amino acids are the *monomers* (i.e., building blocks) of proteins.

Proteins must be *hydrolyzed* (catabolized) into monopeptides, dipeptides, or tripeptides for absorption in the duodenum of the small intestine.

D: lipids are degraded into free fatty acids and glycerol for absorption in the small intestine.

59. A is correct.

Adding H_2O to break bonds (i.e., hydrolysis) is used during digestion when fats are catabolized (i.e., degraded) into fatty acids by detaching from glycerol or proteins that are digested (catabolized) into amino acids.

60. A is correct.

Dipole interactions joining complementary strands of DNA are *hydrogen bonds*.

These bonds form from the acid protons between the amides and imide functional groups and the carbonyl and amide Lewis basic sites of the matched nitrogen base pairs.

61. D is correct.

DNA molecule (shown) has a deoxyribose sugar-phosphate backbone with bases (A, C, G, T) projecting into the center to join the antiparallel strand of DNA (i.e., double helix).

Deoxyribose sugar-phosphate backbone is negatively charged due to the formal charge of the oxygen attached to the phosphate group.

deoxyadenosine 5'-phosphate

deoxythymidine 5'-phosphate

deoxyguanosine 5'-phosphate

deoxycytosine 5'-phosphate

Nucleosides contain ribose sugar, phosphate, and base (A, C, G, T)

continued...

Purines (adenine and guanine) are double-ringed nitrogenous bases.

Pyrimidines (cytosine, thymine, and uracil-in RNA) are single-ringed.

Nucleotides have deoxyribose sugar, base, and phosphate.

Nucleosides have deoxyribose sugar and base without a phosphate group.

62. B is correct.

Transcription (DNA → RNA) is a biomolecular event in the nucleus.

During transcription, RNA molecules are synthesized using complementary base pairs of DNA single strands.

63. D is correct.

Amino acids are *monomers* that comprise proteins.

Nucleotides have a *nitrogenous base* (i.e., adenosine, cytosine, guanine, thymine, or uracil), *phosphate group*, and a *five-carbon sugar* (i.e., ribose for RNA or deoxyribose for DNA).

64. B is correct.

Four standard nucleotides are in DNA molecules: adenine (A), cytosine (C), guanine (G), and thymine (T)

Four standard nucleotides are in RNA molecules: adenine (A), cytosine (C), guanine (G), and uracil (U)

65. A is correct.

One strand is a template for a new strand synthesized at the replication fork during DNA replication.

Continuously synthesized strand is the *leading strand* and, when combined with one original (parental) strand of DNA, makes one new (daughter) DNA molecule. A new DNA molecule is created as the other parent strand is a template for its complementary strand.

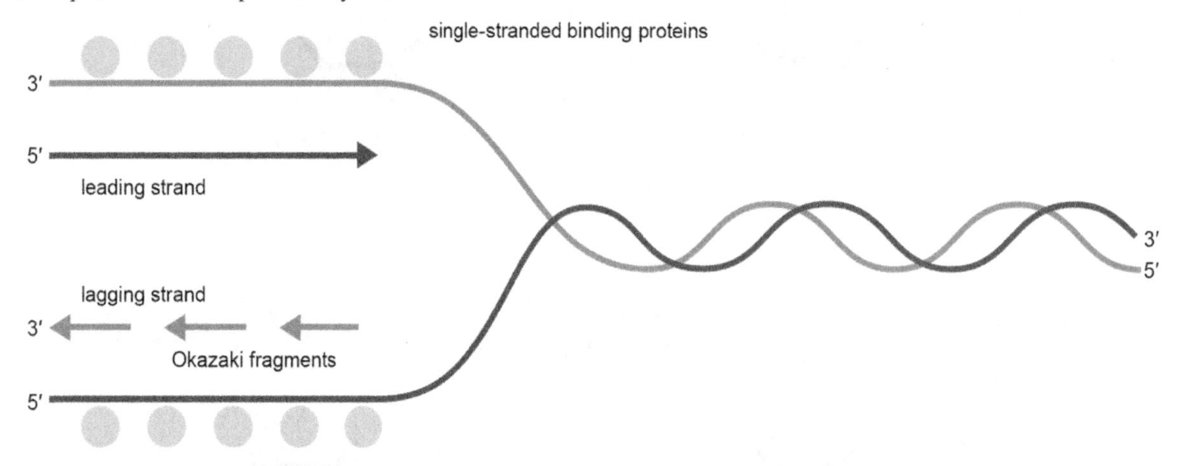

DNA replication with the leading and lagging strands indicated

Lagging strand is made of smaller segments called *Okazaki fragments* (about 150-200 nucleotides long).

Okazaki fragments are combined with DNA *ligase* (enzyme).

66. D is correct.

RNA molecules contain ribose as the carbohydrate component of the backbone

DNA contains deoxyribose (lacking a 2'-hydroxy) sugar as part of the backbone

67. D is correct.

Adenine forms *two hydrogen bonds* with thymine (A=T); cytosine forms *three hydrogen bonds* with guanine (C≡G).

A complementary nitrogen base is used by DNA polymerase (in the S phase of interphase) for strand synthesis.

68. C is correct.

DNA molecules hold genetic information.

RNA molecules are synthesized from the DNA strand to make proteins for the cell.

Genes are the sections of DNA responsible for *synthesizing proteins* in cells.

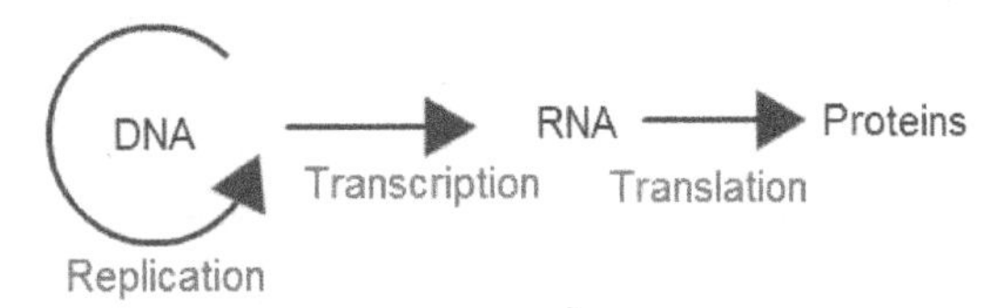

Central dogma of molecular biology designates information flow

69. D is correct.

There are five nucleotides, four appear in DNA: adenine (A), cytosine (C), guanine (G), and thymine (T).

In RNA molecules, thymine is replaced with the pyrimidine nucleotide of uracil.

Nucleotides contain ribose sugar, phosphate, and base (adenine shown)

Nucleotides have a phosphate group (note the negative charge on oxygens), deoxyribose sugar (lack a 2'hydroxyl), and a nitrogenous base (adenine, cytosine, guanine, thymine, or uracil).

Nucleosides are nucleotides (sugar and base) with one or more phosphates added.

70. D is correct.

DNA	DNA	mRNA	tRNA
A	T	A	U
C	G	C	G
G	C	G	C
T	A	U	A

Complementary base pairing for nucleotides

DNA → DNA (replication); DNA → RNA (transcription); RNA → protein (translation)

Guanine and cytosine with three hydrogen bonds

continued...

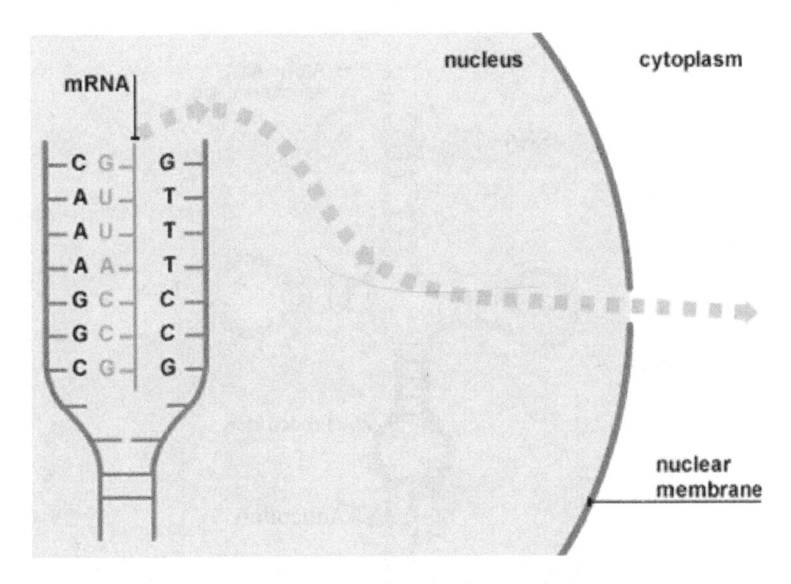

A single strand of DNA is the template for RNA synthesis during transcription

mRNA (after processing) is translocated to the cytoplasm for *translation into proteins*.

71. A is correct.

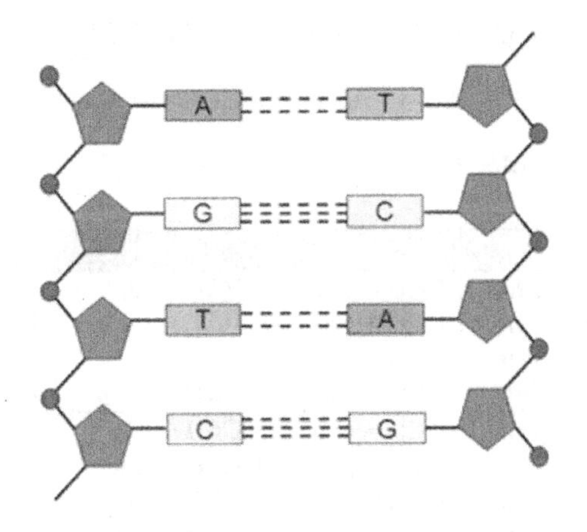

Double-stranded DNA with two hydrogen bonds between A=T and three between C≡G

DNA backbone is deoxyribose sugars (pentagons), and phosphates (circles) joined by covalent bonds.

72. D is correct.

Codons (schematically shown) are three-nucleotide sequences on the mRNA.

Anticodons are nucleotide sequences of three bases on the tRNA.

Codon-anticodon sequences hybridize by forming hydrogen bonds to the complementary base pair.

Relationship between codon (on mRNA), anticodon (on tRNA), and the resulting amino acid:

continued...

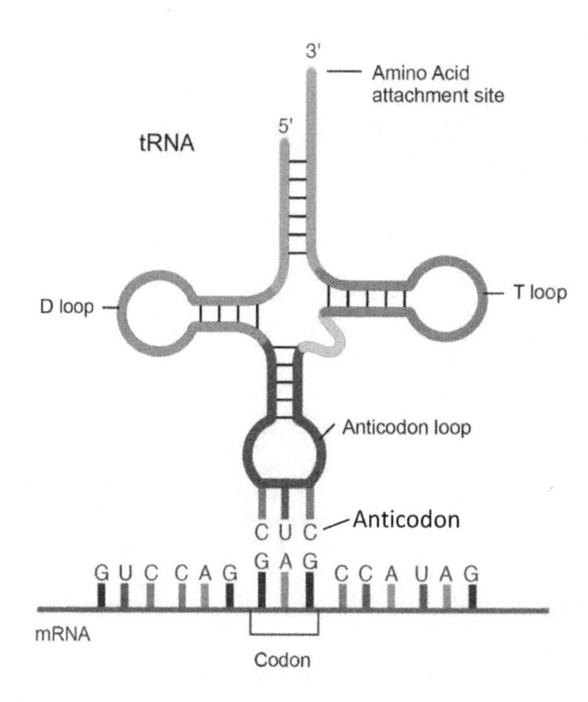

Three nucleotide codon/anticodon bonding with associated cloverleaf tRNA

Codon (mRNA): 5'–AUG–CAA–CCC–GAC–UCC–AGC–3'

Anticodon (tRNA): 3'–UAC–GUU–GGG–CUG–AGG–UAG–5'

Amino acids: Met–Gln–Pro–Asp–Phe–Ser

	U	C	A	G
U	UUU = phe UUC = phe UUA = leu UUG = leu	UCU = ser UCC = ser UCA = ser UCG = ser	UAU = tyr UAC = tyr UAA = stop UAG = stop	UGU = cys UGC = cys UGA = stop UGG = trp
C	CUU = leu CUC = leu CUA = leu CUG = leu	CCU = pro CCC = pro CCA = pro CCG = pro	CAU = his CAC = his CAA = gln CAG = gln	CGU = arg CGC = arg CGA = arg CGG = arg
A	AUU = ile AUC = ile AUA = ile AUG = met	ACU = thr ACC = thr ACA = thr ACG = thr	AAU = asn AAC = asn AAA = lys AAG = lys	AGU = ser AGC = ser AGA = arg AGG = arg
G	GUU = val GUC = val GUA = val GUG = val	GCU = ala GCC = ala GCA = ala GCG = ala	GAU = asp GAC = asp GAA = glu GAG = glu	GGU = gly GGC = gly GGA = gly GGG = gly

Genetic code of nucleotides and corresponding amino acids

Genetic code is the nucleotide sequence of the codon (on mRNA) that complementary base pairs with the nucleotide sequence of the anticodon (on tRNA).

Amino acid encoded by a gene (synthesized during translation into mRNA) derives from the *genetic code*.

73. A is correct.

Nucleotide consisting of sugar, phosphate, and a nitrogenous base

The hexose sugar, nitrogen base, and phosphoric acid group comprise nucleotides, and these nucleotides are used to make larger molecules like *nucleic acids*.

74. D is correct.

Identical copies of DNA are necessary for the division of cells; these cells are *daughter cells*.

When the daughter strand is synthesized, a complementary nitrogenous base containing nucleotides (A ↔ T and C ↔ G) is incorporated into the growing strand.

Replication (i.e., synthesis of DNA) occurs during the S phase (i.e., within interphase) of the cell cycle.

75. B is correct.

Hydrogen bonding between complementary strands of antiparallel DNA strands

continued...

Two antiparallel strands of DNA (schematically as vertical arrows) indicate the 3'-hydroxyl of the sugar (from the point of chain elongation).

Nucleotide is the building block of DNA and has sugar (i.e., deoxyribose), phosphate, and base (adenosine, cytosine, guanine, and thymine)

Two hydrogen bonds (A=T) hold adenine and thymine base pairs.

Cytosine and guanine nitrogen base pairs use three hydrogen bonds (C≡G) to support the nucleic acid structure.

76. B is correct.

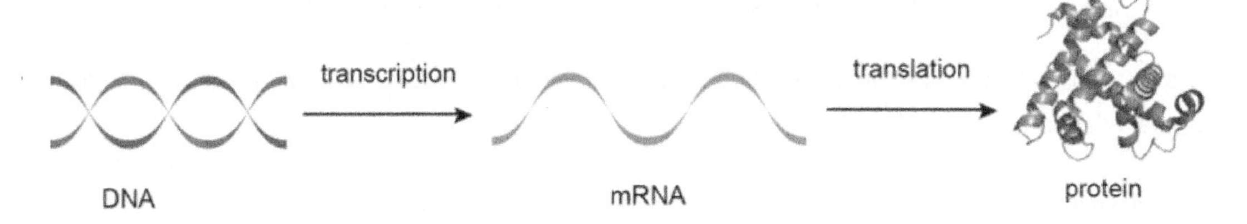

Central dogma of molecule biology: DNA → RNA → protein

tRNA and ribosomes are used to make peptide chains from mRNA.

Nucleotide triplets known as codons are combined with a complementary tRNA (i.e., containing the anticodon complementary in base pairing with the codon of the mRNA).

Each tRNA brings an appropriate (i.e., anticodon ↔ amino acid) to the growing polypeptide during translation.

Ribosomes combine *amino acid residues* in the order of the codon sequence.

77. C is correct.

After transcription (DNA → mRNA), the synthesized mRNA is transported out of the nucleus and the ribosome to synthesize protein during translation (mRNA → protein).

RNA contains ribose, a sugar similar to deoxyribose of DNA molecules, except it has a hydroxyl group (~OH) at the 2' position on the sugar.

Ribonucleotide (left) and deoxyribonucleotide (right): note the 2' position of the sugars

Nucleic acids (DNA and RNA) bind via hydrogen bonds between bases (A=T/U and C≡G).

Sugar and phosphate groups form the backbone and do not affect (to any appreciable degree) the hydrogen bonding between bases.

continued…

A hydroxyl group (~OH) in RNA causes the backbone to experience steric and electrostatic repulsion.

Therefore, the grooves formed in helixes or hairpin loops between chains are larger.

Larger groove of DNA permits nucleases (i.e., enzymes that digest DNA or RNA) to efficiently bind to the RNA chain and digest the covalent bonds between the alternating sugar-phosphate monomers.

78. A is correct.

Nitrogen bases of nucleotides hydrogen bond one nucleic acid strand to the other.

The number of hydrogen bonds between the pairs varies between two (A=T) and three (C≡G) bonds.

> Adenine and thymine nitrogenous base pairs bond with two hydrogen bonds (A=T).
>
> Cytosine and guanine nitrogenous base pairs bond with three hydrogen bonds (C≡G).

79. A is correct.

Three nucleotides are combined to make a *codon* (on mRNA) or *anticodon* (on tRNA) required for translation.

A larger segment of DNA is a *gene*, and sections of different genes comprise nucleic acid strands.

Two single strands of DNA are used to make one DNA double helix.

80. B is correct.

Each thymine nitrogen base forms two hydrogen bonds with adenine in DNA molecules, and there is an equal number of nitrogen bases in the molecule.

81. D is correct.

Ribose sugar differs from deoxyribose sugars because ribose lacks one alcohol (i.e., hydroxyl) group.

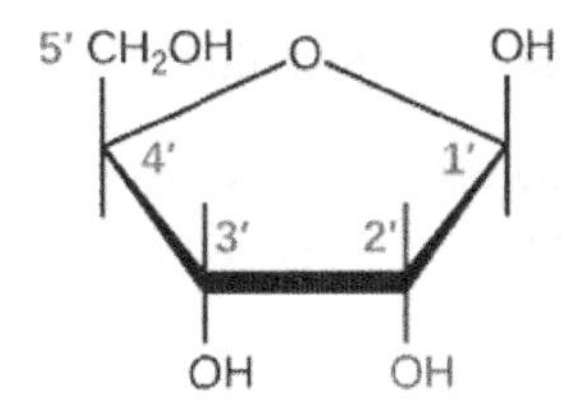

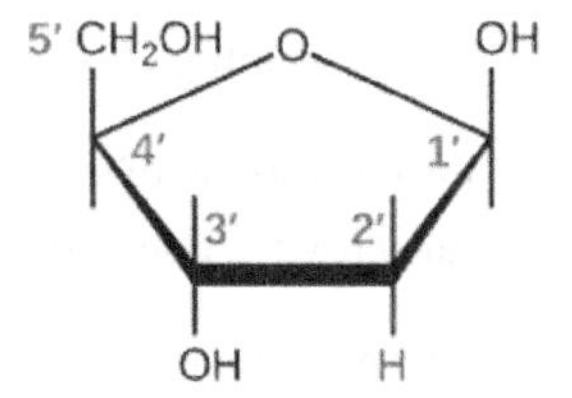

Ribose (left) and deoxyribose have a 3'-OH, but deoxyribose lacks a 2'-OH

Ribose sugar (RNA) and *deoxyribose* sugar (DNA) are used to synthesize nucleic acid polymers.

82. B is correct.

Replication is DNA → DNA during the S phase of the cell cycle.

A: *translation* is the process of synthesizing proteins from mRNA.

C: *transcription* is the process of synthesizing mRNA from DNA.

D: *complementation* is observed in genetics when two organisms with different homozygous recessive mutations that produce the same mutant phenotype (e.g., thorax differences in *Drosophila* flies), when mated or crossed, produce offspring with the wild-type phenotype.

Complementation only occurs if the mutations are in different genes.

Each organism's genome supplies the wild-type allele το *complement* the mutated allele. Since the mutations are recessive, the offspring display the wild-type phenotype.

Complementation (i.e., *cis*/*trans*) test can evaluate whether the mutations are in different genes.

83. D is correct.

Central dogma of molecular biology:

DNA → RNA → protein

DNA → RNA is *transcription*

RNA → protein is *translation*

DNA is the nucleic acid biomolecule that codes for nucleic acids and proteins.

DNA strands are synthesized from parental DNA strands during replication.

84. C is correct.

The peptide chain is assembled depending on the amino acid residue order, dictated by the mRNA sequence.

rRNA is the nucleic acid that comprises the ribosome used during translation (converting the codon into a corresponding amino acid in the growing polypeptide chains of the nascent protein).

Each *codon of RNA* has a corresponding *anticodon on tRNA*.

tRNA molecules have 3-nucleotide sequences of the anticodon and the appropriate amino acid corresponding to the anticodon at its 3' end.

The genetic code is the language for converting DNA (i.e., nucleotides) to proteins (i.e., amino acids).

DNA → mRNA → protein

DNA to RNA is *transcription*

mRNA to protein is *translation*

There are 20 naturally occurring amino acids with one start codon (i.e., methionine) and three stop codons (containing releasing factors that dissociate the ribosome).

85. D is correct.

RNA utilizes uracil (U) nitrogenous base instead of thymine (T).

Therefore, thymine should not appear in the codon.

86. A is correct.

Thymine is a *pyrimidine nitrogenous base* that forms two hydrogen bonds with adenine (purine) in the base-paired structure of DNA.

In RNA molecules, the nitrogenous base thymine is replaced by uracil.

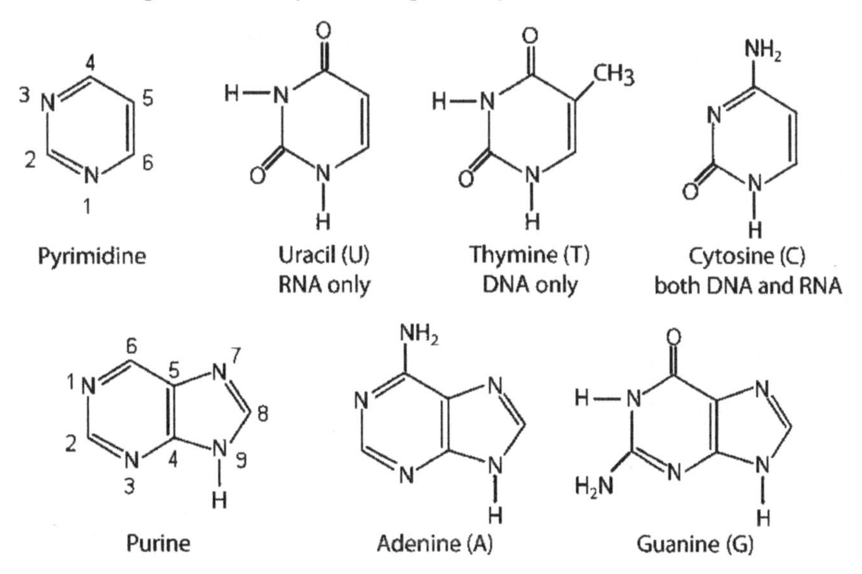

Purines (A, G) are single-ring structures, while pyrimidines (C, T, U) are double-ring structures

87. B is correct.

Three components of nucleotides are a phosphate group, cyclic five-carbon sugar, and a nitrogenous base.

Fat molecules are biomolecules in phospholipid membranes, storage fat molecules, and other lipid molecules.

88. A is correct.

There are three major nucleotide components in nucleic acids.

Nucleic acids have a nitrogen base used for hydrogen bonding, a hexose sugar (ribose or deoxyribose), and a phosphate group with a phosphate linkage with the sugar.

Ester linkages are in fats, *glycosidic linkages* in sugars, and *peptide linkages* in proteins.

89. B is correct.

Genetic code necessary for constructing peptide chains is the codon of three mRNA nucleotides complementary to the anticodon of tRNA molecules.

90. C is correct.

Because RNA contains uracil, these nitrogenous bases form hydrogen bonds with adenine.

Note that RNA molecules are single-stranded, and DNA molecules are double-stranded.

Adenosine (A) forms two hydrogen bonds with thymine (T) in DNA.

Cytosine (C) forms three hydrogen bonds with guanine (G) in DNA.

91. C is correct.

Thymine is a pyrimidine nucleotide base in DNA but not in RNA.

Instead, RNA has uracil.

92. C is correct.

In DNA, thymine hydrogen bonds with adenine.

In RNA, the thymine is exchanged for uracil.

Uracil (RNA) | Thymine (DNA)

93. C is correct.

Nucleic acids determine the sequences of amino acids because of groupings of nucleotides along a sequence corresponding to a particular amino acid.

The information of specific nucleic acids (i.e., mRNA) is translated on ribosomes by tRNA.

Prions are infectious, disease-causing agents of misfolded proteins.

94. C is correct.

DNA (deoxyribonucleic acid) is a long biological molecule composed of smaller nucleotides (i.e., sugar, phosphate, and base).

The sugar is deoxyribose (compared to ribose for RNA), and the bases are adenine, cytosine, guanine, and thymine (with thymine replaced by uracil in RNA).

The strands that these nucleotides are nucleic acids.

95. D is correct.

Ribose is the structural sugar of RNA, while deoxyribose is the sugar for DNA.

Uracil is a nucleotide (i.e., sugar, phosphate, and base) containing ribose sugar, like deoxyribose; however, one difference is that deoxyribose has one fewer alcohol group (2' position of the sugar) than ribose.

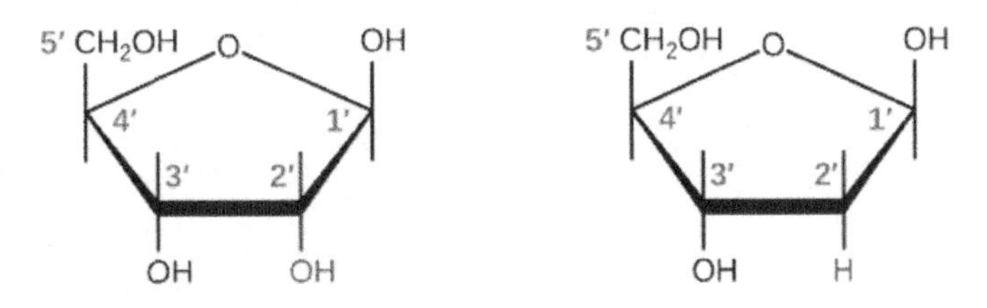

Ribose (left) and deoxyribose have a 3'-OH, but deoxyribose lacks a 2'-OH

Uracil is a *nucleotide base* of RNA and does not appear in DNA strands.

96. A is correct.

The two nucleic acid strands of DNA dissociate during transcription, and mRNA is synthesized (transcription) using the nitrogen bases as a template.

Therefore, the mRNA strand is a complementary strand to the DNA strand.

mRNA *exits the nucleus* to be used as a template to produce proteins (translation).

97. C is correct.

Covalent bonds link single strands of DNA.

Hydrogen bonds link antiparallel strands of DNA.

Two hydrogen bonds join adenine and thymine (A=T).

Three hydrogen bonds join cytosine and guanine (C≡G).

Notes for active learning

Eukaryotic Cell: Structure and Function – Detailed Explanations

1. D is correct.

Facilitated transport (or *passive transport*) uses a protein pore/channel but is differentiated from *active transport that requires energy*.

2. A is correct.

Cell is the unit of function and reproduction because subcellular components cannot regenerate whole cells.

3. C is correct.

I: water relies on *aquaporins* to readily diffuse across a plasma membrane.

Without aquaporins, only a small fraction of water molecules can diffuse through the cell membrane per unit of time because of the polarity of water molecules.

II: *small hydrophobic molecules* readily diffuse through the hydrophobic tails of the plasma membrane.

III: *small ions* rely on ion channel transport proteins to diffuse across the membrane.

IV: *neutral gas molecules* (e.g., O_2, CO_2) readily diffuse through the hydrophobic tails of the plasma membrane.

4. C is correct.

Integral proteins often span the plasma membrane.

Plasma membrane is a phospholipid bilayer with an inner span of hydrophobic (or *water-fearing*) regions.

Diameter of a plasma membrane is 20 to 25 amino acids thick.

Spans of 20-25 hydrophobic residues prefer to be embedded in the plasma membrane and isolated from water.

Hydropathy analysis determines the degree of *hydrophobicity* (i.e., nonpolar or *water-fearing*) or *hydrophilicity* (i.e., polar, or *water-loving*) of amino acids in a protein. It characterizes the possible structures of a protein.

Each residue (i.e., individual amino acid) has a hydrophobicity value (analogous to electronegativity).

Hydropathy analysis plots the degree of hydrophobicity (or hydrophilicity) on the *y*-axis and the amino acid sequence on the *x*-axis, hydrophobicity *vs.* amino acid position.

Amino acids have lower energy when polar amino acids occupy a polar environment (e.g., cytoplasm) and nonpolar amino acids occupy a nonpolar environment (e.g., the interior of plasma membrane).

5. B is correct.

Lysosome is the digestive region of the cell and is a membrane-bound organelle with a low pH (around 5) that stores hydrolytic enzymes.

A: *vacuoles* and *vesicles* are membrane-bound sacs involved in the transport and storage of materials ingested, secreted, processed, or digested by cells.

Vacuoles are larger than vesicles and are in plant cells (e.g., central vacuole).

C: *chloroplasts* are the site of photosynthesis and are only in algae and plant cells. Chloroplasts contain their DNA and ribosomes and may have similarly evolved via endosymbiosis like mitochondria.

D: *phagosomes* are vesicles for transporting and storing materials ingested by the cell through phagocytosis. Vesicles form by fusion of the cell membrane around the particle.

Phagosome is a cellular compartment in which pathogenic microorganisms are digested.

Phagosomes *fuse with lysosomes* in their maturation process to form *phagolysosomes.*

6. C is correct.

DNA damage checkpoints are *signal transduction pathways* that block cell cycle progression in G1, G2, and metaphase and slow the S phase progression rate when DNA is damaged.

Pausing cell cycle allows the cell to repair the damage before dividing.

G1 → S → G2 → prophase → metaphase → anaphase → telophase
Interphase — Mitosis (PMAT)

Cell cycle divides into interphase (G1. S, G2) and mitosis (prophase, metaphase, anaphase, and telophase)

7. A is correct.

(C≡G) base pairs are linked in the double helix by *three hydrogen bonds.*

(A=T) base pairs are linked in the double helix by *two hydrogen bonds.*

Therefore, it takes more energy to separate G-C base pairs.

Less G–C rich strands of double-stranded DNA require less energy to separate (i.e., denature).

Chargaff's rule specifies complementary base pairing; double-stranded DNA has equal G and C (and A and T).

8. A is correct.

Phospholipids are lipids as major components of cell membranes; they form lipid bilayers.

Phospholipids contain a glycerol backbone, a phosphate group, and a simple organic molecule (e.g., choline).

The 'head' is *hydrophilic* (i.e., attracted to water), while the 'tails' are *hydrophobic* (i.e., repelled by water), and the tails aggregate (via hydrophobic forces).

Hydrophilic heads contain negatively charged phosphate groups and glycerol.

Hydrophobic tails usually consist of 2 long fatty acids (saturated or unsaturated) hydrocarbon chains.

Cholesterol is embedded within animal lipid bilayers but is absent in plant cell membranes. Embedded cholesterol in the phospholipid bilayer in eukaryotic animal cells allows for protective cell membranes that can also change shape.

Plant and bacterial cell walls are primarily composed of cellulose and peptidoglycan glucose polymers, respectively, which are rigid and restrict movement.

9. B is correct.

Cytoskeleton determines the overall shape of a cell.

Cytoskeleton is composed of:

a. *Microtubules*: help synthesize cell walls in plants which primarily contribute to shape; centrosomes organize microtubules cilia and flagella (9+2). They form *mitotic spindles* and *centrioles* (non-membrane-bound organelles).

b. *Intermediate filaments*: anchor organelles (e.g., nucleus) and bear tension, contributing to cell shape.

c. *Microfilaments:* resist compression, thus contributing to cell shape.

10. B is correct.

Osmolarity is determined by the total concentration of dissolved particles in the solution.

Compounds that dissociate into ions (i.e., electrolytes) increase the concentration of particles and produce a higher osmolarity.

To determine which molecule (after dissociation into ions) generates the highest osmolarity, determine the number of individual ions each molecule dissociates into in H_2O.

$CaCl_2$ dissociates into 1 Ca^{2+} and 2 Cl^-

As a result, $CaCl_2$ generates the greatest osmolarity, which equals 250 mOsmoles for Ca^{2+} + 500 mOsmoles for Cl^- = 750 mOsmoles when $CaCl_2$ dissociates into ions within the solution.

A: NaCl dissociates in water with an osmolarity of 600 mOsmoles because it dissociates into 1 Na^+ and 1 Cl^-.

Na^+ cations and Cl^- anions are added: 300 mOsmoles for Na^+ + 300 mOsmoles for Cl^- = 600 mOsmoles.

C: glucose does *not* dissociate in water and has the same osmolarity as the starting molecule—500 mOsmoles.

D: urea does *not* dissociate in water and has the same osmolarity as the starting molecule— 600 mOsmoles.

11. C is correct.

The two ribosomal subunits are synthesized in the nucleolus, a region within the nucleus. The ribosomes are the sites of protein production.

Prokaryotic ribosomes (30S small + 50S large subunit = 70S complete ribosome) are smaller than *eukaryotic ribosomes* (40S small + 60S large subunit = 80S complete ribosome).

A: *Golgi apparatus* is a membrane-bound organelle that modifies (e.g., glycosylation), sorts, and packages proteins synthesized by the ribosomes.

B: *lysosomes* have a low pH of about 5 and contain hydrolytic enzymes involved in digestion.

D: *rough endoplasmic reticulum* (RER) is part of the endomembrane extending from the nuclear envelope.

The RER has ribosomes associated with its membrane and is the site of the production and folding of proteins.

Misfolded proteins exit the rough ER and are sent to the *proteasome* for degradation.

12. C is correct.

Cyclins are phosphorylated proteins responsible for specific events during cycle division, such as microtubule formation and chromatin remodeling.

Cyclins are four classes based on their behavior in the cell cycle: G1/S, S, M, and G1 cyclins.

p53 is not a transcription factor but is a tumor suppressor gene. The p53 protein is crucial in multicellular organisms, where it regulates the cell cycle and functions as a tumor suppressor (preventing cancer).

p53 is *the guardian of the genome* because it conserves stability by preventing genome mutation.

13. B is correct.

Codon is a three-nucleotide segment of an mRNA that hybridizes (via complementary base pairing) with the appropriate anticodon on the tRNA to encode one amino acid in a polypeptide chain during protein synthesis.

The tRNA molecule interacts with the mRNA codon after the ribosomal complex binds the mRNA.

A: tRNA molecules interact with the mRNA codon after (not before) the ribosomal complex binds mRNA

C: *translation* involves the conversion of mRNA into protein.

D: *operons* regulate the transcription of genes into mRNA and are not involved in translating mRNA into proteins.

14. C is correct.

Peroxisomes are organelles in most eukaryotic cells; a major function is the breakdown of very-long-chain fatty acids through *beta-oxidation*.

Peroxisome convert the very long fatty acids to medium-chain fatty acids in animal cells, subsequently shuttled to the mitochondria.

Medium-chain fatty acids are degraded, via oxidation, into CO_2 and H_2O.

Peroxisomes are membrane bound, while ribosomes are non-membrane-bound organelles.

15. C is correct.

Vacuole is a membrane-bound organelle in plant and fungal cells and some protist, animal, and bacterial cells.

Vacuoles are enclosed compartments filled with water. They contain inorganic and organic molecules (including enzymes in solution) and may contain solids that have been engulfed.

Function and significance of vacuoles vary by cell type, with much greater prominence in plants, fungi, and certain protists than in animals or bacteria.

Mitochondria and chloroplasts have circular DNA resembling DNA in prokaryotes, as supported by the endosymbiotic *theory* for the evolution of mitochondria and chloroplasts from prokaryotes.

Ribosomes are the site of protein synthesis.

Central dogma of molecular biology proposes that DNA makes RNA, which makes proteins.

16. C is correct.

I-cell disease patients cannot correctly direct newly synthesized peptides to their target organelles. The Golgi apparatus is part of the endomembrane system and serves as a cellular distribution center.

Golgi apparatus packages proteins before they are sent to their destination. It modifies, sorts, and packages proteins for cell secretion (i.e., exocytosis) or use within the cell.

A: *nucleus* is the largest organelle and contains genetic material (i.e., DNA), and is the site of rRNA synthesis (within the nucleolus).

D: *smooth ER* (endoplasmic reticulum) forms the endomembrane system, is connected to the nuclear envelope, and functions in several metabolic processes. It synthesizes lipids, phospholipids, and steroids.

Cells secreting lipids, phospholipids, and steroids (e.g., testes, ovaries, and skin oil glands) have an extensive smooth endoplasmic reticulum.

Smooth ER carries out the metabolism of carbohydrates and drug detoxification. It is responsible for the attachment of receptors on cell membrane proteins and steroid metabolism.

17. D is correct.

Cytochrome c oxidase is a large transmembrane protein complex in bacteria and the mitochondrion of eukaryotes. It receives an electron from each of four cytochrome c molecules and transfers the electrons to an O_2 molecule, converting molecular oxygen to two molecules of H_2O.

Cytochrome c oxidase is the *last enzyme in the electron transport chain* (ETC) of mitochondria (or bacteria) in the mitochondrial (or bacterial) inner membrane.

Mitochondria and chloroplasts have circular DNA resembling DNA in prokaryotes.

Endosymbiotic theory illustrates the evolution of mitochondria and chloroplasts from prokaryotes, thus explaining the resemblance.

18. A is correct.

Cytoskeleton is integral to proper cell division because it forms the mitotic spindle and separates sister chromatids during cell division.

The cytoskeleton is composed of microtubules and microfilaments, provides mechanical cell support to maintain shape, and functions in cell motility.

19. B is correct.

Biochemical events during the cell cycle include DNA damage repair and replication completion, centrosome duplication, assembly of the spindle, and attachment of the kinetochores to the spindle.

20. A is correct.

Mitochondria divide autonomously to produce daughter mitochondria that incorporate new nonradioactive phosphatidylcholine and inherit radioactive phosphatidylcholine from the parent via semiconservative replication.

Therefore, the daughter mitochondria have equal radioactivity.

B: mitochondria divide *autonomously*, and daughter mitochondria retain parental (original) radioactive label.

C: original sample was 100% radiolabeled.

DNA replication is *semiconservative*, whereby one strand of parental DNA (radiolabeled) and one strand of newly replicated (non-radiolabeled) are in each daughter cell after the first round of division.

D: requires the daughter mitochondria to be synthesized *de novo* (i.e., new) with newly-synthesized, nonradioactive phosphatidylcholine.

If the mitochondria divide autonomously, the daughter mitochondria retain the radioactive label evenly via *semiconservative replication.*

21. C is correct.

Golgi apparatus (i.e., Golgi complex) is a eukaryotic cell organelle.

Golgi apparatus processes proteins via *post-translational modifications* for three destinations:

1) *secreted* from the cell,

2) transported into *organelles,* or

3) targeted to the *plasma membrane.*

Golgi complex mainly processes proteins synthesized by the ER

In plant cells, the central vacuole functions as a lysosome, stores nutrients, and maintains osmotic balance.

Peroxisomes are similar to lysosomes in size, are bound by a single membrane, and are filled with enzymes.

However, peroxisomes *bud from* the endoplasmic reticulum.

22. B is correct.

Prokaryotic cells (bacteria) have a typical cell width of 0.2 to 2.0 micrometers in diameter.

Eukaryotic cells (animal cells) have a typical cell width of 10-100 micrometers in diameter.

1 millimeter = 1×10^{-3} m

1 micrometer = 1×10^{-6} m

1 nanometer = 1×10^{-9} m

Light microscopes visualize objects from 1 millimeter (10^{-3} m) to 0.2 micrometers (2×10^{-7} m).

Electron microscopes visualize objects as small as an atom (1 angstrom or 10^{-10} m).

Microscopic scale ranges from 1 millimeter (10^{-3} m) to a ten-millionth of a millimeter (10^{-10} m). There are immense variations in objects' sizes even within the microscopic scale.

10^{-3} m is 10 million times larger than 10^{-10} m, equivalent to the Earth's size *vs.* a beach ball.

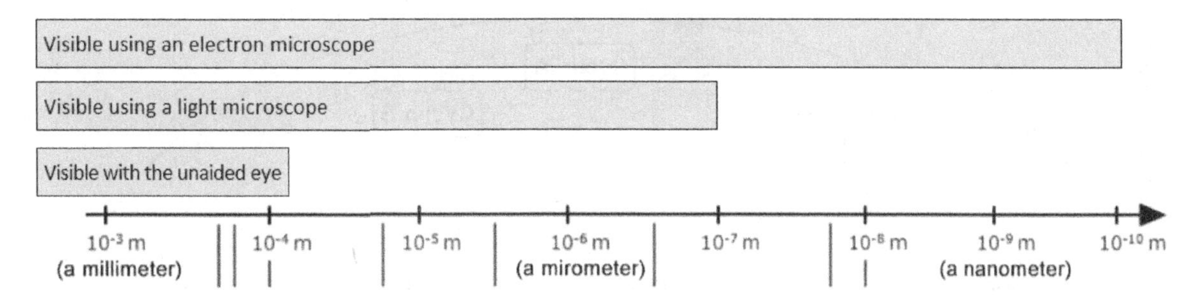

Comparison of resolution by unaided eyes, light, and electron microscopes

23. B is correct.

Ribosomes are composed of specific rRNA molecules and associated proteins.

Ribosomes are identified by the sedimentation coefficients (i.e., S units for Svedberg units) for density.

Prokaryotes have a 30S small and a 50S large subunit (i.e., complete ribosome = 70S; based on density).

Eukaryotes have a 40S small and 60S large subunit (i.e., complete ribosome = 80S).

A: *peroxisomes* are organelles involved in hydrogen peroxide (H_2O_2) synthesis and degradation. They function in cell detoxification and contain the catalase that decomposes H_2O_2 into H_2O and O_2.

C: *mitochondria* are organelles as the site of cellular respiration (i.e., oxidation of glucose to yield ATP) and plentiful in cells with high demands for ATP (e.g., muscle cells).

The number of mitochondria within a cell varies widely by organism and tissue type. Many cells have a single mitochondrion, whereas others contain several thousand mitochondria.

D: *nucleus* is the largest membrane-bound organelle in eukaryotes, containing the genetic code (i.e., DNA).

The *nucleus* directs the cell by storing and transmitting genetic information. Cells can contain multiple nuclei (e.g., skeletal muscle cells), one nucleus, or none (e.g., red blood cells).

24. A is correct.

Osmosis is a type of diffusion involving water and is a form of passive transport.

Hypertonic means a solution of high solute and low solvent concentrations.

Hypotonic means a solution of high solvent and low solute concentrations.

Solvents flow spontaneously from an area of high solvent to a low solvent concentration.

During *osmosis*, water flows from a hypotonic to a hypertonic environment.

25. B is correct.

Complex of Cdk and cyclin B is maturation or mitosis-promoting factor (MPF).

Cyclin B is necessary to progress cells into and out of the M phase of the cell cycle.

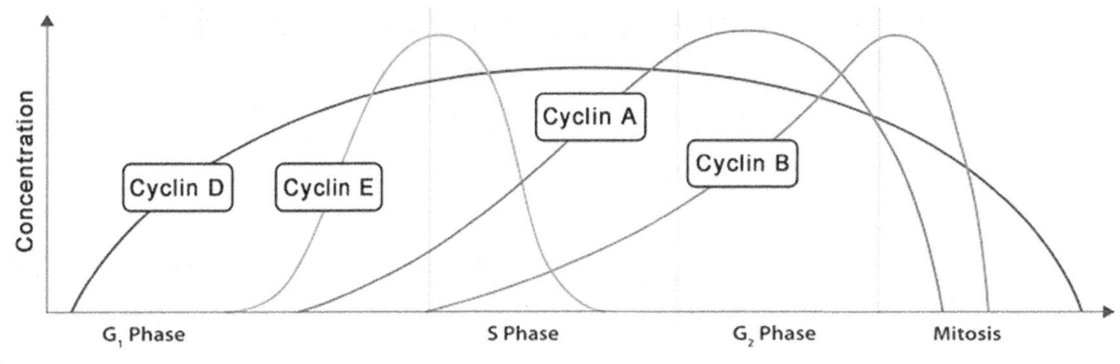

26. B is correct.

Mitochondria have their DNA genetic material and machinery to manufacture their RNAs and proteins.

In the example, the trait is recessive (not observed in a limited number of offspring) and encoded by a nuclear gene.

A: like organisms that reproduce sexually, mice inherit the *mitochondrial organelle* from their mother and display maternal inheritance of mitochondrial genes.

C: if X-linked, selectively male (not female) progeny would display the trait.

D: mitochondrial genes cannot be *recessive* because mitochondria are *inherited from the mother.*

27. C is correct.

Smooth endoplasmic reticulum (smooth ER) participates in synthesizing phosphatidylcholine.

Phosphatidylcholine is a class of phospholipids.

Smooth ER functions include synthesis of lipids, phospholipids, and steroids; metabolism of carbohydrates and steroids; detoxification of alcohol and drugs; and regulation of Ca^{2+} concentration in muscle cells.

28. D is correct.

Plastids (e.g., chloroplast and chromoplast) are major organelles in plants and algae. They are the site of manufacturing and storing critical chemical compounds used by cells. They often contain pigments used in photosynthesis. Pigments change to determine cell color.

Plastids, like prokaryotes, contain a circular double-stranded DNA molecule.

29. A is correct.

Thyroid gland synthesizes calcitonin in response to high blood calcium levels. It acts to reduce blood calcium (Ca^{2+}), opposing the effects of parathyroid hormone (PTH).

Calcitonin lowers blood Ca^{2+} levels in three ways:

1) inhibiting Ca^{2+} absorption by the intestines,

2) inhibiting osteoclast activity in bones, and

3) inhibiting renal tubular cell reabsorption of Ca^{2+}, allowing it to be excreted in the urine.

B: *kidneys* serve several essential regulatory roles. They are essential in the urinary system and serve homeostatic functions such as regulating electrolytes, maintaining acid-base balance, and regulating blood pressure (maintaining salt and water balance).

Kidneys secrete *renin* (involved in blood pressure regulation) that induces the release of aldosterone from the adrenal cortex (it increases blood pressure via sodium reabsorption, increasing blood pressure).

C: *parathyroid glands* synthesize parathyroid hormone (PTH), which increases blood calcium.

PTH increases the concentration of calcium in the blood by acting upon the parathyroid hormone receptor (elevated levels in bone and kidney) and the parathyroid hormone receptor (high levels in the central nervous system, pancreas, testes, and placenta).

D: *liver* is the largest organ with many functions, including detoxification, protein synthesis, and the production of biomolecules necessary for digestion. The liver synthesizes bile, which is necessary for dietary lipid emulsification (in the small intestine).

30. B is correct.

Rough *endoplasmic reticulum* (rough ER) is involved in synthesizing plasma membrane proteins.

Oxidative phosphorylation is a series of redox reactions in the electron transport chain (ETC), leading to the production of ATP. In Eukaryotes, this occurs in the *mitochondrial inner membrane* and prokaryotes in the intermembrane space.

Endocytosis is when a cell membrane invaginates, forming a vacuole to store molecules from the extracellular space actively transported across the cell's plasma membrane.

Post-translational modification is after ribosomes translate mRNA into polypeptide chains; the polypeptide chains become a mature protein by undergoing biochemical reactions (e.g., cleavage, folding).

31. B is correct.

Active transport uses a carrier protein and energy to move a substance across a membrane against (i.e., up) a concentration gradient: from low solute to a region of high solute concentration.

Donnan equilibrium refers to some ionic species passing through the barrier while others cannot.

Charged substances that cannot pass through the membrane create an uneven electrical charge. The electric potential arising between the solutions is the Donnan potential.

32. D is correct.

Cyclin D synthesis is initiated during G1 and drives the G1/S phase transition.

Apoptosis is programmed cell death (PCD) that may occur in multicellular organisms. Biochemical events lead to characteristic cell changes (morphology) and death.

Apoptotic changes include blebbing (i.e., an irregular bulge in the plasma membrane), cell shrinkage, chromatin condensation, nuclear fragmentation, and chromosomal DNA fragmentation.

In contrast to necrosis, traumatic cell death resulting from acute cellular injury, apoptosis confers advantages during an organism's life cycle.

For example, the differentiation of fingers and toes in a developing human embryo occurs because cells between the fingers undergo apoptosis, and the digits are separated.

Unlike necrosis, apoptosis produces cell fragments called *apoptotic bodies* that phagocytic cells can engulf and quickly remove before the cell's contents can spill out onto surrounding cells and cause damage.

33. C is correct.

During meiosis I, *homologous chromosomes* separate.

Sister chromatids (identical copies, except for recombination) separate during meiosis II.

Klinefelter syndrome (XXY karyotype) contains two X and one Y chromosome.

X and Y would be "homologous chromosomes" and typically separate during meiosis I. Failure to do so could create a sperm containing an X and a Y, which causes Klinefelter syndrome.

Anaphase is when the *centromere splits*, and the *homologous chromosomes / sister chromatids* are drawn away (via spindle fibers) from each other toward opposite sides of the two cells.

Homologous chromosomes separate during anaphase I, while sister chromatids separate during anaphase II.

In females, Turner's syndrome is due to the single X karyotype (single X chromosome and lacking a Y).

34. B is correct.

Most proteins that are secretory, membrane-bound, or targeted to an organelle use the *N-terminal signal sequence* (i.e., 5 to 30 amino acids) to target the protein.

Signal sequence of the polypeptide is recognized by a signal recognition particle (SRP), while the protein is synthesized on ribosomes.

Synthesis pauses while the ribosome-protein complex transfers to an SRP receptor on the ER (in eukaryotes) or plasma membranes (in prokaryotes) before polypeptide translation resumes.

35. C is correct.

Ribosomes anchored to the endoplasmic reticulum create the rough endoplasmic reticulum. It is *rough* because it is "studded" with ribosomes in contrast to the smooth endoplasmic reticulum, which lacks ribosomes.

"*Free*" and "*attached*" ribosome comparisons:

1) *free ribosomes* are in the cytoplasm, while *attached ribosomes* are anchored to the endoplasmic reticulum (ER), and

2) *free ribosomes* produce proteins in the cytosol, while *attached ribosomes* produce proteins inserted into the ER lumen (i.e., interior space).

36. D is correct.

Anterior pituitary hormones (including GH) are peptides. Peptide hormones are *hydrophilic* and *cannot* cross the hydrophobic phospholipid bilayer; peptide hormones bind to receptors on the plasma membrane.

Destruction of the plasma membrane dramatically *reduces* the concentration of GH receptors.

37. C is correct.

Urea, a byproduct of amino acid metabolism, is a small uncharged molecule that crosses cell membranes by simple diffusion – a passive process that does not require energy.

A: export of Na^+ from a neuron is coupled with the import of K^+; the sodium-potassium-ATPase pump is an ATP-dependent process necessary to maintain a voltage potential across the neuron membrane.

B: movement of Ca^{2+} into a muscle cell occurs against the concentration gradient, and Ca^{2+} enters cells by *active transport*, which requires ATP.

D: *synaptic vesicles* contain neurotransmitters, and their exocytosis at a nerve terminus is an ATP-dependent process triggered by an action potential propagating along the neuron.

Vesicle fusion requires Ca^{2+} to enter the cell upon axon depolarization reaching the terminus.

38. C is correct.

p53 is a *tumor suppressor protein* that regulates the cell cycle and prevents cancer in multicellular organisms.

p53 is *the guardian of the genome* because of its role in conserving genetic stability by inhibiting genome mutations. The name p53 refers to its apparent molecular mass of 53 kDa.

Dalton is defined as 1/12 the mass of carbon and is a unit of a convention for expressing (i.e., often in kilodaltons or kDa) the molecular mass of proteins.

39. D is correct.

Newly synthesized secretory protein pathway:

rough ER → Golgi → secretory vesicles → exterior of the cell (via exocytosis)

Peroxisomes and *lysosomes* are destinations for proteins but do not involve secretory path exocytosis.

Ribosomes synthesize proteins, but the Golgi is the final organelle before exocytosis.

40. B is correct.

Plant cell membranes have higher amounts of unsaturated fatty acids.

The ratio of saturated and unsaturated fatty acids determines membrane fluidity.

Unsaturated fatty acids have kinks in their tails (due to double bonds) that push the phospholipids apart, so the membrane retains its fluidity.

A: some textbooks state that plant membranes lack cholesterol, but a small amount is present, which is negligible compared to animal cells.

Cholesterol is usually dispersed in varying amounts throughout animal cell membranes in the irregular spaces between the hydrophobic lipid tails of the membrane.

Cholesterol functions as a *bidirectional buffer.*

At elevated temperatures, c*holesterol* decreases membrane fluidity because it confers stiffening and strengthening effects on the membrane.

At low temperatures, cholesterol intercalates between the phospholipids, preventing clustering and stiffening of the membrane.

41. D is correct.

Nucleus, chloroplast, and mitochondria are organelles enclosed in a double membrane.

Endosymbiotic theory illustrates the evolution of mitochondria and chloroplasts from prokaryotes, thus explaining the resemblance.

42. C is correct.

Golgi apparatus processes *secretory proteins* via post-translational modifications.

Proteins targeted to the Golgi (from the rough ER) have three destinations: secreted out of the cell, transported into organelles, or targeted to the plasma membrane (as a receptor, channel, or pore).

43. C is correct.

Carbon, hydrogen, and oxygen are in macromolecules (i.e., proteins, carbohydrates, nucleic acids, and lipids).

Nitrogen is in nucleic acids and proteins, which may contain sulfur or phosphorus.

Amino acids are *monomers* (building blocks) of proteins, and *nitrogen* is an *amino acid* and *urea* component.

Organic nitrogen is a nitrogen compound originating from a living organism.

Carbohydrates and lipids are made of only carbon, hydrogen, and oxygen

Carbohydrates have about 2 H and 1 O atom for every C atom.

Proteins are composed of C, H, O, N, and sometimes S.

Nucleic Acids are composed of: nucleotides composed of C, H, O, N, and P.

44. A is correct.

Albumin is the most abundant plasma protein. It is primarily responsible for *osmotic pressure* in circulatory systems. Albumin is too large to pass from the circulatory system into the interstitial space.

Osmotic pressure is the force of H_2O flowing from an area of a lower solute to a higher solute concentration.

If a membrane is impermeable to a solute, H_2O flows across the membrane (i.e., osmosis) until the differences in solute concentrations have equilibrated.

Capillaries are impermeable to albumin (i.e., solute). Increasing albumin concentration in the arteries and capillaries increases the movement of H_2O from the interstitial fluid to reduce the osmotic pressure in the arteries and capillaries.

45. B is correct.

Retinoblastoma protein (i.e., pRb or *RB1*) is a dysfunctional tumor suppressor protein.

pRb inhibits excessive cell growth by regulating the cell cycle through G1 (first gap phase) into S (DNA synthesis) phase. It recruits chromatin remodeling enzymes, such as methylases and acetylases.

46. D is correct.

Glycolysis occurs in the *cytoplasm.*

Krebs (TCA) cycle and *pyruvate oxidation* to acetyl-CoA occurs in the mitochondrial *matrix.*

Electron transport chain (ETC) uses cytochromes in the inner mitochondrial membrane and a proton (H^+) gradient in the intermembrane space).

A: *pyruvate* is oxidized to acetyl-CoA preliminarily and transported from the cytoplasm into the matrix before joining oxaloacetate in the Krebs cycle.

B: Krebs cycle is the second stage of cellular respiration and occurs in the matrix of the mitochondrion.

C: *electron transport chain* is the final stage of cellular respiration occurring in the inner membrane (i.e., cytochromes) / intermembrane space (i.e., H^+ proton gradient) of the mitochondrion.

47. D is correct.

Triglycerides are derived from glycerol and three fatty acids, commonly called "fats" and lipids, and are the most abundant lipid.

Teichoic acids are bacterial copolymers of carbohydrates and phosphate.

Peptidoglycan is formed by monosaccharide and amino acid polymers in bacterial cell walls.

Glycogen is a polysaccharide of glucose, a monosaccharide.

48. D is correct.

Secretory sequence in the flow of newly synthesized protein for export from the cell is:

rough ER → Golgi → plasma membrane

49. B is correct.

Minerals (e.g., potassium, sodium, calcium, and magnesium) are essential nutrients because they must be consumed in the diet and act as cofactors (i.e., nonorganic components) for enzymes.

Lysosomes do not digest minerals.

Organic molecules, such as nucleotides, proteins, and lipids, are hydrolyzed (i.e., degraded) into monomers.

Nucleotides have phosphate, sugar, and base; proteins have amino acids; lipids have glycerol and fatty acids.

50. D is correct.

Recycling of organelles within the cell is accomplished through autophagy by *lysosomes.*

51. B is correct.

Albumins are globular proteins in the circulatory system.

Carotenoids are organic pigments in chloroplasts of plants and photosynthetic organisms, such as some bacteria and fungi. They are fatty acid-like carbon chains containing *conjugated double bonds* and sometimes have six-membered carbon rings at ends. They produce red, yellow, orange, and brown colors in plants and animals as pigments.

Waxes (esters of fatty acids and alcohols) are protective coatings on the skin, fur, leaves of higher plants, and on the exoskeleton cuticle of many insects.

Steroids (e.g., cholesterol, estrogen) have three fused cyclohexane rings and one cyclopentane ring.

52. A is correct.

Defective attachment of a chromosome to the spindle blocks activation of the *anaphase-promoting complex*.

Spindle checkpoint prevents anaphase onset in mitosis and meiosis until all chromosomes are attached to the spindle with the proper bipolar orientation.

53. B is correct.

Human gametes, formed during meiosis, are cells with a single copy (1N) of the genome.

After the second meiotic division, cells have a single unreplicated copy (i.e., devoid of a sister chromatid).

54. D is correct.

Smooth endoplasmic reticulum is the organelle for fatty acid, phospholipid, and steroid synthesis.

Smooth endoplasmic reticulum (SER) synthesizes lipids, phospholipids, and steroids; metabolism of carbohydrates and steroids; detoxification of alcohol and drugs; regulates Ca^{2+} concentration in muscle cells.

Endosome is a transport pathway starting at the Golgi.

Peroxisome undergoes beta-oxidation of long chain fatty acids, which eventually yield $CO_2 + H_2O$.

Rough endoplasmic reticulum (RER) assembles proteins.

55. C is correct.

Centrioles are cylindrical structures mainly of *tubulin* in eukaryotic cells (except flowering plants and fungi).

Centrioles participate in the organization of the *mitotic spindle* and the completion of *cytokinesis.* They contribute to the structure of centrosomes and organize microtubules in the cytoplasm.

Centriole position determines the location of the nucleus and is crucial in the spatial arrangement of cells.

56. A is correct.

Centrioles are the organizational sites for microtubules (i.e., spindle fibers) that assemble during cell division (e.g., mitosis and meiosis).

Four phases of mitosis are prophase, metaphase, anaphase, and telophase. These are followed by cytokinesis, which physically divides cells into two identical daughter cells.

Condensed chromosomes align along the *equatorial plane* in metaphase before the centromere (i.e., heterochromatin region of DNA) splits. The two sister chromosomes begin their journey to the respective poles of the cell.

57. A is correct.

cAMP is a second messenger triggered when a ligand (e.g., peptide hormone or neurotransmitter) binds a membrane-bound receptor.

Adenylate cyclase (enzyme) is activated through a G-protein intermediate and converts ATP into cAMP.

Adenylate cyclase is attached to the inner layer of the phospholipid bilayer and is not in the cytoplasm.

cAMP

ATP

58. C is correct.

Cyclin and its associated *protein kinase* ensure a proper progression of cell division.

Cyclins are phosphorylated proteins responsible for specific events during cycle division (e.g., microtubule formation, chromatin remodeling).

Cyclins are divided into *four classes* based on their behavior in the cell cycle: G1/S, S, M, and G1 cyclins.

59. A is correct.

Hypertonic solution is when there is a higher concentration of solutes outside the cell than inside.

When a cell is in a *hypertonic solution*, the tendency is for *water to flow out* of the cell to balance the concentration of the solutes.

Osmotic pressure draws water out of the cell, and the cell shrivels (i.e., crenation).

60. A is correct.

Peroxisomes are organelles abundant in the liver containing oxidases and detoxifying substances (i.e., alcohol and hydrogen peroxide).

61. B is correct.

Microtubules are hollow proteins composed of *tubulin* monomers necessary for:

1) formation of the *spindle apparatus* that separates chromosomes during cell division,

2) synthesis of *cilia* and *flagella*, and

3) formation of the *cytoskeleton* (within the cytoplasm).

II: actin and myosin are contractile fibers in muscle cells composed of microfilament (not microtubules).

62. D is correct.

If a cell (e.g., pancreatic exocrine cell) is producing large amounts of proteins (i.e., enzymes) for export, this involves the *rough endoplasmic reticulum* (RER).

Protein synthesis begins in the nucleus with mRNA transcription, translated into polypeptides with the RER.

Exported proteins are packaged and modified in the Golgi; this cell would have a prominent nucleolus for rRNA (i.e., ribosomal components) synthesis.

63. A is correct.

Mitosis is cell division when new somatic (i.e., body) cells are added to multicellular organisms as they grow, and tissues are repaired or replaced.

Mitosis does not produce genetic variations. A daughter cell is identical in chromosome number and genetic makeup to the parental cell.

Eukaryotes divide by mitosis. Mitosis distributes identical genetic material to two daughter cells. The fidelity of DNA transmission between generations without dilution is remarkable.

64. B is correct.

Amoeboids move using pseudopodia as bulges of cytoplasm powered by the elongation of flexible microfilaments (not microtubules).

Microtubules are long, hollow cylinders of polymerized α- and β-tubulin dimers critical in cellular processes such as maintaining cell structure and forming the cytoskeleton with microfilaments and intermediate filaments.

Microtubules comprise the internal structure of *cilia* and *flagella*. They provide platforms for intracellular transport and participate in cellular processes, including the movement of secretory vesicles, organelles, and intracellular substances.

Microtubules are involved in cell division (i.e., mitosis and meiosis), including the formation of mitotic spindles that pull apart eukaryotic chromosomes.

65. B is correct.

Apoptosis is programmed cell death that occurs during fetal development and aging.

Synaptic cleft development, the formation of separate digits in the hand of a fetus, and tadpole tail reabsorption are examples of apoptosis during development.

The synthesis of the uterine lining is an *anabolic* process that involves mitosis (i.e., cell division).

66. A is correct.

A cell involved in active transport (e.g., intestinal epithelial cells) requires much ATP.

Therefore, many mitochondria are needed to meet cellular respiration needs (i.e., glucose → ATP).

B: high levels of *DNA synthesis* occur in cells using mitosis for rapid reproduction (i.e., skin cells).

C: high levels of *adenylate cyclase* (i.e., cAMP second messenger) are in the target cells of peptide hormones.

D: *polyribosomes* are in cells with a high protein synthesis level.

67. D is correct.

Coat proteins, like clathrin, form small vesicles to transport molecules within and between cells.

Endocytosis and *exocytosis* of vesicles allow cells to transfer nutrients, import signaling receptors, mediate immune responses, and degrade cell debris after tissue inflammation.

Endocytosis is when cells internalize receptor-ligand complexes from the cell surface, such as cholesterol bound to its receptor. The receptor-ligand complexes cluster in clathrin-coated pits at the cell surface and pinch off the vesicles that join acidic vesicles (i.e., endosomes).

68. D is correct.

Cells respond to peptide hormones through biochemical reactions involving membrane receptors and kinase activation. The first and second messengers communicate for cells to respond because the G protein links the first and second messengers.

cAMP is a second messenger triggered when a ligand (e.g., peptide hormone or neurotransmitter) binds a membrane-bound receptor.

Adenylate cyclase (enzyme) is activated through a G-protein intermediate and converts ATP into cAMP.

Adenylate cyclase is attached to the inner layer of the phospholipid bilayer and is not in the cytoplasm.

cAMP

ATP

Notes for active learning

Notes for active learning

Microbiology – Detailed Explanations

1. B is correct.

The *major* distinction between prokaryotic and eukaryotic cells is that prokaryotic cells do not have a nucleus, but eukaryotic cells do.

2. B is correct.

Penicillin prevents the formation of the bacterial *peptidoglycan cell wall* by covalently binding to a serine residue at the transpeptidase active site.

Binding the enzyme's active site is characteristic of an *irreversible competitive* inhibitor.

Irreversible binding with a covalent bond creates a stable and permanent attachment.

Competitive because it competes with the substrate for the active site.

Penicillin (β-lactam antibiotic) inhibits the formation of peptidoglycan cross-links in the bacterial cell wall. The enzymes that hydrolyze the peptidoglycan cross-links continue to function, but those that form crosslinks do not. This weakens the bacterium cell wall, and osmotic pressure rises, causing cell death (cytolysis).

A: *reversible competitive inhibitors* utilize weak molecular attachment (i.e., van der Waals or hydrogen bonds) when attaching to the enzyme active site.

C: penicillin does not digest the cell wall but prevents cross-linking of bacterial *cell wall peptidoglycan*. The effect inhibits the bacteria's ability to remodel their cell wall or prevent progeny from forming a necessary cell wall to counter osmotic pressure.

3. D is correct.

Viruses are simple, non-living organisms that take on living characteristics when they infect a host cell. Their genetic material is RNA or DNA; not arranged into chromosomes but associated with a complex of nucleic acids and histone proteins.

Viruses contain DNA or RNA and a protein coat (i.e., capsule).

Cellular machinery and biomolecules in a host cell (prokaryotic or eukaryotic) are required for viral replication.

4. D is correct.

Replica plating technique of Joshua and Esther Lederberg demonstrated in 1952 that streptomycin revealed the presence of streptomycin-resistant bacteria.

5. B is correct.

Operon is a functional unit of genomic DNA with a cluster of genes under the control of a single regulatory signal or promoter. Genes (i.e., nucleotide sequences) are transcribed together into mRNA strands.

The genes contained in the operon are expressed together or not at all.

Several genes must be *co-transcribed* and *co-regulated* to be defined as an operon.

6. C is correct.

Neurospora is a fungus and haploid for most of its life cycle.

For fungus, a brief diploid (2N) stage after fertilization transitions via meiosis to produce haploid (1N) cells, which repeatedly divide via mitosis before entering another sexual cycle.

A: most fungi undergo meiosis and a sexual cycle.

B: separation of fertilization and meiosis is characteristic of the life cycle of plants.

D: *fertilization* immediately following meiosis is characteristic of diploid organisms.

7. D is correct.

Enzymes are biomolecules in prokaryotic cells.

8. A is correct.

Endomembrane system extends the nuclear envelope and includes the endoplasmic reticulum and Golgi apparatus.

Golgi receives proteins within vesicles from the RER and modifies, sorts, and packages proteins destined for the secretory pathway (i.e., plasma membrane, exocytosis from the cell, or organelles within the cell).

Golgi is essential for synthesizing *proteoglycans* (i.e., components of connective tissue) in the extracellular matrix of animal cells.

Golgi primarily modifies proteins delivered from the rough endoplasmic reticulum. It participates in lipid transport, and the synthesis of lysosomes and is site of carbohydrate synthesis.

B: *lysosomes* are organelles with low pH that function to digest intracellular molecules.

C: *peroxisomes* are organelles in most eukaryotic cells. A significant function of the peroxisomes is the breakdown of very-long-chain fatty acids through *beta-oxidation*.

In animal cells, the very-long-chain fatty acids are converted to medium-chain fatty acids and subsequently shuttled to mitochondria. They are degraded, via oxidation, into *carbon dioxide* and *water*.

D: *smooth endoplasmic reticulum* connects to the nuclear envelope and functions in metabolic processes. It synthesizes lipids, phospholipids, and steroids. It carries out the metabolism of carbohydrates, drug detoxification, attachment of receptors on cell membrane proteins, and steroid metabolism.

Cells secreting lipids, phospholipids, and steroids (e.g., testes, ovaries, skin oil glands) have a robust, smooth endoplasmic reticulum.

Smooth endoplasmic reticulum contains *glucose-6-phosphatase* (enzyme), which converts glucose-6-phosphate to glucose during *gluconeogenesis*.

9. C is correct.

Hfr (high-frequency recombination) cell is a bacterium with a conjugative plasmid (F factor) integrated into its genomic DNA instead of being in an autonomous circular DNA element in the cytoplasm (i.e., a plasmid).

F^+ denotes cells with the F plasmid, while F^- denotes cells that do not.

Unlike a typical F^+ cell, Hfr strains attempt to transfer their *entire* DNA through the mating bridge (pili).

The F factor tends to transfer during conjugation, and often, the entire bacterial genome is dragged along, but the transfer is often aborted before the complete plasmid is transferred.

Hfr cells are useful for studying gene linkage and recombination. Because the genome's transfer rate through the mating bridge is constant, investigators can use the Hfr strain of bacteria to study genetic linkage and map the chromosome.

A: during conjugation, the transfer of Hfr DNA is interrupted by the spontaneous breakage of the DNA molecule at random points. F^+ denotes cells with the F plasmid, while F^- denotes cells that do not.

Typically, the chromosome is broken before the F factor is transferred to the F^- cell.

Therefore, the conjugation of a Hfr cell with an F^- cell does not usually result in an F^+ cell, and the F factor usually remains in the Hfr cell.

B: Hfr cells produce sex pili (i.e., mating bridge in this example), and the F^- cell is the recipient of the transfer.

D: F factor is integrated into and is a part of the bacterium's chromosome, and the F factor is replicated along with the cells' genome before conjugation.

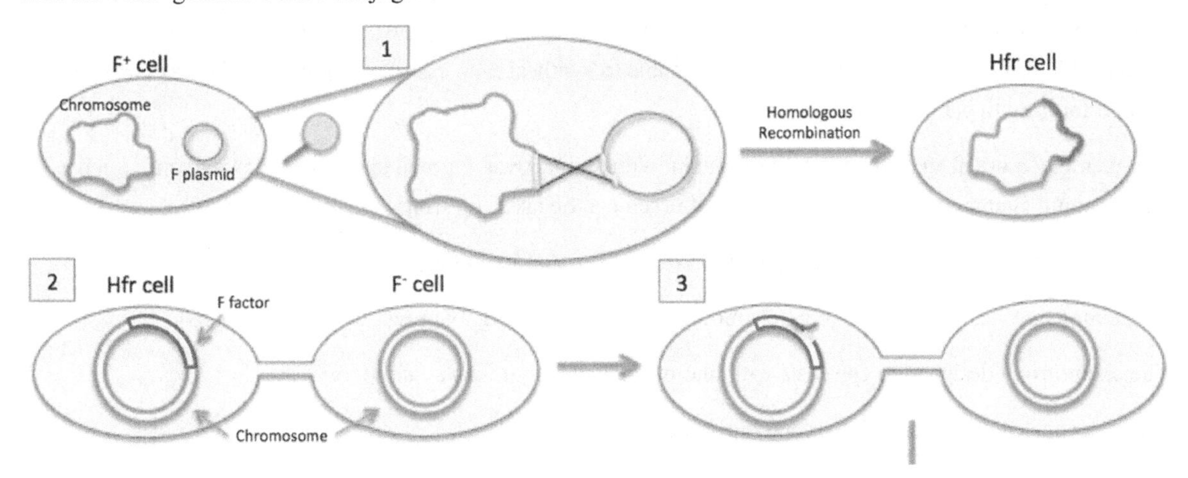

F^+ cell integrates plasmid to form Hfr cell that transfers the F factor by conjugation to an F^- cell

10. B is correct.

Ames test (1970s) uses bacteria to evaluate whether a chemical likely causes cancer. It assesses the mutagenic potential of chemical compounds. A positive test indicates that the chemical is mutagenic and may function as a carcinogen because cancer is often linked to genetic mutations.

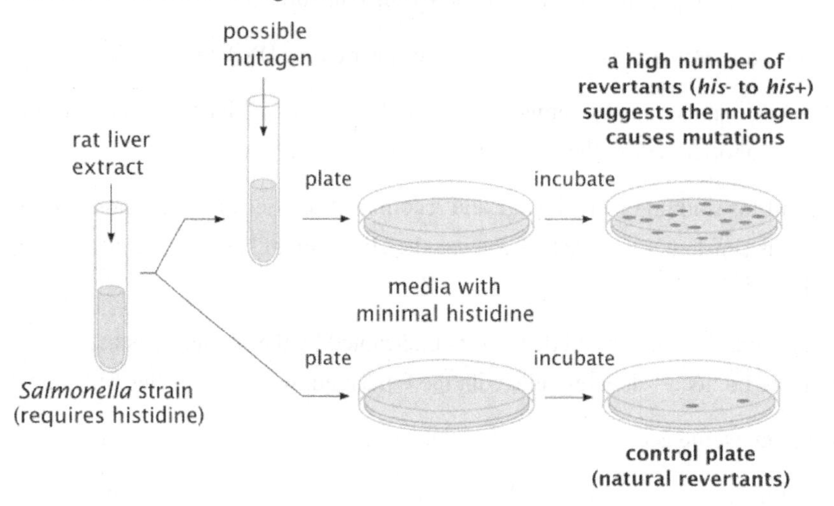

Ames test evaluates potential mutagens for the ability to transform nutrient-deficient cells upon exposure

11. A is correct.

Plants are generally autotrophs; animals are heterotrophs, and bacteria can be either.

Auxotrophs are unable to synthesize an organic compound required for growth. In genetics, a strain is auxotrophic if it has a mutation that renders it unable to synthesize an essential compound (i.e., *essential* is needed for growth but cannot be synthesized).

For example, a uracil auxotroph is a yeast mutant with an inactivated uracil synthesis pathway gene. Such a strain cannot synthesize uracil and will grow if uracil can be taken up from the environment.

B: *chemotrophs* obtain energy by the oxidation of electron donors in their environments.

These molecules can be organic (e.g., chemoorganotrophs) or inorganic (e.g., chemolithotrophs).

The chemotroph designation contrasts with phototrophs, which utilize solar energy.

Chemotrophs can be autotrophic or heterotrophic.

C: *heterotrophs* use energy derived from another organism's metabolism (*hetero* means other).

D: *prototrophs* are characterized by synthesizing the compounds needed for growth.

12. B is correct.

Endospore is a dormant, tough, non-reproductive structure produced by certain bacteria.

The endospore consists of bacterium DNA and cytoplasm, surrounded by a tough outer coating.

Endospores can survive without nutrients. A lack of nutrients usually triggers endospore formation.

13. A is correct.

Fungi are a large group of eukaryotes, including microorganisms such as mold, yeasts, and mushrooms.

Fungi are a kingdom (Fungi) separate from plants, animals, protists, and bacteria.

One significant difference is that fungal cells have cell walls with chitin.

The cell walls of plants and some protists contain cellulose, while bacterial cell walls contain peptidoglycan.

Fungi reproduce by sexual and asexual means and produce spores like basal plant groups (e.g., ferns, mosses).

Like algae and mosses, fungi typically have haploid (1N) nuclei with a small percentage of their life cycle in a diploid (2N) phase.

14. C is correct.

Cyanide is a poison interfering with the electron transport chain (ETC) of the inner plasma membrane (for prokaryotes) or the inner mitochondrial membrane (for eukaryotes) by binding to cytochromes (mainly *cytochrome c oxidase*) of the electron transfer complexes.

Cyanide inhibits the flow of electrons down their reduction potential and effectively inhibits the transport chain.

Consequently, the proton pump stops, and ATP cannot be generated aerobically.

Electron carriers such as NADH and $FADH_2$ cannot be oxidized and yield high-energy electrons to the electron transport chain because they are blocked. NAD^+ and FAD are not regenerated, and aerobic *respiration ceases*.

DNA replication, RNA transcription, and protein synthesis require energy (ATP or GTP) and are processes necessary for host cell functions and viral replication.

If aerobic ATP formation is inhibited, there will be a deficiency of ATP for cell functions and viral replication.

Energy is required for a bacteriophage (a virus that infects bacteria) to replicate.

15. A is correct.

Transformation is the genetic alteration of a cell resulting from the direct uptake, incorporation, and expression of exogenous genetic material (exogenous DNA) from its surroundings and passes through the cell membrane.

Transformation introduces genetic material into nonbacterial cells, including animal and plant cells.

B: *conjugation* transfers genetic material (plasmid) between bacterial cells by direct cell-to-cell contact or a bridge-like connection between two cells (i.e., pili).

Conjugation is a mechanism of *horizontal gene transfer*, as are transformation and transduction.

Other gene transfer mechanisms do not use cell-to-cell contact (conjugation uses a pilus).

C: *transduction* is how a virus transfers DNA from one bacterium to another.

In molecular biology, foreign DNA is introduced via a viral vector into another cell.

D: *recombination* is when DNA molecules exchange genetic information, forming new allele combinations.

In eukaryotes, genetic recombination between homologous chromosomes during prophase I of meiosis leads to a novel set of genetic information passed on to progeny.

Most recombination occurs spontaneously to increase genetic variation.

16. D is correct.

Viruses can have a genome consisting of double-stranded DNA (dsDNA).

Retroviruses have RNA genomes (single-stranded or double-stranded). After infecting the host cell, the retrovirus uses *reverse transcriptase* to convert its RNA into DNA.

17. B is correct.

Cells of the same strain transfer their genomes in the same order and at the same rate. Transfer is interrupted at times, and by matching the genes transferred to the length of time necessary for the transfer, the linear order of the genes is mapped.

A: *polycistronic* refers to the expression of bacterial genes on a single mRNA in an operon.

C: *rate of chromosome (i.e., F factor) transfer* must be constant because differences in the transfer rate would obscure the results.

D: F factors and the bacterial chromosome are replicated by the same method during *conjugation* (bacterial mating).

18. C is correct.

Prokaryotic ribosomes (30S small & 50S large subunit = 70S complete ribosome).

Eukaryotic ribosomes (40S small & 60S large subunit = 80S complete ribosome).

19. A is correct.

Retroviruses are a family of enveloped viruses that use reverse transcription to replicate within a host cell.

Retrovirus is a single-stranded RNA virus with nucleic acid as a single-stranded mRNA genome (including 5' cap and 3' poly-A tail).

Retrovirus is an obligate parasite within the host cell. Once inside the host cell cytoplasm, the virus uses its reverse transcriptase (enzyme) to produce DNA from its RNA genome.

Retro describes this backward flow of genetic information. *Integrase* (enzyme) incorporates this new reverse-transcribed DNA into the host cell genome. *Provirus* is the integrated retroviral DNA.

The host cell treats the viral DNA as part of its genome, translating and transcribing the viral genes and the cell's genes, producing the proteins required to assemble new copies of the virus.

20. C is correct.

Virus is a simple non-living organism that takes on living characteristics when it enters host cells.

Since viruses are not free-living organisms, they must replicate within a host cell.

Viruses contain DNA (single-stranded or double-stranded) or RNA (single-stranded or double-stranded) and have a protein coat.

Bacteriophage (i.e., a virus that infects bacteria) injects its genome into the bacterium while leaving the protein coat on the cell surface.

However, in eukaryotes, the entire virus (including the protein capsid) may enter the host cell. After entering the cytoplasm, the protein coat is removed (i.e., a virus is unencapsulated).

21. A is correct.

Bacterial conjugation transfers genetic material (plasmid) between bacterial cells by direct cell-to-cell contact or a bridge-like connection between two cells (i.e., pili). Conjugation is *horizontal gene transfer*, as are transformation and transduction. The other mechanisms do not involve cell-to-cell contact (conjugation requires a pilus).

B: *transformation* is the genetic alteration resulting from the direct uptake, incorporation, and expression of exogenous genetic material (exogenous DNA) from its surroundings and through the cell membranes.

In molecular biology, transformation introduces genetic material into nonbacterial cells, including animal and plant cells.

C: *transduction* is how a virus transfers DNA from one bacterium to another.

In molecular biology, *transduction* is when foreign DNA is introduced into another cell via a viral vector.

D: *recombination* is when DNA molecules exchange genetic information, resulting in a new combination of alleles. Most recombination occurs spontaneously to increase genetic variation.

continued...

In eukaryotes, *genetic recombination* between *homologous chromosomes* during prophase I of meiosis leads to a novel set of genetic information passed on to progeny.

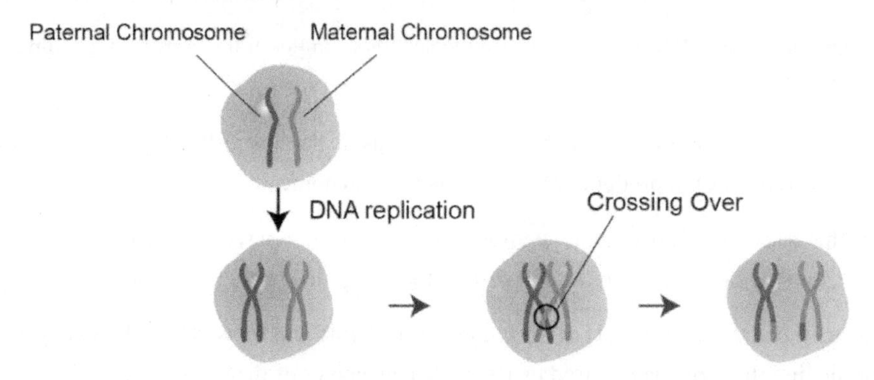

Crossing over occurs during prophase I at the tetrad during prophase I of meiosis as the product of recombination

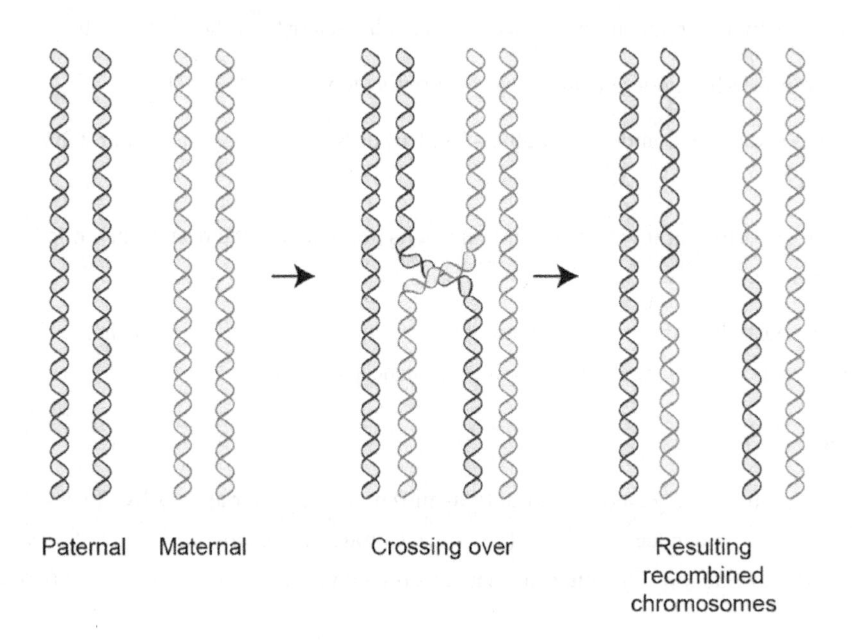

Recombination between homologous chromosomes during prophase I of meiosis

22. D is correct.

E. coli on the soft agar produces a solid growth (i.e., lawn) covering the agar.

Phages lyse cells, releasing phages (i.e., viruses). *Clear spots on the agar plate* correspond to where the bacteria were lysed and are *plaques* (i.e., clear spots).

A: *viral replication* produces clear spots on the lawn of *E. coli* growth.

B: *colonies* on the agar surface indicate *E. coli* growth, not locations where the virus lysed the bacteria cells.

C: *smooth layer* of bacterial growth on the agar plate indicates the absence of the virus.

23. D is correct.

Gram staining differentiates bacterial species into Gram-positive and Gram-negative by the chemical and physical properties of peptidoglycan cell walls.

Gram stain is usually the first assay in identifying a bacterial organism.

Gram-negative bacteria are more resistant to antibiotics than Gram-positive bacteria, despite their thinner peptidoglycan layer. The pathogenic capability of Gram-negative bacteria is often associated with specific components of their membrane, in particular, the lipopolysaccharide layer (LPS).

Penicillins are β-lactam antibiotics to treat bacterial infections by, usually, Gram-positive organisms.

Penicillin core structure, where "R" is the variable group

Gram-positive bacteria take up the violet stain used in Gram staining. This distinguishes them from the other large group of bacteria, Gram-negative bacteria that cannot retain the crystal violet stain.

Gram-negative bacteria take up the counterstain (e.g., safranin or fuchsine) and appear red or pink.

Gram-positive bacteria retain crystal violet stain by a thick *peptidoglycan layer* superficial to cell membranes.

In Gram-negative bacteria, this peptidoglycan layer is thinner and between two cell membranes.

The cell membrane, peptidoglycan layer, and cell wall are three distinct structures.

Cell walls provide structural support, protection, and rigidity to the cell.

Gram-positive bacteria have a thicker peptidoglycan cell wall, giving them a purple-blue color from staining.

Gram-negative bacteria stain a pink-red color.

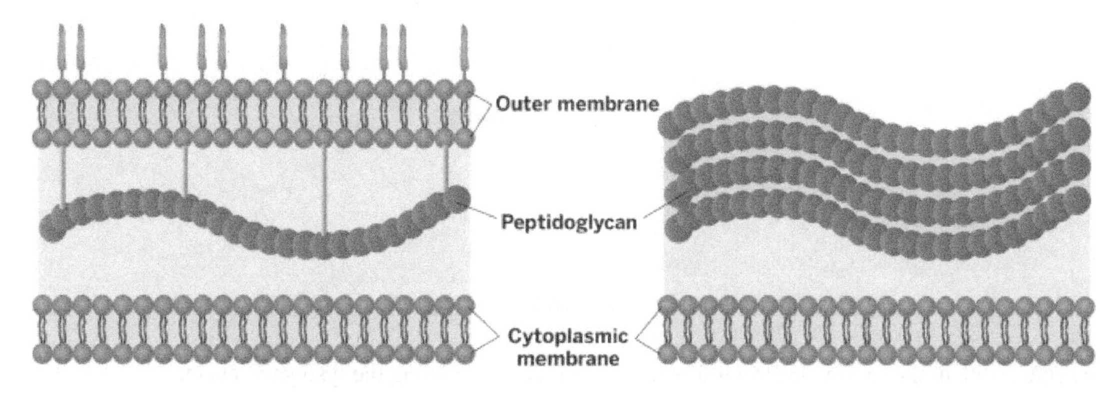

Gram-negative (left) comparison with gram-positive (right) cell walls

24. B is correct.

Viral genomes are single-stranded DNA, double-stranded DNA, single-stranded RNA, or double-stranded RNA.

Retroviruses contain a single-stranded RNA (i.e., mRNA as its genome).

Retroviruses have *reverse transcriptase* and *integrase* to facilitate their infective ability within the host cell.

25. C is correct.

Operons are mainly in prokaryotes and encode for clusters of related (similar function) genes.

Lac operon of *E. coli* allows the digestion of lactose and consists of a set of control and structural genes.

Three structural genes are controlled by an operator on another part of the genome.

Lac genes encoding enzymes are *lacZ, lacY,* and *lacA*.

The fourth *lac* gene is *lacI*, encoding the lactose repressor—"I" stands for *inducibility*.

Without lactose, a repressor protein (*lacI*) is bound to the operator, preventing RNA polymerase from binding.

The binding of the repressor protein prevents the translation of the structural genes (*lacZ, lacY,* and *lacA*).

When lactose is present (i.e., glucose is absent), *lacI* binds the repressor that dissociates from the operator region. RNA polymerase (i.e., *inducible system*) attaches to the promoter, and translation occurs.

26. D is correct.

Prophage is a viral genome inserted and integrated into the circular bacterial DNA chromosome or as an extrachromosomal plasmid.

Lysogenic phase (i.e., latent form) of a bacteriophage is when viral genes are in bacterium without disrupting the cell.

Prophase formation with a virus infecting a bacterial cell

Lytic cycle is one of the two cycles of viral reproduction, the other being the lysogenic cycle.

The lytic cycle destroys the infected cell and its membrane.

A critical difference between the lytic and lysogenic phage cycles is that in the *lytic phage*, the viral DNA exists as a separate molecule within the bacterial cell and *replicates separately from host bacterial DNA*.

The location of viral DNA in the lysogenic phage cycle is within the host DNA (i.e., integrated); the virus (phage) replicates using the host DNA machinery.

Phage is a free-floating separate molecule to the host DNA in the lytic phage cycle.

27. C is correct.

Retrovirus has an RNA genome transcribed (by the virus-encoded reverse transcriptase enzyme) into single- and then double-stranded DNA incorporated into the host cell genome.

B: *reverse transcriptase* (enzyme) converts the RNA of the virus into DNA when infecting host cells.

28. B is correct.

E. coli are normal flora of the human gut and are adapted to live in the human intestine. Therefore, the optimal temperature for growth is 37 °C, whereby enzyme activity is optimal.

A: temperature of the human intestine is 37 °C. Bacteria growing optimally at this temperature exhibit the typical phenotype.

C: *conjugation* by bacteria is not necessary for growth. Conjugation is mediated by a small genetic element (i.e., fertility or F factor) as independent or integrated into the bacterial chromosome.

F factor encodes for the F pili, which forms a conjugation bridge and allows for the transfer of genetic material between mating cells.

Cells carrying the F factor are F^+ and transfer to an F^- cell. Part of the bacterial chromosome can be transferred during conjugation, but the point of origin and the gene order are the same.

D: oxygen utilization is irrelevant to the growth temperature of bacteria.

29. A is correct.

Some bacteria can propel themselves through liquid using a *flagellum*.

30. C is correct.

When a virus infects a cell (eukaryotic or prokaryotic), it must attach to a host cell via specific proteins on the viral capsid or envelope. These proteins bind to receptor proteins on the membrane of the target cell.

Following this process, the virus enters cells via one of the three mechanisms: membrane fusion, endocytosis, or viral penetration. The latter mechanism is specific to bacteriophages.

Membrane fusion is the most well-known mechanism for enveloped viruses to enter eukaryotic cells.

The viral envelope fuses with the host cell's membrane, and the contents of the virus are released into the cell.

Endocytosis is utilized by enveloped and non-enveloped viruses that infect eukaryotic cells.

In endocytosis, the virus is engulfed by the cell and shuttled by cellular vesicles to the cytoplasm.

31. C is correct.

Bacteria are prokaryotes and have *no membrane-bound organelles* such as peroxisomes or nucleolus.

32. A is correct.

Lysogen is a bacterial cell where a phage (i.e., virus) exists as DNA in its dormant state (prophage).

Prophage is integrated into the host bacterial chromosome (i.e., lysogenic cycle) or (rarely) exists as a stable plasmid in the host cell.

The prophage expresses genes that repress the phage's lytic action until this repression is disrupted.

The virus enters the *lytic life cycle*, ultimately rupturing the cell and releasing virions.

B: *temperate* refers to the ability of some bacteriophages to enter the lysogenic lifecycle.

33. D is correct.

Protein synthesis (like for eukaryotes) occurs in three phases: initiation, elongation, and termination.

For translation, hydrogen bonds join codons on mRNA and anticodons on tRNA, not amino acid and mRNA.

The prokaryotic cellular translation machinery is the 70S ribosome (30S small and 50S large subunits).

F-met is used only in prokaryotic translation initiation. First, an initiation complex forms with the 30S subunit, mRNA, initiation factors, and a special initiator formyl methionine F-met tRNA.

50S subunit binds the initiation complex to form the 70S ribosome.

The complete large subunit of the ribosome complex has two binding sites: the P (peptidyl transferase) site and the A (aminoacyl) site.

Initiator formyl methionine (F-met) tRNA is in the P site.

Elongation begins with binding a second tRNA (charged with its corresponding amino acid) to the vacant A site of the large ribosomal subunit.

The appropriate amino acid is determined by the complementary hydrogen bonding between the anticodon of the tRNA and the next codon of mRNA.

The orientation for the mRNA (from 5' to 3') is E-P-A (ribosomes move towards the 3' end of mRNA).

Peptide bonds are catalyzed by peptidyl transferase (at the P site) with a nucleophile attack from the lone pair of electrons on the N of the amino terminus on the carbonyl of the C terminus (at the A-site).

tRNA in the P site, now uncharged (without amino acid), moves to the E site and dissociates.

tRNA in the A site (after peptide bond formation and the ribosome translocates) is now in the P site, the A site is vacant, and this is where the incoming tRNA (carrying the next amino acid to join the polypeptide) binds.

This binding cycle to the A site, peptide bond formation, and translocation creates a growing polypeptide chain.

Termination occurs when one of the three tRNA stop codons (i.e., not charged with an amino acid) hybridizes to the mRNA in the A site.

Termination factors catalyze the hydrolysis of the polypeptide chain from the tRNA, and the ribosomal complex dissociates.

H_3C S H O OH HN H O

N-Formylmethionine (fMet) is a derivative of methionine whereby a formyl group adds to the amino group

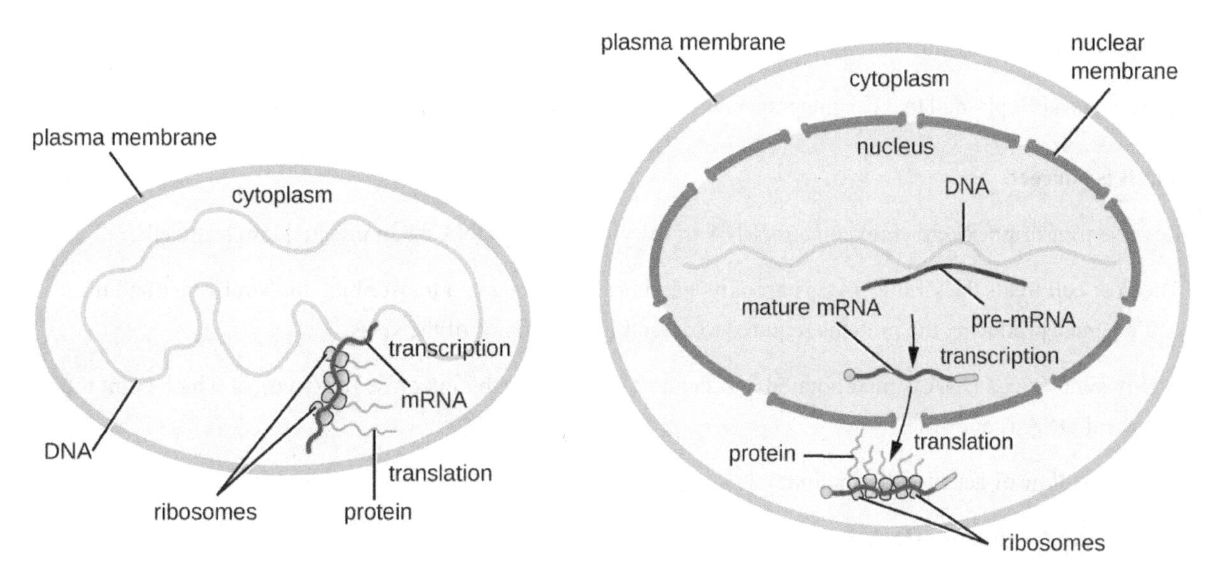

Prokaryotic cell (left) and eukaryotic cell (right). Prokaryotes have concurrent transcription and translation, while eukaryotes separate the processes by the presence of a nucleus.

A: prokaryote mRNA does not undergo splicing to remove introns.

B: *translation* in prokaryotes uses N-terminal formyl methionine (F-met) as the initiator amino acid.

C: *prokaryotes* have no nucleus, the mRNA has no nuclear membrane to cross, and translation begins before its synthesis is complete.

Eukaryotic mRNA must be processed (5' G-cap, 3' poly-A tail, and splicing of exons with the removal of introns) and transported across the nuclear membrane before translation begins in the cytoplasm.

34. B is correct.

Surface-to-volume ratio limits the size of biological cells because when the volume increases, so does the surface area, but the surface area increases at a slower rate.

Eukaryotes grow beyond the apparent limitation of surface-to-volume ratios because of organelles (specialized environment) and extensive cytoplasmic matrix, utilizing microfilaments and motor proteins for cargo transport.

35. D is correct.

Prokaryotes have *peptidoglycan cell walls*, 30S and 50S ribosomes, and plasma membranes without cholesterol.

36. B is correct.

Viruses consist of genetic material with single-stranded DNA, double-stranded DNA, single-stranded RNA, or double-stranded RNA packaged within a protein coat.

A: viruses do not have membrane-bound organelles but consist entirely of nucleic acid (RNA or DNA) and, for retroviruses, reverse transcriptase (enzyme).

C: bacteria have *peptidoglycan* (i.e., N-linked glucose polymers) cell walls.

D: viruses do not have a phospholipid bilayer membrane.

37. A is correct.

Episome is an F^- plasmid that can integrate into the bacterial chromosome by homologous recombination.

38. B is correct.

Reverse transcriptase (enzyme) converts RNA of the virus into ds-DNA when infected into host cells.

The host cell treats the viral DNA as part of its genome, translating and transcribing the viral genes and the cell's genes, producing the proteins required to assemble new copies of the virus.

Newly synthesized DNA is incorporated into the host cell genome by integrase (enzyme), at which point the retroviral DNA is a *provirus*.

Retrovirus flow of genetic information:

RNA (virus) → DNA (from virus template) → RNA (host cell machinery) → polypeptide

39. A is correct.

T4 has a DNA genome transcribed and translated by the host's machinery. Transcription and translation occur in the cytoplasm since the bacterial cell does not contain a nucleus. Therefore, both processes occur in the same locations and are concurrent.

B: a late gene encodes lysozyme enzymes because the host is not lysed until the viruses are assembled and packaged into protein capsids to be released for infection of other host cells.

C: the assembly must be complete before lysis.

D: bacterial cells have a *peptidoglycan cell wall*, so budding cannot occur. The cell wall is lysed by lysozyme, and the host cell ruptures, which causes the release of the virus.

40. C is correct.

Gram-positive bacteria take up the violet stain used in the Gram staining.

Differential staining distinguishes them from the other large group of Gram-negative bacteria that cannot retain the crystal violet stain.

Gram-negative bacteria take up the counterstain (e.g., safranin, fuchsine) and appear red or pink.

Gram-positive bacteria retain the crystal violet stain due to a *thick peptidoglycan layer* superficial to the cell membrane.

Gram-negative bacteria, the peptidoglycan layer is much thinner between cell membranes.

The cell membrane, peptidoglycan layer, and cell wall are three distinct structures.

Cell walls provide structural support, protection, and rigidity to the cell.

D: *teichoic acids* are in cell walls of Gram-positive bacteria (e.g., *Staphylococcus*, *Bacillus*, *Streptococcus*, *Clostridium, Listeria*) and extend to the surface of the peptidoglycan layer.

Teichoic acids are *not* in Gram-negative bacteria.

41. C is correct.

A bacterium with an outer lipopolysaccharide layer is Gram-negative and protects against penicillin.

A: *fimbriae* (i.e., a proteinaceous appendage in many Gram-negative bacteria) is thinner and shorter than a flagellum and allows a bacterium to attach to solid objects.

B: *bacterial cell membranes* have a phospholipid bilayer like eukaryotes, except it lacks cholesterol.

D: *Gram-negative bacteria* have a thinner peptidoglycan cell wall that does not retain Gram stain.

42. B is correct.

DNase is an enzyme that degrades DNA by hydrolysis of the DNA molecule.

Bacterial cells treated with DNase die because bacteria have DNA genomes, while RNA viruses are unaffected by DNase and continue to synthesize proteins following treatment with DNase.

A: having multiple copies of a gene is not enough to prevent DNase from degrading the DNA.

C: *viral genomes* typically contain multiple reading frames to use their limited nucleic acid efficiently, but multiple reading frames do not prevent DNA hydrolysis.

D: viral protein coat is not able to denature DNase. Denaturation involves breaking weak (e.g., hydrogen, dipole, and hydrophobic) bonds from heat or chemical treatment.

43. C is correct.

F^- recipient remains F^- in mating between Hfr and F^- cells.

44. A is correct.

Translation in prokaryotes uses the *initiation* amino acid of N-terminal formyl methionine (F-met).

Specific cells in the human immune system can identify f-MET and release local toxins to inhibit bacterial (i.e., prokaryote) infections.

45. C is correct.

As a large polysaccharide, dextran does *not pass* through the cell membrane.

Osmotic pressure of the solution increases, H_2O moves out of the cell to reduce the osmotic pressure difference, and the cell undergoes crenation (i.e., shrinking).

46. A is correct.

Gram staining differentiates bacterial species into two large groups: Gram-positive and Gram-negative.

Gram staining differentiates the chemical and physical properties of *peptidoglycan cell walls.*

Gram-positive bacteria have a thicker peptidoglycan cell wall which gives Gram-positive bacteria a purple-blue color from staining, while Gram-negative results in a pink-red color. The Gram stain is usually the first assay in identifying a bacterial organism.

47. A is correct.

DNA polymerase replicates strands of DNA by synthesizing a new strand using a template strand. DNA polymerase replicates the DNA F factor in F^+ cells before conjugation.

B: *reverse transcriptase* is a retroviral enzyme synthesizing DNA from an RNA (virus) template.

C: *DNA ligase* catalyzes the formation of phosphodiester bonds that link adjacent DNA bases.

D: *integrase* is a retroviral enzyme that integrates provirus DNA into host genomes.

48. B is correct.

Conjugation occurs between bacterial cells of different mating types. "Maleness" in bacteria is determined by the presence of a small extra piece of DNA that can replicate independently of the larger chromosome.

Male bacteria having this *sex factor* (the *F factor*) are denoted F^+ if the sex factor exists as extrachromosomal.

F^+ bacteria can conjugate only with F^- bacteria, the "female" that do not possess the F factor.

Genes on the F factor determine the formation of *sex pili* (hair-like projections) on the surface of the F^+ bacterium, which forms cytoplasmic bridges to transfer genetic material. The pili aid the F^+ cell in adhering to the F^- cell during conjugation.

During conjugation (bacterial mating) of an F^+ cell with an F^- cell, and before the transfer, the F factor replicates, and the F factor is the DNA likely to be transferred to the female. F^- becomes an F^+ by receiving one copy of the F factor, while the original F^+ retains a copy.

If this were the only genetic exchange in conjugation, all bacteria would become F^+ and cease conjugation. In F^+ bacterial cultures, a few bacteria with the F factor incorporated into their chromosome can be isolated and are *Hfr* bacteria, which may conjugate with F^- cells.

They do not transfer their F factor during conjugation but often transfer linear portions of their chromosomes; the transfer is interrupted by the spontaneous breakage of the DNA molecule at random sites, usually before the F factor crosses to the F^- cell.

This process is *unidirectional*, and no genetic material from the F^- cell is transferred to the *Hfr* cell.

49. B is correct.

Retrotransposons (or transposons via RNA intermediates) are a subclass of transposons. They are endogenous genetic elements that amplify in a genome as ubiquitous components of DNA in many eukaryotic organisms.

Around 42% of the human genome is made up of retrotransposons.

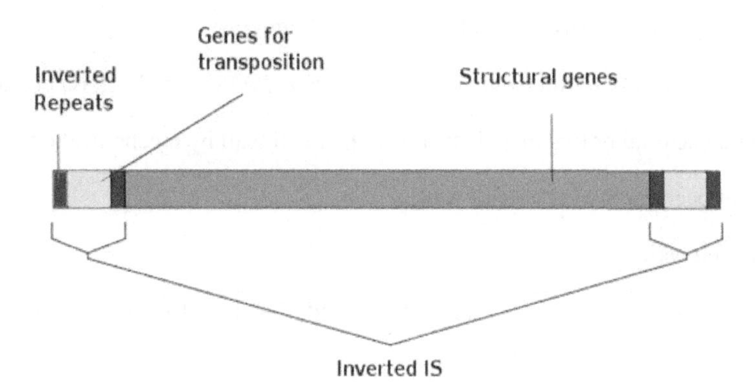

Bacterial DNA transposon with flanking inverted sequences encompassing structural genes

Retrotransposons are copied into RNA and back into DNA that may integrate into the genome.

The second step of forming DNA may be carried out by a reverse transcriptase encoded by the retrotransposon.

50. B is correct.

Plasmids are small circular double-stranded DNA in bacteria carrying extrachromosomal genetic information. Plasmids (with an origin of replication) are replicated by bacterial proteins and inherited by progeny.

The proteins encoded by genes on plasmids often provide resistance to antibiotics by degrading the antibiotic.

Through recombinant DNA technology, plasmids are engineered to carry genes not typically in bacteria.

Plasmids are introduced into cells by transforming DNA across the cell wall and plasma membrane without killing bacterial cells.

After transformation, exposure to the specific antibiotic allows the selection of bacteria that received plasmid.

Bacteriophages, such as bacteriophages λ are viruses that infect bacterial cells.

Bacteriophage λ are engineered to carry novel genes, not in bacteria or bacteriophages.

I: *plasmids* are extra-chromosomal circular DNA molecules and not organelles because organelles are membrane-bound cellular components present only in eukaryotes.

II: like the bacterial genome, plasmids are in the cytoplasm.

Without a nucleus, prokaryotic ribosomes translate plasmid mRNA into proteins while transcribed into mRNA from DNA.

III: plasmids rely on bacterial machinery for metabolic processes (e.g., replication, transcription, translation).

51. B is correct.

Fungi are members of a large group of eukaryotic organisms that includes microorganisms such as yeasts, molds, and mushrooms.

These organisms are classified as a Fungi kingdom (separate from plants, animals, protists, and bacteria).

One major difference is that fungal cells have cell walls with *chitin.*

The cell walls of plants contain *cellulose*), some protists contain *cellulose,* and bacteria contain *peptidoglycan.*

A: *protoplasts* are plant, bacterial or fungal cells that lose their cell wall by mechanical or enzymatic means.

C: L forms are strains of bacteria that lack a cell wall.

D: viruses do not have cell walls.

A virus particle (or *virion*) has nucleic acid enclosed in a capsid as a protective protein coat.

52. B is correct.

Prokaryotes do *not* have membrane-bound organelles (e.g., nuclei, mitochondria, lysosomes).

Prokaryotes have *peptidoglycan* cell walls.

Fungi have cell walls with *chitin.*

53. C is correct.

Bacteriophages are viruses that infect bacteria and typically consist of a protein coat (i.e., head) and a core containing nucleic acid. Like viruses, bacteriophages contain host-specific protein tail fibers for attachment.

Upon infection, bacteriophages can enter one of two life cycles (image below).

In the *lytic cycle*, the viral nucleic acid enters the bacterial cell. It begins using host machinery to produce new virions (i.e., virus particles), lysing the host cell and infecting other cells.

Lysogenic cycle is when viral DNA integrates into the bacterial chromosome, replicating with it and being passed to daughter cells (integrated into their genome) in this inactive form.

Lytic cycle destroys the infected cell and its membrane.

A critical difference between the lytic and lysogenic phage cycles is that in the lytic phage, the viral DNA exists as a separate molecule within the bacterial cell and replicates separately from the host bacterial DNA.

The location of viral DNA in the lysogenic phage cycle is within the host DNA (i.e., integrated); the virus (phage) replicates using the host DNA machinery.

Phage is a free-floating separate molecule to the host DNA in the lytic phage cycle.

continued...

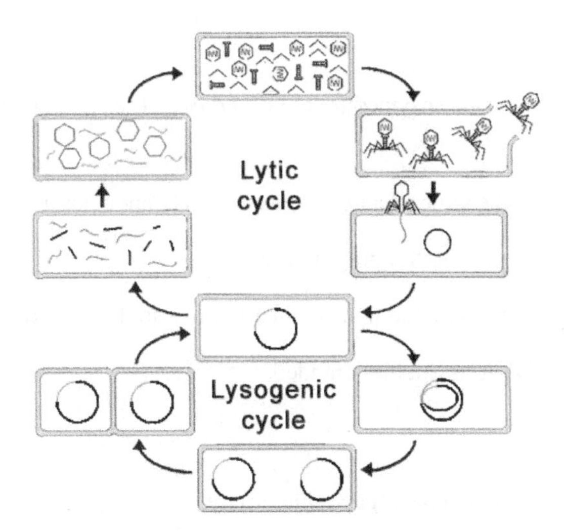

Lytic phase lysis the cell and releases virions while lysogenic cycles involve the integration of the viral genome into the host cell

When an integrated virus (i.e., prophage) becomes activated, it exits the lysogenic and enters the lytic cycle.

Activation triggers for the virus to enter the lytic cycle include *cellular or metabolic stresses* such as UV light, depleted nutrients, or cellular abnormalities.

Retroviruses are RNA-containing viruses replicating by reverse transcriptase (enzyme) through a DNA intermediate via a viral-coded *RNA-dependent DNA polymerase*.

Human immunodeficiency virus (HIV), the causative agent of AIDS, is an example of a retrovirus.

Retroviral life cycle consists of four main events:

1) virus binds its host and injects its RNA and a few viral enzymes;

2) RNA is converted to DNA by reverse transcriptase;

3) DNA integrates into the host cell's genome; and

4) viral genes are expressed, and virions are assembled and released from the cell by budding.

Bacteriophage and retrovirus integrate into the host genome (i.e., lysogenic) or lyse cells (i.e., lytic cycle).

A: *bacteriophage*s have host-specific protein tail fibers and infect bacteria.

B: bacteria (the target of bacteriophage) have no immune system. Bacteria have a defense against infection by nucleotide-specific *restriction enzymes* used for molecular biology and biotechnology.

D: *retroviruses* contain an RNA genome (ss-RNA or ds-RNA) and reverse transcriptase, not in bacteriophages.

54. C is correct.

Integration of phage DNA into bacterial chromosomes uses *site-specific recombinase* encoded in the phage.

55. A is correct.

Sequences recognized by most restriction enzymes are *inverted repeats* (i.e., palindromes) that read the same if inverted (i.e., rotated by 180°).

Sticky ends for DNA fragments are the same in either orientation, so ligation occurs from either orientation.

B: DNA strands do serve as primers for DNA polymerase

C: DNA *ligase* creates a phosphodiester bond that covalently links sticky ends of DNA.

D: *plasmid DNA*, like bacterial DNA, is double-stranded.

56. D is correct.

Virulence describes disease severity or a pathogen's infectivity.

The virulence factors of bacteria are typically proteins or other molecules synthesized by enzymes.

Virulent viruses use the *lytic* lifecycle.

Proteins are coded for by genes in chromosomal DNA, bacteriophage DNA or plasmids.

57. C is correct.

Promoter is a region on DNA recognized and bound by RNA polymerase as the initiation site for transcription.

Inducer is the molecule that inactivates the repressor.

When the inducer binds the *repressor*, the bound repressor dissociates from DNA, allowing polymerase to bind and activate the operon.

Repressor binds the *operator* (i.e., a segment of DNA within the operon).

Notes for active learning

Notes for active learning

Cellular Metabolism and Enzymes – Detailed Explanations

1. D is correct.

α-helix (alpha helix) is a typical secondary structure of proteins. It is a *right-handed coiled* or spiral conformation (helix) when each backbone amino (N-H) group donates partial positive hydrogen to form a hydrogen bond with a lone pair of electrons from the backbone carbonyl (C=O) group of another amino acid four residues earlier.

2. A is correct.

ATP is a nucleotide composed of adenosine (A), ribose, and three phosphate groups.

3. C is correct.

Hydrophobic side chain groups (e.g., phenylalanine, methionine, leucine, and valine) interact through hydrophobic interactions, excluding water from the attraction region.

B: *hydrogen bonds* require hydrogen to be connected to an electronegative atom of fluorine, nitrogen, oxygen, or chlorine (weaker hydrogen bond due to the larger valence shell size) to establish a $\delta+$ and $\delta-$ (partial positive and negative regions that attract).

D: *cysteine* is the only amino acid capable of forming disulfide bonds because the side chain contains sulfur.

4. B is correct.

Cellular respiration uses enzyme-catalyzed reactions and is a catabolic pathway to use the potential energy stored in glucose.

While glycolysis yields two ATP per glucose, cellular respiration (i.e., glycolysis, Krebs/TCA cycle, and electron transport chain) produces about 30–32 ATP. Around 2004, research results reduced the original estimate of 36-38 ATP due to inefficiencies of the ATP synthase.

Cellular respiration is an aerobic process whereby O_2 is the final acceptor of electrons passed from cytochrome electron carriers during the final stage of the electron transport chain.

Glycolysis (glucose to pyruvate) occurs in the cytoplasm.

Krebs cycle (TCA) occurs in the matrix (i.e., the cytoplasm of mitochondria), while the electron transport chain occurs in the intermembrane space of the mitochondria for eukaryotes.

For prokaryotes, both processes occur in the cytoplasm because prokaryotes lack mitochondria.

Some forms of anaerobic respiration use an electron acceptor other than O_2 (e.g., iron, cobalt, or manganese reduction) at the end of the electron transport chain.

Glucose molecules are entirely oxidized in these cases because glucose products enter the Krebs cycle.

Highly reduced chemical compounds (e.g., NADH or $FADH_2$) establish an electrochemical gradient across a membrane in the Krebs cycle. The reduced chemical compounds are oxidized by integral membrane proteins that transfer the electron to the final electron acceptor.

5. B is correct.

K_m is the substrate concentration [S] at half the maximum reaction velocity (V_{max}) and increases when the antibody binds the substrate. This reaction kinetics follow the profile of a *competitive inhibitor*.

The substrate binds the antibody and is not available to react with the enzyme; therefore, an additional substrate is needed to bind the same amount of enzyme (as a lower concentration of substrate in the absence of antibody).

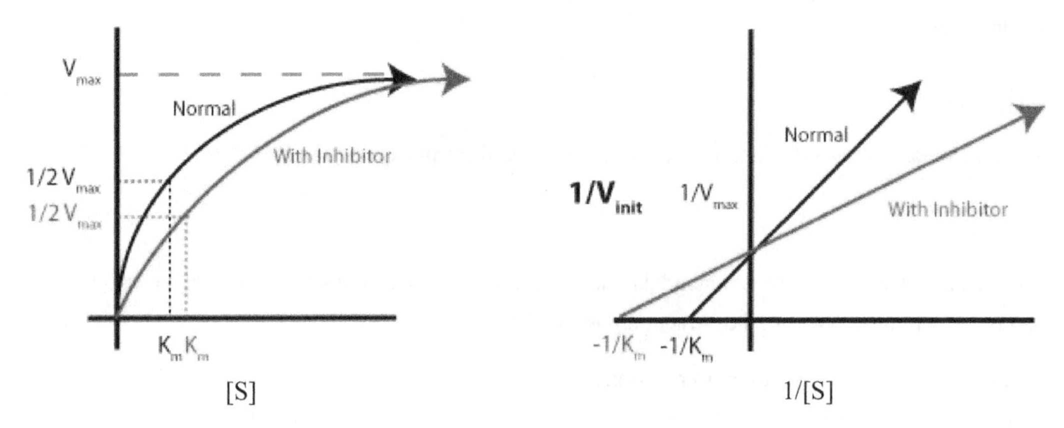

Michaelis-Menten equation (left) and Lineweaver-Burke (double reciprocal) plot

Graph on the *left* illustrates the Michaelis-Menten equation for enzyme kinetics.

Graph on the *right* is the Lineweaver-Burke (double reciprocal) plot showing the change in K_m when the substrate is subjected to competitive inhibition.

V_{max} does not change when the number of available substrates changes.

Binding to a substrate does not affect V_{max} but affects K_m because the amount of available substrate is reduced, altering the reaction kinetics because it binds the substrate.

6. C is correct.

Metabolism means change and refers to life-sustaining chemical transformations within cells.

Enzyme-catalyzed reactions allow organisms to maintain structures, grow, reproduce, and respond.

Metabolism includes *anabolism* (or *buildup*) and *catabolism* (or *breakdown*).

Catabolism is the breakdown of organic matter and harvests energy from cellular respiration (e.g., glycolysis, Krebs cycle, and the electron transport chain).

Anabolism utilizes energy (e.g., ATP) to *synthesize biomolecules* (e.g., lipids, nucleic acids, proteins).

7. D is correct.

Fermentation is an anaerobic process and occurs in the absence of oxygen.

The purpose of fermentation is to regenerate the high-energy nucleotide intermediate of NAD^+.

Oxidative phosphorylation occurs during the electron transport chain as the final stage of cellular respiration.

8. A is correct.

Acid hydrolysis has several effects:

1) partial destruction of tryptophan prevents the proper estimate of the tryptophan concentration;

2) conversion of asparagine into aspartic acid prevents the direct measure of asparagine;

3) conversion of glutamine to glutamic acid.

Therefore, the concentration of glutamic acid is an indirect measure of glutamine.

9. B is correct.

When plasma glucose levels are low, the body utilizes other energy sources for cellular metabolism.

These energy sources are used in preferential order:

glucose → other carbohydrates → fats → proteins

These molecules are converted to glucose or glucose intermediates degraded in the glycolytic pathway and the Krebs cycle (i.e., citric acid cycle).

Proteins are used last for energy because there is no protein storage in the body.

Catabolism of protein results in muscle wasting and connective tissue breakdown, which is harmful in the long term.

10. D is correct.

Activation energy is the minimum amount of energy needed for a reaction. It is considered an "energy barrier" because energy must be added to the system.

Enzymes act by decreasing the activation energy and lowering the energy barrier, allowing the reaction, and increasing the reaction rate.

11. A is correct.

A phosphate group from ATP is transferred to glucose, which creates a phosphodiester bond.

12. D is correct.

Second messengers are common in eukaryotes.

Cyclic nucleotides (e.g., cAMP and cGMP) are second messengers transmitting extracellular signals from the cell membrane to intracellular proteins.

Second messengers are used by hydrophilic protein hormones (e.g., insulin, adrenaline) that cannot cross the plasma membrane.

Steroid hormones (e.g., testosterone, estrogen, progesterone) are lipid-soluble and can pass through the plasma membrane and enter the cytoplasm without second messengers.

13. A is correct.

Greatest direct source of ATP synthesis involves the electron transport chain. Glycolysis occurs in the cytoplasm, the Krebs cycle (TCA) in the matrix of mitochondria, and oxidative phosphorylation (i.e., the electron transport chain) in the intermembrane space and inner membrane of mitochondria.

Glycolysis produces pyruvate, converted into acetyl CoA, and joined to oxaloacetate in the Krebs cycle, producing citrate as the first intermediate.

Krebs cycle produces two GTP (i.e., ATP) per glucose molecule (or 1 GTP per pyruvate). Most ATP is formed by *oxidative phosphorylation* when NADH and $FADH_2$ nucleotides are oxidized and donate their electrons to the cytochromes in the electron transport chain.

14. D is correct.

V_{max} is the reaction velocity at a fixed enzyme concentration and depends on the total enzyme concentration. Adding enzymes allows more enzyme reactions per minute.

II: V, not V_{max}, depends on [S]. V_{max} is a constant for a specified amount of enzyme.

III: *competitive inhibition* is when the inhibitor binds reversibly to the active site. Adding enough substrate overcomes competitive inhibition, and the original V_{max} is obtained.

15. B is correct.

There are two major models of enzyme-substrate binding.

Induced-fit model is when the initial interactions between enzyme and substrate (e.g., hexokinase and glucose) are weak, but the weak interactions induce *conformational changes* that strengthen binding.

Lock-and-key model is when the molecules conform for binding and do not change.

16. D is correct.

Gibbs free energy (ΔG) of a reaction is not dependent on the amount of enzyme. It measures the energy difference (Δ) between the reactants and products.

ΔG is *positive* for endergonic reactions with products higher in energy than the reactants (absorbs energy).

ΔG is *negative* for exergonic reactions when products are lower in energy than the reactants (releases energy).

17. C is correct.

Zymogens are inactive forms of enzymes and have an ~ogen suffix (e.g., pepsinogen). From the question, glucokinase has a higher Michaelis constant (K_m).

A higher value for K_m is due to enzymes having a lower affinity for the reactant (e.g., glucose). Information about K_m does not answer the question and is merely a distraction.

A: *hexokinase* is a control point enzyme (i.e., irreversible steps) regulated by negative feedback inhibition.

B: *hexokinase* and glucokinase catalyze the same reaction (from the question); by definition, they are *isozymes*.

D: *fructose* is not a reactant in glycolysis.

18. B is correct.

Secondary structure (2°) is the repetition of α-helices or β-pleated sheets in the polypeptide backbone.

Primary structure (1°) is the linear sequence of amino acids.

Tertiary structure (3°) involves interactions between the side chains of the amino acids.

Quaternary structure (4°) requires the interaction of two or more polypeptides. 4° requires more than one polypeptide chain in the mature protein (e.g., hemoglobin).

19. C is correct.

Cofactors are organic or inorganic molecules classified depending on how tightly they bind to an enzyme.

Coenzymes are loosely bound *organic cofactors* released from the enzyme's active site during the reaction (e.g., ATP, NADH).

Prosthetic groups are tightly bound organic cofactors.

20. B is correct.

Quaternary (4°) *structure* of proteins involves two or more polypeptide chains.

Hydrophobic interactions and disulfide bridges between cysteines maintain the quaternary structure between the different polypeptide chains (e.g., 4 chains of 2 α and 2 β in hemoglobin).

21. A is correct.

Mitochondrion is the organelle bound by a double membrane, where the Krebs (TCA) cycle, electron transport, and oxidative phosphorylation occur.

In eukaryotes, the Krebs cycle (i.e., TCA) occurs in the matrix of the mitochondria.

Matrix is an interior space in the mitochondria analogous to the cell cytoplasm.

B: *smooth ER* (endoplasmic reticulum) is connected to the nuclear envelope and synthesizes lipids, phospholipids, and steroids.

Cells secreting lipids, phospholipids, and steroids (e.g., testes, ovaries, skin oil glands) have prominent smooth endoplasmic reticulum.

Smooth ER carries out the metabolism of carbohydrates, drug detoxification, attachment of receptors on cell membrane proteins, and steroid metabolism.

C: *cytosol* is common to eukaryotes and prokaryotes and equivalent to the cytoplasm.

D: *nucleolus* is the organelle within the nucleus responsible for synthesizing ribosomal RNA (rRNA).

22. B is correct.

Pyruvate is the product of glycolysis and is converted into acetyl Co-A as the starting reactant for the Krebs cycle. Pyruvate is *not* a waste product of cellular respiration. Metabolic waste products are produced during enzymatic processes.

Pyruvate, made during glycolysis (as an intermediate of cellular respiration), is converted to acetyl CoA and enters the Krebs cycle to be oxidized into CO_2 and H_2O or converted into the waste product of lactate under anaerobic conditions. Waste products can damage cells and must be removed.

A: *lactate* (2 carbon chain) is produced from *pyruvate* (3 carbon chain) as the waste product of anaerobic respiration. Lactate is converted to pyruvate in the liver when O_2 becomes available.

If lactate is not metabolized, it can lead to lactic acidosis (acidification of the blood) and death.

C and D: CO_2 and H_2O are waste products of aerobic respiration.

CO_2 and H_2O are removed from the lungs via expiration during regular breathing.

CO_2 increases lead to acidosis (lowering blood pH) because CO_2 reacts with H_2O to form carbonic acid (H_2CO_3).

23. A is correct.

V_{max} is proportional to the number of active sites on the enzyme (i.e., [enzyme] or enzyme concentration).

K_m remains constant because it is a measure of the active site affinity for the substrate. Regardless of the number of enzyme molecules, each enzyme interacts with the substrate similarly.

Models propose mechanisms of enzymatic catalysis.

The Michaelis–Menten model describes enzyme-substrate interactions, whereby enzymatic catalysis occurs at a specific site on enzymes – the active site.

Substrate (S) binds the enzyme (E) at the active site for an enzyme-substrate (ES) complex. ES complex dissociates into enzyme and substrate or moves forward in the reaction to form product (P) and original enzyme.

$$E + S \underset{k_{-1}}{\overset{k_1}{\rightleftharpoons}} ES \xrightarrow{k_2} P + E$$

Rate constants for different steps in the reaction are k_1, k_{-1}, and k_2.
The overall rate of product formation is a combination of each rate constant.

At constant enzyme concentrations, varying [S] changes the rate of product formation.

At low [S], a small fraction of enzyme molecules is occupied with the substrate.

ES and [P] formation rate increases linearly with substrate concentration.

At high [S], all active sites are occupied with the substrate, and increasing the substrate concentration further does not increase the reaction rate, and the reaction rate is V_{max}.

Equation describing the relationship between substrate concentration and reaction rate is:

$$V = \frac{[S]}{[S] + K_m} V_{max}$$

24. C is correct.

Apoenzyme, with its cofactors, is a *holoenzyme* (an active form). Enzymes that require a cofactor, but do not have one bound, are *apoenzymes* (or apoproteins).

Cofactors can be inorganic (e.g., metal ions) or organic (e.g., vitamins).

Organic cofactors are coenzymes or prosthetic groups. Most cofactors are not covalently attached to an enzyme but are tightly bound. Organic prosthetic groups can be covalently bound.

Holoenzyme refers to enzymes containing multiple protein subunits (e.g., DNA polymerases), whereby the holoenzyme is the complete complex with all subunits needed for the activity.

25. C is correct.

Each ATP releases about –7.4 kcal/moles.

As an approximation, 1 kcal/mol = ~ 4.2 kJ/mol

Structure of the nucleotide of ATP
(3 phosphates + ribose sugar + adenosine)

ATP contains three phosphate groups and is produced by enzymes (e.g., ATP synthase) from adenosine diphosphate (ADP) or adenosine monophosphate (AMP) and phosphate group donors.

Three central mechanisms of ATP biosynthesis are *oxidative phosphorylation* (in cellular respiration), *substrate-level phosphorylation*, and *photophosphorylation* (in photosynthesis).

Metabolic processes using ATP convert it back into its precursors; ATP is continuously recycled.

26. D is correct.

Cysteine is the only amino acid capable of forming a disulfide (S–S covalent) bond and serves an essential structural role in many proteins. The *thiol side chain* in cysteine often participates in enzymatic reactions, serving as a nucleophile. Thiol is susceptible to oxidization to give the disulfide derivative cystine.

27. C is correct.

Electron transport chain (ETC) uses cytochromes in the inner mitochondrial membrane and is a complex carrier mechanism of electrons that produces ATP through *oxidative phosphorylation*.

A: Krebs (i.e., TCA) cycle occurs in the *matrix* of the mitochondria. It begins when acetyl CoA (i.e., 2-carbon chain) combines with oxaloacetic acid (i.e., 4-carbon chain) to form citrate (i.e., 6-carbon chain).

A series of additional enzyme-catalyzed reactions result in the oxidation of citrate and the release of two CO_2, and oxaloacetic acid is regenerated to begin the cycle again once it is joined to an incoming acetyl CoA.

B: *long-chain fatty acid degradation* occurs in peroxisomes that hydrolyze fat into smaller molecules fed into the Krebs cycle and used for cellular energy.

D: *glycolysis* occurs in the cytoplasm as the oxidative breakdown of glucose (i.e., 6-carbon chain) into two pyruvates (i.e., 3-carbon chain).

28. A is correct.

Apoenzyme is an inactive enzyme without its cofactor. An apoenzyme, with its cofactor(s), is a *holoenzyme* (an active form).

Enzymes that require a cofactor, but do not have one bound, are *apoenzymes* (or apoproteins).

Cofactors are inorganic (e.g., metal ions) or organic (e.g., vitamins).

Organic cofactors are *coenzymes* or *prosthetic groups.*

29. B is correct.

Disulfide bond is a covalent bond derived by coupling two thiols (~S-H) groups as R–S–S–R.

C: *peptide bonds* join adjacent amino acids and make the protein's linear sequence (i.e., primary structure).

30. B is correct.

Enzyme prosthetic groups attach via strong molecular forces (e.g., covalent bonds).

A: *Van der Waals* interactions, like dipole/dipole, are weak molecular forces.

C: *ionic bonds* are powerful in non-aqueous solutions but are not used to attach prosthetic groups because they are weak in aqueous environments such as plasma. For example, NaCl dissociates in water.

D: *hydrogen bonds* (like hydrophobic interactions) are an example of a weak molecular force.

31. C is correct.

Cellular respiration begins via glycolysis in the cytoplasm but is completed in the mitochondria.

Glucose (six-carbon chain) is cleaved into two pyruvate molecules (three-carbon chain).

Pyruvate is converted to acetyl CoA that enters the Krebs cycle in the mitochondria.

NADH (from glycolysis and the Krebs cycle) and $FADH_2$ (from the Krebs cycle) enter the electron transport chain on the inner membrane of the mitochondria.

32. C is correct.

Primary activity of thyroid hormone is to *increase* the *basal metabolic rate.*

33. D is correct.

Cofactors are organic or inorganic molecules classified depending on how tightly they bind to an enzyme.

Coenzymes are loosely bound organic cofactors released from the enzyme's active site during the reaction (e.g., ATP, NADH).

Prosthetic groups are tightly bound organic cofactors.

34. B is correct.

Primary structure is the *linear sequence* of amino acids in the polypeptide.

35. D is correct.

Denaturing the polypeptide disrupts the 4°, 3° and 2° structures, while the 1° structure (i.e., linear sequence of amino acids) is unchanged.

In folded proteins, 1° structure determines subsequent 2°, 3° and 4° structures.

36. B is correct.

$FADH_2$ is produced in the Krebs cycle (TCA) in cellular respiration.

A: final product of glycolysis is pyruvate (i.e., pyruvic acid), which is converted to lactic acid (in humans) or ethanol & CO_2 (in yeast) *via* anaerobic conditions.

Yeast is used for alcoholic production and baking for the dough to rise.

C: in glycolysis, the first series of aerobic (or anaerobic) reactions occur in the cytoplasm by breaking the 6-carbon glucose into two 3-carbon pyruvate molecules.

D: two ATP are required, and four ATP are produced = net of two ATP at the end of glycolysis.

37. A is correct.

There are 13 essential (i.e., must be consumed) vitamins: A, B_1 (thiamine), B_2 (riboflavin), B_3 (niacin), B_5 (pantothenic acid), B_6 (pyridoxine), B_7 (biotin), B_9 (folate) and B_{12} (cobalamin), C, D, E and K.

The four fat-soluble vitamins A, D, E, and K are stored in adipose tissue.

38. D is correct.

Hemoglobin is a *quaternary protein* with two α and two β chains with Fe^{2+} (or Fe^{3+}) as the prosthetic group.

Prosthetic groups are *tightly bound* cofactors (i.e., nonorganic molecules such as metals).

39. A is correct.

Glycine is the only achiral amino acid because hydrogen is the R group (i.e., side chain).

Optical activity is the ability of a molecule to rotate plane-polarized light and requires a chiral center (i.e., carbon atom bound to 4 different substituents).

D: *cysteine* contains sulfur in the side chain and is the only amino acid forming disulfide bonds (i.e., S–S).

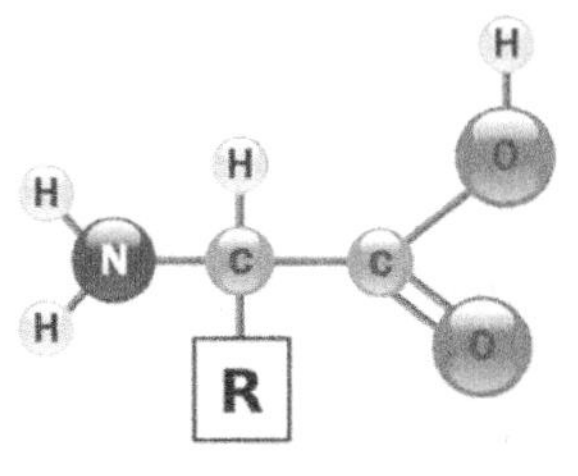

Amino acid structure with the α carbon attached to the side chain R

40. A is correct.

During glycolysis, two net (four gross = total) molecules of ATP are produced by *substrate-level phosphorylation*, and two molecules of NAD^+ are reduced (i.e., gain electrons) to form NADH.

B: during glycolysis, *two pyruvates* form from each starting molecule of glucose.

C: *glycolysis* is an anaerobic process and does not require O_2.

D: *glucose* is partially *oxidized* (not reduced) into *two pyruvate* molecules during glycolysis.

41. B is correct.

Krebs (TCA) cycle and the *electron transport chain* are metabolic processes in the mitochondria.

42. C is correct.

Feedback inhibition occurs when a product binds an enzyme to prevent it from catalyzing further reactions.

Since it is *allosteric inhibition*, this product binds a site other than the active site and changes the conformation of the active site to inhibit the enzyme.

Although the allosteric inhibitor can be the same product of the enzyme-catalyzed reaction *or* the product of the metabolic pathway, it is usually the final product that inhibits the entire metabolic pathway, thus saving the energy necessary to produce the intermediates as well as the final product.

When levels of the final product are low, the enzyme resumes its catalytic activity.

43. A is correct.

Obligate anaerobe reactions occur in the *absence* of O_2.

Oxidative phosphorylation occurs during the electron transport chain and requires a molecule of oxygen as the final acceptor of electrons shuttled between the cytochromes.

44. D is correct.

Peptide bonds join adjacent amino acids.

The amino acid (written on the left by convention) contributes an amino group ($\sim NH_2$).

The other amino acid (written on the right by convention) contributes a carboxyl group ($\sim COOH$) that undergoes condensation (i.e., joining of two pieces to form a connected unit) *via* dehydration (i.e., removal of H_2O during bond formation).

45. A is correct.

Oxidative phosphorylation (O_2 as substrate/reactant) occurs only in the electron transport chain (the last step for cellular respiration) in the inner membrane (i.e., cristae) of the mitochondria.

NADH and $FADH_2$ donate electrons to a series of cytochrome (i.e., protein) molecules embedded in the inner membrane and create an electron gradient, which establishes a proton (H^+) gradient within the intermembrane space of the mitochondria.

H^+ gradient drives a proton pump coupled with an enzyme, producing ATP via *oxidative phosphorylation.*

Electrons from NADH and $FADH_2$ are transferred to ½ O_2 (i.e., oxidative phosphorylation) to generate ATP and form H_2O as a metabolic waste (along with CO_2) from cellular respiration.

H_2O and CO_2 (as metabolic wastes) are expired from the lungs during breathing.

Each Krebs cycle $FADH_2$ yields two ATP, while each NADH yields three ATP in the electron transport chain.

NADH from glycolysis only produces two ATP because energy is expended to shuttle the NADH from glycolysis (in the cytoplasm) through the double membrane of the mitochondria.

46. C is correct.

Enzymes do not affect free energy (ΔG); they decrease the activation energy required, increasing the reaction rate.

Enzymes do *not* affect the position or direction of equilibrium; they only affect the speed of equilibrium.

47. C is correct.

Zymogen (or proenzyme) is an inactive enzyme precursor. Proteolysis (i.e., cleavage) of the zymogen makes it active to catalyze reactions. Changes in substrate concentration regulate enzyme activity; an increase in substrate concentration increases enzyme activity (at saturation, V_{max} is achieved).

Post-translational modifications occur during protein biosynthesis (after translation), and they may involve cleaving proteins or introducing new functional groups to arrive at the mature protein product.

The enzyme may not be functional until post-translational modifications, a crucial regulatory aspect.

48. B is correct.

2° structure consists of numerous local conformations, such as α-helixes and β-sheets. Secondary conformations are stabilized by hydrogen bonds or the covalent disulfide bonds between S–S of two cysteines to form cystine.

To be classified as 2° structure, the bonds must be formed between amino acids within about 12-15 amino acids along the polypeptide chain.

Otherwise, interactions (e.g., H bonds or disulfide bonds) that connect amino acid residues of more than 15 amino acids along the polypeptide chain qualify as 3° protein structure.

If the bonds occur between different polypeptide strands, the interactions qualify as 4° protein structures (e.g., two α and two β chains in hemoglobin).

49. C is correct.

Glycogen is a polysaccharide (i.e., carbohydrate) storage form with *highly branched glucose monomers*.

Extensive branching in glycogen provides numerous ends to the molecule to facilitate the rapid hydrolysis (i.e., cleavage and release) of individual glucose monomers when needed *via* epinephrine (i.e., adrenaline).

Glycogen is synthesized in the liver because of high plasma glucose concentrations and stored in muscle cells for release during exercise.

A: *glycogenesis* involves the synthesis of glycogen.

B: *glycogenolysis* involves the degradation of glycogen.

D: plants produce *starch* (i.e., analogous to glycogen) as their storage carbohydrate.

50. B is correct.

The fraction of occupied active sites for an enzyme equals V/V_{max} which = $[S]/([S] + K_m)$.

If $[S] = 2K_m$, the fraction of occupied active sites is 2/3.

51. C is correct.

Allosteric regulators bind enzymes at allosteric sites (i.e., other than active sites) with *non-competitive inhibition.*

Once bound to the allosteric site, the enzyme changes its conformational shape.

If the shape change causes the ligand (i.e., molecule destined to bind to the active site) to bind to the active site less efficiently, the modulator is *inhibitory*.

Modulator is excitatory if the shape change causes the ligand to bind to the active site more efficiently (i.e., the active site becomes open and accessible).

52. B is correct.

Biological reactions can be *exergonic* (releasing energy) or *endergonic* (consuming energy).

Biological reactions have *activation energy*, the minimum amount of energy required for the reaction.

These reactions use *enzymes* (i.e., *biological catalysts*) to lower activation energy and increase the reaction rate.

53. C is correct.

Oxidative phosphorylation (in the electron transport chain) uses ½ O_2 as the ultimate electron acceptor.

Electron transport chain (ETC) is on the inner mitochondrial membrane. It uses cytochromes (i.e., proteins) in the inner membranes of the mitochondria to pass electrons released from the oxidation of NADH & $FADH_2$.

Mitochondrial matrix (i.e., the cytoplasm of mitochondria) is the site for the Krebs cycle (TCA).

Outer mitochondrial membrane does not directly participate in oxidative phosphorylation or the Krebs cycle.

Glycolysis and Krebs cycle produce ATP via *substrate-level phosphorylation*, while *oxidative phosphorylation* requires O_2 and occurs during the ETC.

54. D is correct.

Enzymes are often proteins and function as biological catalysts at an optimal temperature (physiological temperature of 36 °C) and pH (7.35 is the pH of blood).

At higher temperatures, proteins *denature* (i.e., unfolding by disrupting hydrogen and hydrophobic bonds and changing shape) and lose their function.

Proteins often interact with inorganic minerals (i.e., *cofactors*) or organic molecules (i.e., *coenzymes or tightly bound prosthetic groups*) for optimal activity.

Mutations affect *DNA sequences* that encode proteins, resulting in a change in the amino acid sequence of the polypeptide and a change in conformation within the enzyme.

A change in the conformation of enzymes often results in a change in function.

55. D is correct.

Gibbs free energy is:

$$\Delta G = \Delta G° + RT\ln Q$$

where $\Delta G°$ = the Gibbs free energy change per mole of reaction for unmixed reactants and products at standard conditions (i.e., 298K, 100kPa, 1M of each reactant and product), R = the gas constant ($8.31\ J{\cdot}mol^{-1}{\cdot}K^{-1}$), T = absolute temperature and Q = [product] / [reactant]

56. D is correct.

Allosteric enzymes have allosteric sites that bind metabolites.

Allosteric sites are distinct from the active sites that bind substrate.

An enzyme must have a *quaternary structure* (multiple polypeptides) to bind more than one molecule.

Allosteric enzymes show *cooperative* substrate binding with the binding of a molecule at one site affecting the binding at another.

If an enzyme binds an inhibitor at an allosteric site, this *decreases the affinity* of the active site for the substrate.

57. C is correct.

Monoamine oxidases (MAO) are a family of enzymes that catalyze the oxidation of monoamine neurotransmitters. Monoamine neurotransmitters and neuromodulators contain one amino group connected to an aromatic ring by a two-carbon chain ($\sim CH_2–CH_2$).

Monoamines are derived from the aromatic amino acids phenylalanine, tyrosine, tryptophan, and thyroid hormones by aromatic amino acid decarboxylase (enzyme). Monoamines trigger crucial components such as emotion, arousal, and cognition.

Monoamine oxidases are linked to some psychiatric and neurological disorders.

High or low levels of MAOs are associated with schizophrenia, depression, attention deficit disorder, substance abuse, and migraines. MAO degrades serotonin, melatonin, norepinephrine, and epinephrine.

Excessive levels of catecholamines (e.g., epinephrine, norepinephrine, dopamine) leads to hypertensive crisis (e.g., hypertension), and excessive serotonin leads to serotonin syndrome (e.g., increased heart rate, perspiration, dilated pupils).

58. C is correct.

ΔG for hydrolysis of ATP to ADP and Pi is –7.3 kcal/mole.

59. C is correct.

I: *prosthetic groups* are tightly bound chemical compounds required for the enzyme's catalytic activity, and it is often involved at the active site.

II: *zymogens* are inactive enzyme precursors requiring biochemical changes to become active enzymes. This activation is usually a proteolysis (protein cleaving) reaction that reveals the active site.

60. B is correct.

Hydrolysis of ATP $\rightarrow$ ADP + phosphate forms glucose-6-phosphate from glucose and phosphate.

Enzymatic coupling of reactions allows ATP hydrolysis energy to drive the synthesis of glucose-6-phosphate.

61. A is correct.

Protein function can be altered by *post-translational modifications* (often in Golgi) after synthesis.

The common post-translational modification in eukaryotes is *phosphorylation* which forms the "*mature*" protein. Phosphorylation is the "activator" *or* "deactivator" of proteins/enzymes.

Secondary structure of proteins (e.g., alpha helix and beta pleated sheets) is stabilized by hydrogen bonds and hydrophobic interactions.

Quaternary structure requires two or more polypeptide chains.

Integral membrane proteins are embedded within the plasma membrane. Integral proteins are amphipathic (i.e., hydrophobic, and hydrophilic portions). They have a similar structural motif with a hydrophobic domain, α-helical or β-sheet, which traverses the hydrophobic core of the lipid-bilayer membrane.

62. D is correct.

CO_2 is a product of alcohol fermentation (ethanol) and pyruvate oxidation (lactic acid) under aerobic conditions.

In yeast, *alcoholic fermentation* occurs in an anaerobic (i.e., without oxygen) process, producing ATP and the waste products ethanol (alcohol) and carbon dioxide (CO_2).

Pyruvate oxidation occurs in the mitochondria and cytosol in eukaryotes and prokaryotes, respectively. The pyruvate dehydrogenase complex (PDC) has enzymes that oxidize pyruvate to acetyl-CoA, NADH, and carbon dioxide waste products.

Under anaerobic conditions (e.g., exercise in humans), pyruvate is converted to 2 moles of *lactic acid*, and NADH is oxidized (i.e., loss of hydrogen atom) to NAD^+.

63. D is correct.

Glucose and fructose have different chemical properties despite the same *molecular formula* ($C_6H_{12}O_6$).

Molecular formula of fructose and glucose are identical; however, the *structural formulas* (shown below) are different, giving rise to many physical and chemical differences between the two monosaccharides.

Haworth projections (above) and Fisher projections (below) for glucose on the left and fructose on right

Glucose has an aldehyde (i.e., terminal carbonyl) functional group; fructose is a ketone (i.e., internal carbonyl).

Compared to glucose, fructose has an increased density and decreased melting point with an increased BP.

Glucose, commonly referred to as blood sugar, is the "preferred" metabolic energy source.

Insulin is secreted from the *beta cells of the pancreas* in response to increased blood sugar (i.e., glucose) and facilitates glucose's entry into cells. Fructose does not stimulate the release of insulin as glucose does.

Glucose fuels cellular respiration, but fructose does not.

Glucose relies on glucokinase or hexokinase enzymes.

Fructose is more lipogenic and relies on fructokinase to initiate metabolism.

Fructose is the sweetest natural carbohydrate.

Notes for active learning

Photosynthesis – Detailed Explanations

1. D is correct.

C_4 plants use C_4 carbon fixation.

There are three carbon fixation mechanisms: C_3, C_4 and CAM (*crassulacean acid metabolism*).

C_4 is named the 4-carbon molecule in carbon fixation compared to a 3-carbon molecule product in C_3 plants.

C_4 plants have a competitive advantage over plants that use the C_3 carbon fixation pathway under drought, hot temperatures, and nitrogen or CO_2 limitation conditions.

About 8,100 plant species use C_4 carbon fixation, representing about 3% of terrestrial species of plants.

C_4 and CAM overcome the tendency of the RuBisCO to fix O_2 rather than CO_2 in photorespiration. They use a more efficient enzyme to fix CO_2 in mesophyll cells and shuttling this fixed carbon to bundle-sheath cells.

In bundle-sheath cells, RuBisCO is isolated from atmospheric oxygen and saturated with CO_2 released by decarboxylation of malate or oxaloacetate.

C_4 fixation is hypothesized to have evolved later.

Because these additional steps require more energy from ATP, C_4 plants can efficiently fix carbon in specific conditions, with the C_3 pathway being efficient in other conditions.

2. D is correct.

CAM (*crassulacean acid metabolism*) photosynthesis is a carbon fixation pathway that evolved in some plants to adapt to arid conditions.

In a plant using CAM, the stomata in the leaves remain shut during the day to reduce evapotranspiration but open at night to collect carbon dioxide (CO_2).

CO_2 is stored as the four-carbon acid malate and used for photosynthesis during the day.

The pre-collected CO_2 is concentrated around the RuBisCO enzyme, increasing photosynthetic efficiency.

3. A is correct.

Autotrophs (i.e., *producers*) synthesize complex organic compounds (i.e., carbohydrates, fats, proteins) from simple substances in their environment, generally using energy from light (i.e., photosynthesis) or inorganic chemical reactions (i.e., chemosynthesis).

Autotrophs are the producers in a food chain (plants on land and algae in water), in contrast to heterotrophs that consume autotrophs. They can make their food and do not need living energy or organic carbon source.

Autotrophs can reduce carbon dioxide to make organic compounds.

Most autotrophs use water as the reducing agent, but some can use other hydrogen compounds.

4. B is correct.

Adenosine triphosphate (ATP) is a *nucleotide* composed of adenosine (A), ribose, and three phosphate groups.

ATP has three phosphate groups and is produced by enzymes (e.g., ATP synthase) from adenosine diphosphate (ADP) or adenosine monophosphate (AMP) and phosphate groups.

Mitochondria are the site of most ATP molecules produced during aerobic respiration.

5. C is correct.

Photosynthesis reaction:

$$6\ CO_2 + 6\ H_2O \rightarrow C_6H_{12}O_6 + 6\ O_2$$

The reactants are six carbon dioxide (CO_2) and six water (H_2O) molecules, converted by light energy captured by chlorophyll pigments into one sugar ($C_6H_{12}O_6$) and six oxygen (O_2) molecules.

Chloroplasts are the site of photosynthesis and are only in algae and plant cells.

Chloroplasts contain DNA and ribosomes and may have similarly evolved via endosymbiosis.

6. D is correct.

ATP is a nucleoside triphosphate with a nitrogenous base (adenine), ribose sugar, and triphosphate.

The complete structure represents ATP.

Structure A represents *adenine* (nitrogenous base).

Structure B represents *ribose.*

Structure C represents *diphosphate.*

Structure D represents *phosphate*

Adenosine triphosphate

7. A is correct.

Stroma is the colorless fluid surrounding the thylakoids within the chloroplast.

Within stroma are *grana* (i.e., stacks of thylakoids) – the sub-organelles, where photosynthesis begins before the chemical changes are completed in the stroma.

8. B is correct.

During photosynthesis, autotrophs produce carbohydrates (e.g., glucose).

Photosynthesis:

$$6\ CO_2 + 6\ H_2O \rightarrow C_6H_{12}O_6 + 6\ O_2$$

Reactants are six carbon dioxide (CO_2) and six water (H_2O) molecules, converted by light energy captured by chlorophyll pigments into one sugar ($C_6H_{12}O_6$) and six oxygen (O_2) molecules.

9. A is correct.

Stomata are composed of a pair of specialized epidermal cells known as *guard cells*.

Stomata regulate gas exchange (e.g., CO_2) and control water loss by changing the size of the stomatal pore.

10. D is correct.

Plants use photosynthesis to make food. During photosynthesis, plants absorb photons (light energy) with their leaves. Plants use energy from the sun to convert water (H_2O) and carbon dioxide (CO_2) into glucose ($C_6H_{12}O_6$), six-carbon chain sugar.

Plants use glucose ($C_6H_{12}O_6$) for cellular energy to make biomolecules (e.g., cellulose and starch in plants; glycogen in animals).

Cellulose builds cell walls, while starch is stored in seeds and plant parts as a food source.

Chlorophylls *a* and *b* are photosynthetic pigments produced in chloroplasts of photosynthetic tissues of leaves. Chlorophyll molecules are water-repelling because of the long phytol tail in the molecule.

Photopigments chlorophyll a (top) and chlorophyll b (bottom) that absorb energy during photosynthesis

continued...

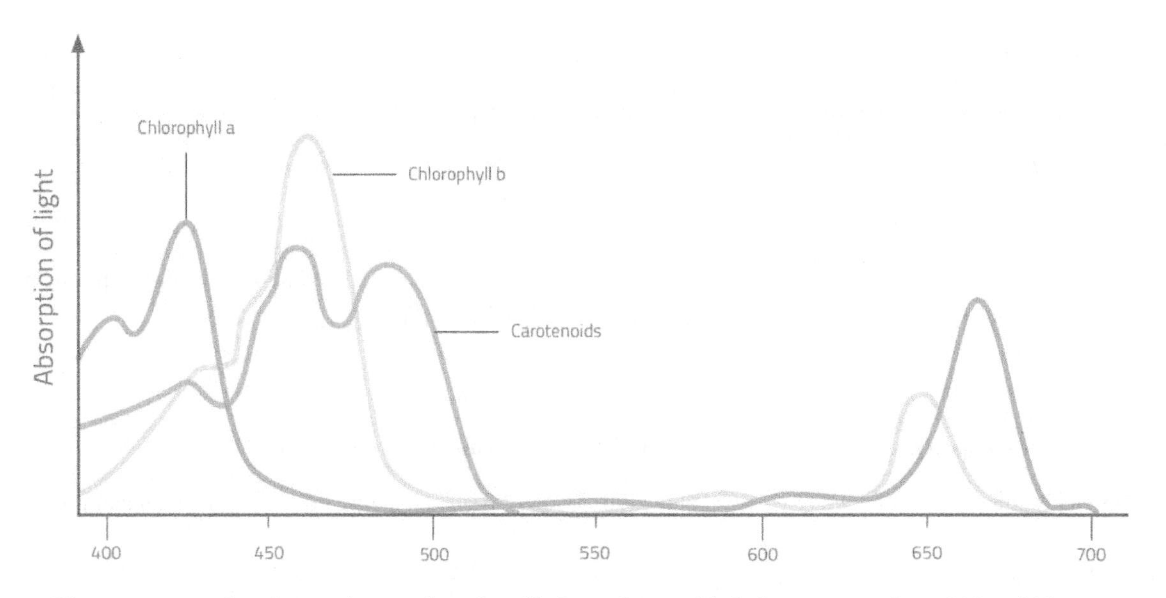

Photopigments absorb specific wavelengths of light with a visible light spectrum from 380 to 700 nm

11. C is correct.

Roots are used by plants to obtain most of their water.

12. C is correct.

Thylakoids are labeled in the figure.

13. B is correct.

Thylakoids are membrane-bound compartments inside chloroplasts and cyanobacteria. They are the site of photosynthesis.

Thylakoids consist of a thylakoid membrane surrounding a thylakoid lumen.

Thylakoids stack as disks (i.e., grana).

Outer Membrane
Granum
Lumen
Inner Membrane
Stroma
Thylakoids

Chloroplast with internal structures

14. B is correct.

The chlorophyll is within the thylakoid membrane.

15. A is correct.

Granum (pl. grana) is a stack of thylakoid discs. Chloroplasts can have from 10 to 100 grana.

Grana are connected by stroma thylakoids (or lamellae).

Grana thylakoids and stroma thylakoids are distinguished by their protein composition.

16. A is correct.

Electron carrier molecule in the figure is $NADP^+$.

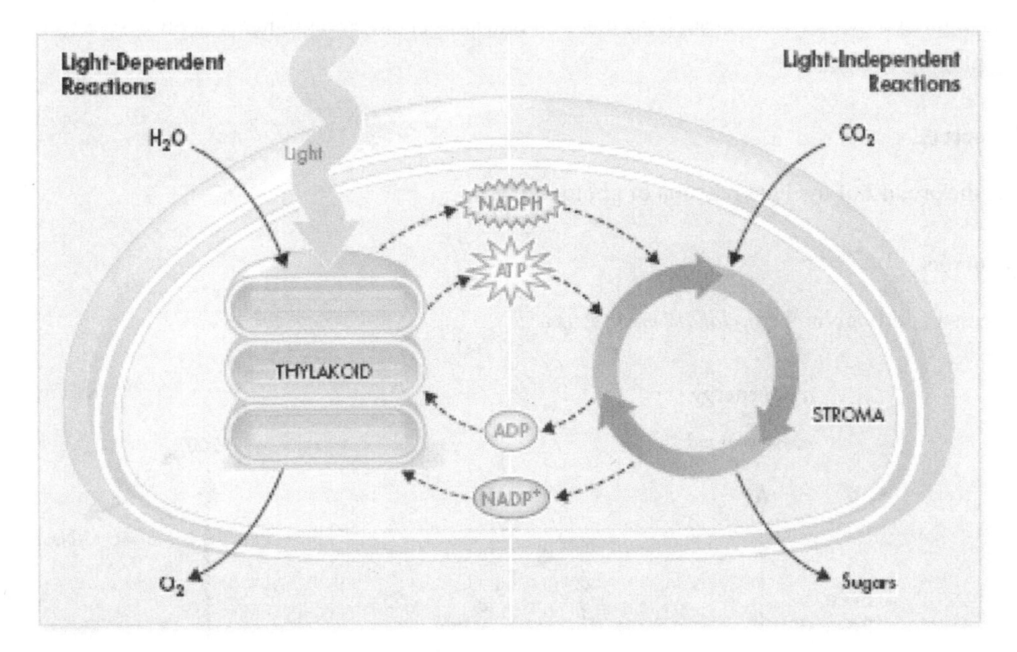

Chloroplast with light-dependent (ATP and NADPH) and light-independent reactions (sugars)

17. B is correct.

Low ATP production is likely if a shade-tolerant plant has minimal water intake.

18. C is correct.

High-energy electrons are highly reactive and are transported in the chloroplast by *electron carriers* ($NADP^+$).

19. D is correct.

Photosynthesis reaction:

$$6\ CO_2 + 6\ H_2O \rightarrow C_6H_{12}O_6 + 6\ O_2$$

Reactants are six carbon dioxide (CO_2) and six water (H_2O) molecules, converted by light energy captured by chlorophyll pigments into one sugar ($C_6H_{12}O_6$) and six oxygen (O_2) molecules.

20. A is correct.

Rate of photosynthesis *increases* and then levels off as the intensity of light increases.

21. A is correct.

In the redox reactions of photosynthesis, *electron transfer* is from $H_2O \rightarrow CO_2$

22. B is correct.

Steps in the light-dependent reaction include ATP synthase allowing H^+ ions to pass through the thylakoid membrane, high-energy electrons through the electron transport chain, and pigments in photosystem II absorbing photons of light.

23. C is correct.

Oxygen is the product of the light reaction of photosynthesis.

24. C is correct.

Photosystems I and II are in the *thylakoid membrane.*

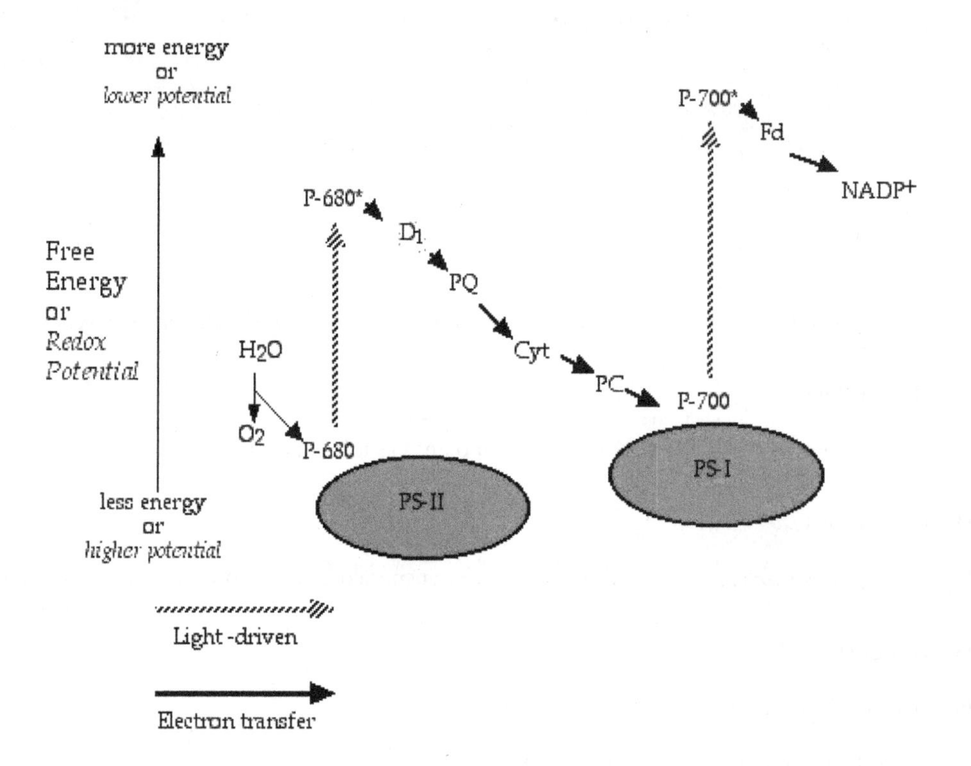

Photosystem II and I in the thylakoid membrane of the chloroplast. The light-driven reactions include electron promotions for P-680 and P-700. $NADP^+$ is the electron carrier.

25. B is correct.

Calvin cycle (i.e., C_3 cycle) is a series of biochemical redox reactions in the stroma of chloroplasts in photosynthetic organisms.

It is one of the light-independent reactions used for carbon fixation. The key enzyme of the cycle is RuBisCO.

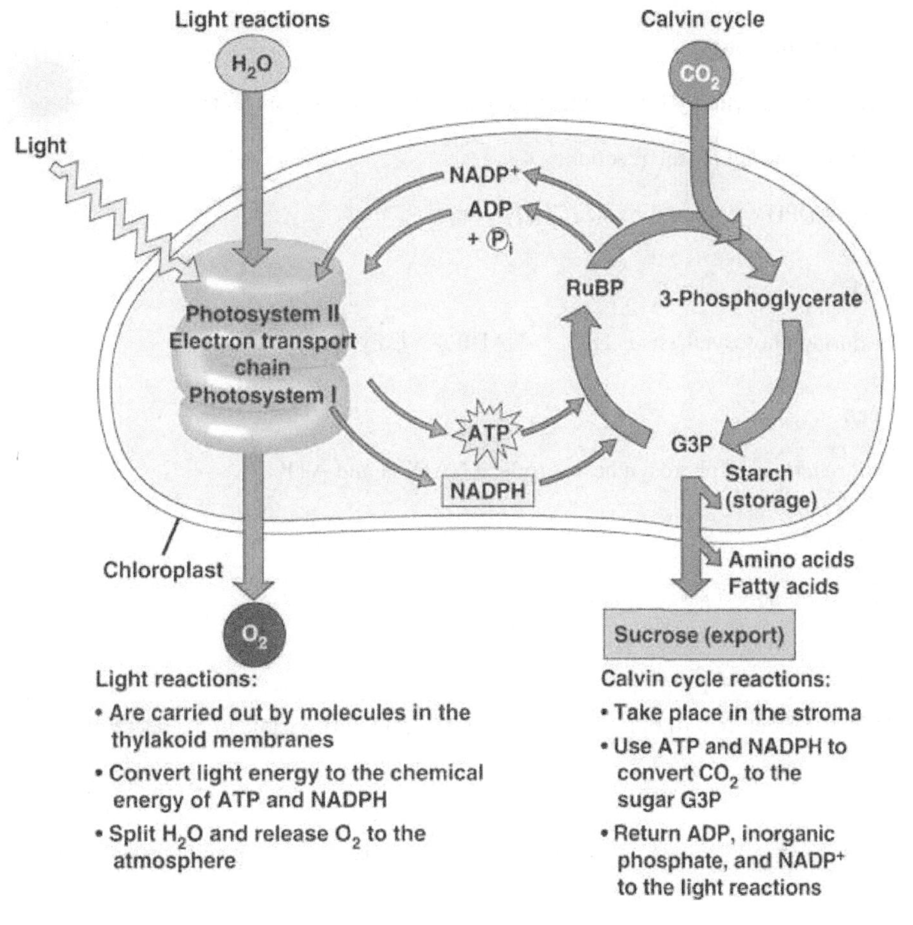

Products of light-dependent (ATP and NADPH) and light-independent reactions (sugars)

Photosynthesis occurs in two stages.

1) *Light-dependent reactions* capture the energy of light and use it to make energy storage and transport molecules ATP and NADPH.

2) *Light-independent reactions* (Calvin cycle) use energy from short-lived electronically excited electron carriers to convert carbon dioxide and water into organic compounds used by the organism (and animals that feed on it).

This set of reactions is *carbon fixation*.

Calvin cycle has four steps:

1) carbon fixation,
2) reduction phase,
3) carbohydrate formation, and
4) regeneration phase.

ATP and NADPH provide energy for the chemical reactions in this sugar-generating process.

Sunlight provides the energy for the reaction:

ATP + NADPH + carbon dioxide (CO_2) → sugar

26. B is correct.

Electrons flow during photosynthesis is H_2O → $NADP^+$ → Calvin cycle.

27. D is correct.

Light-dependent reactions of photosynthesis produce NADPH and ATP.

28. D is correct.

Calvin cycle occurs in the *stroma* of chloroplasts.

29. C is correct.

Blue-colored plants reflect light of blue wavelength (380 – 500 nm); visible light spectrum (380 – 700 nm).

30. A is correct.

Three components of an ATP molecule are adenosine (*base*), ribose (*sugar*), and three *phosphate* groups.

31. C is correct.

The wavelength *reflected* determines the color of an object.

32. A is correct.

Energy is *released* by hydrolysis of ATP (triphosphate) into ADP (diphosphate).

33. C is correct.

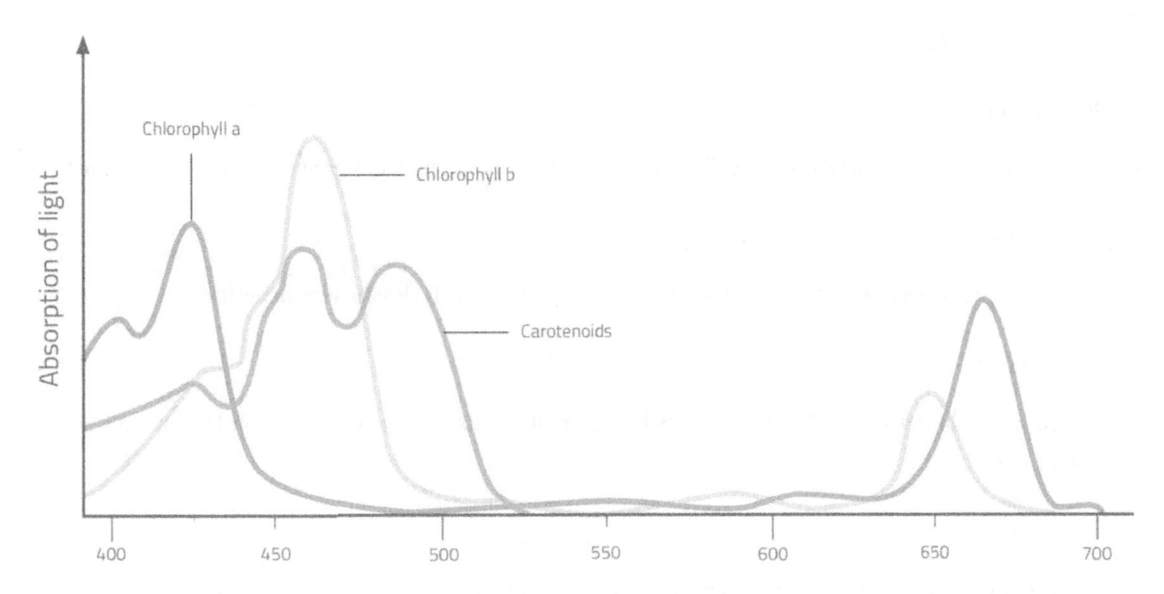

Photopigments absorb specific wavelengths of light with a visible light spectrum from 380 to 700 nm

34. C is correct.

Autotrophs (i.e., *producers*) synthesize complex organic compounds (i.e., carbohydrates, fats, proteins) from simple substances in their environment. They use energy from light (i.e., photosynthesis) or inorganic chemical reactions (i.e., chemosynthesis).

Autotrophs are the producers in a food chain (plants on land and algae in water), in contrast to heterotrophs that consume autotrophs. They can make their food and do not need living energy or organic carbon source.

Autotrophs can reduce carbon dioxide to make organic compounds. Most autotrophs use water to reduce (i.e., a gain of electrons), but some can use other hydrogen compounds.

Phototrophs (i.e., green plants and algae), a type of autotroph, convert physical energy from sunlight into chemical energy in the form of reduced carbon.

35. A is correct.

Carotenoids reflect light with yellow, red, and orange wavelengths.

36. D is correct.

Mushrooms are *heterotrophs* and derive nutrients from *complex organic molecules*.

37. C is correct.

Plants use chlorophyll *a*, chlorophyll *b*, and carotenoid accessory pigments to absorb light over a broad spectrum of wavelengths.

38. B is correct.

The *sun* is the *ultimate energy source* for living organisms.

39. A is correct.

Photons are discrete packets of light.

40. B is correct.

Most plants appear green because chlorophylls do *not* absorb wavelengths of green light (500 – 560 nm).

41. A is correct.

Electromagnetic spectrum (ROY G BIV) has higher energy light with shorter wavelengths.

42. B is correct.

Thylakoids are membrane-bound compartments inside chloroplasts and cyanobacteria and the site of photosynthesis.

43. B is correct.

Energy from photons is transferred to electrons, raising them to a higher energy (i.e., excited) level.

44. C is correct.

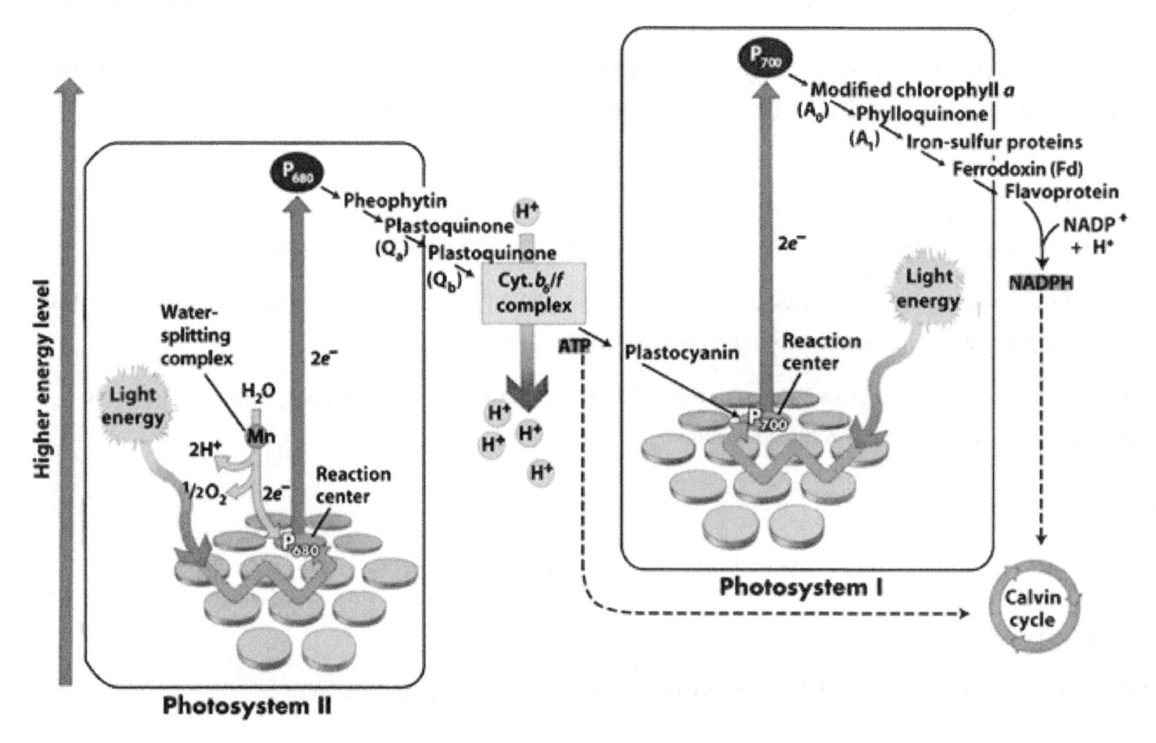

Photosystem II and I in the thylakoid membrane of the chloroplast. The light-driven reactions include electron promotions for P-680 and P-700 with $NADP^+$ as the electron carrier.

45. D is correct.

Molecules can *release energy* as fluorescence, heat, or light.

46. A is correct.

Photosynthesis reaction:

$$6\ CO_2 + 6\ H_2O \rightarrow C_6H_{12}O_6 + 6\ O_2$$

Reactants are six carbon dioxide (CO_2) and six water (H_2O) molecules, converted by light energy captured by chlorophyll pigments into one sugar ($C_6H_{12}O_6$) and six oxygen (O_2) molecules.

47. D is correct.

Photosystems are in the *thylakoid* membrane of chloroplasts.

48. A is correct.

Light-dependent reactions occur within *thylakoid membranes*.

49. A is correct.

Chlorophyll *a* is a form of chlorophyll used in photosynthesis. It absorbs most energy from wavelengths of violet-blue and orange-red light. Chlorophyll *a* reflects green and yellow light and contributes to the green color of many plants. *Photosynthetic pigment* is essential for photosynthesis in eukaryotes, cyanobacteria, and prochlorophytes because it is a primary electron donor in the *electron transport chain*.

50. C is correct.

Products of the *light-dependent reaction* are ATP, NADPH, and O_2 gas.

51. A is correct.

Calvin cycle has four steps:

carbon fixation,

reduction phase,

carbohydrate formation, and

regeneration.

ATP and NADPH provide energy for the chemical reactions in this *sugar-generating process*.

Sunlight provides energy for the reaction:

$$ATP + NADPH + \text{carbon dioxide } (CO_2) \rightarrow \text{sugar}$$

52. B is correct.

Calvin cycle (i.e., C_3 cycle) is a series of biochemical redox reactions in the stroma of chloroplasts in photosynthetic organisms. It is one of the light-independent reactions used for carbon fixation. The key enzyme of the cycle is RuBisCO.

Photosynthesis occurs in two stages in a cell.

Light-dependent reaction captures energy from light and uses it to make the energy storage and transport molecules ATP and NADPH.

*Light-independen*t Calvin cycle uses energy from short-lived electronically excited electron carriers to convert carbon dioxide and water into organic compounds used by the organism (and animals that feed on it).

This set of reactions is *carbon fixation.*

53. D is correct.

Water is the source of *oxygen* and electrons released by a photosystem.

54. C is correct.

Light-independent reaction of photosynthesis used for carbon fixation is the *Calvin cycle.*

55. B is correct.

Water is the source of oxygen and *electrons* released by a photosystem.

56. A is correct.

Electron transport chain occurs in light reactions of photosynthesis (in chloroplasts) and *cellular respiration* (in mitochondria).

57. C is correct.

H^+ gradient is formed across the *thylakoid membranes* of chloroplasts during photosynthesis.

Specialized Cells and Tissues – Detailed Explanations

1. B is correct.

Ca^{2+} in muscle contractions binds the troponin-tropomyosin complex, exposing the myosin-binding sites.

2. A is correct.

Sodium (Na^+) has a positive charge, so the anion is chloride (Cl^-), which has a negative charge.

Potassium (K^+) is a cation with a positive charge.

Magnesium (Mg^{2+}) has a $^{2+}$ charge.

Lithium (Li^+) is a cation with a positive charge.

3. A is correct.

Caffeine does *not inhibit* the signaling pathway commonly stimulated by epinephrine.

*Use the graph to answer questions **4–8***

4. D is correct.

Arrow A points to *Na^+ ions entering axon.*

5. B is correct.

Arrow B points to *K^+ ions leaving axons.*

6. B is correct.

Arrow C points to the *slow close of K^+ voltage-gated channels.*

7. B is correct.

Arrow D points to the *threshold.*

8. D is correct.

Arrow E points to *resting potential.*

9. C is correct.

After acting upon the postsynaptic membrane, acetylcholinesterase inactivates acetylcholine (Ach) in the synaptic cleft.

Because chemical X deactivates acetylcholinesterase, ACh remains in the synaptic cleft and continues depolarizing the postsynaptic membrane.

10. D is correct.

Resting motor neurons are expected to exhibit a *more negative* resting potential than the threshold potential.

11. A is correct.

Na^+/K^+ ATPase transports 3 Na^+ ions *out* for every 2 K^+ ions *into* the cell. When the sodium/potassium pump is inhibited, intracellular [Na^+] *increases* and intracellular [K^+] *decreases.*

12. C is correct.

If a neuron's membrane potential goes from –70 mV to –90 mV, this is an example of *hyperpolarization.*

13. B is correct.

Bone and *cartilage* are connective tissues that connect and support tissues and organs and are related in their lineage and activities. Connective tissue functions to bind and support tissues.

Connective tissue consists of *loose* and *dense connective tissue* (subdivided into dense regular and dense irregular).

Special connective tissue consists of reticular connective tissue, adipose tissue, blood, bone, and cartilage.

14. C is correct.

Resting membrane potential (i.e., voltage results from differences in charge) across a nerve cell membrane depends on the unequal distribution of Na^+ and K^+ ions.

Na^+/K^+ pump is an active transport protein that maintains an electrochemical gradient across the membrane by pumping three Na^+ out and two K^+ into the cell.

Unequal pumping of ions causes:

1) cells to be *negative inside* relative to outside;

2) high [Na^+] *outside* the cell relative to inside; and

3) high [K^+] *inside* relative to outside.

The membrane is more permeable to K^+ than Na^+ ions, and the balance between the pump and the *leaky* membrane determines the resting potential (i.e., –70mV).

15. C is correct.

The first event when a resting axon reaches threshold potential is the *opening of Na^+ gates.*

16. D is correct.

Schwann cells (in the peripheral nervous system) and *oligodendrocytes* (central nervous system) synthesize myelin, which functions as insulation around the axon.

Myelinated axons transmit nerve signals *much faster* than unmyelinated ones.

Multiple sclerosis is a demyelinating disease, which manifests in highly myelinated, fast-conduction neurons.

17. D is correct.

Synaptic summation measures the postsynaptic response after stimulation by the presynaptic cell.

18. B is correct.

A receptor is required for a cell to respond to a signaling molecule.

19. A is correct.

Muscle contraction occurs when the *actin thin filaments* and *myosin thick filaments* slide past each other to shorten the muscle and produce a contraction.

Neither of the filaments shortens nor elongates. The muscle decreases in size because the filaments slide past each other to cause muscle contraction.

20. B is correct.

When an organism dies, its muscles remain in the contracted state of *rigor mortis* for a brief period.

The lack of ATP to break bonds between thick and thin filaments is primarily responsible for this phenomenon.

21. B is correct.

Na^+/K^+ ATPase pumps three Na^+ ions out for every two K^+ ions into the cell. If the activity is blocked, there is a net increase of positive charge within the cell, and the inside becomes less negative.

As the inside becomes more positive, it reaches threshold (i.e., about –50mV), and depolarization ensues. This change in ion concentrations decreases the resting potential (i.e., –70mV).

Ouabain inhibits the Na^+/K^+ pump. If the pump were not working, the consumption of ATP would decrease, [Na^+] increases within the cell (the pump is not moving Na^+ out of the cell), while [K^+] increases in the extracellular environment (the pump is not moving K^+ into the cell).

22. B is correct.

Dendrites are an extension of a nerve cell that receives electrochemical impulses from cells and carry them inwards toward the cell body.

Axons are nerve fibers distinguished from dendrites in that they usually transmit signals rather than receive them. The axon terminus is the inflated portion of the axon that releases neurotransmitters.

T-tubules are extensions of the cell membrane that pass-through muscle cells.

Nodes of Ranvier are gaps in the myelin sheath around an axon or nerve fiber.

23. D is correct.

Myelin sheath covers the axon and increases conduction velocity.

Saltatory conduction occurs by permitting membrane depolarization only at nodes of Ranvier.

Myelin sheath comprises lipids deposited by *Schwann cells* for peripheral nerve cells and *oligodendrocytes* for central nerve cells.

24. D is correct.

Synaptic cleft (i.e., synapse) is the space between the axon terminus (end of one axon) and the abutting dendrite between neurons.

After stimulation, the presynaptic axon releases a neurotransmitter across this cleft, which diffuses and binds receptors on the postsynaptic dendrite of the next neuron.

Neurotransmitter is released by the presynaptic axon, received by the postsynaptic dendrite, and unidirectional.

Dendrite is where the input is received and is (often) near the cell body.

Axon process of the neuron projects away from the cell body and extends towards the axon terminus (where neurotransmitters are released).

Myelin sheath covers the axon and increases conduction velocity (i.e., permits saltatory conduction by preventing (via insulation) the passage of ions during depolarization except at the nodes of Ranvier).

Myelin sheath, composed of lipids, is deposited by Schwann cells for peripheral nerve cells and oligodendrocytes for central nerve cells.

The dendrite receives input, the axon process propagates the all-or-none action potential, and the axon terminus releases neurotransmitters

25. A is correct.

In the communication link between a motor neuron and a skeletal muscle, the motor neuron is presynaptic, and the skeletal muscle is the postsynaptic cell.

26. B is correct.

Mitochondria self-replicate autonomously.

Mitochondria number in a cell varies widely by organism and tissue/type. Many cells have a single mitochondrion, while others contain several thousand mitochondria.

DNA is not an organelle.

Nucleus and *nucleolus* replicate and divide during mitosis and meiosis.

Ribosomes are not self-replicating. They consist of rRNA (synthesized in the nucleolus) and associated proteins. The cellular machinery assembles ribosomes.

27. C is correct.

Resting membrane potential of a neuron would be close to –70 mV.

28. C is correct.

In biochemistry (and pharmacology), a *ligand* is a molecule that forms a complex for a biological purpose.

Ligands include substrates, activators, inhibitors, and neurotransmitters.

In protein-ligand binding, a ligand usually is a signal-triggering molecule that binds a site on a target protein.

In DNA-ligand binding studies, a ligand is any molecule (e.g., protein or ion) binding to the DNA double helix.

Ligand binding to a receptor (ligand-receptor) alters a receptor protein's conformation (i.e., three-dimensional shape) that determines its functional state.

29. D is correct.

Myasthenia gravis causes the production of antibodies that remove acetylcholine (ACh) receptors from muscle fibers. ACh cannot bind to membranes without these receptors and initiate depolarization.

None of the subsequent events occur without depolarization because the conduction of an action potential is impaired across the sarcolemma.

For muscle contraction, a neuromuscular junction is composed of a neuron's presynaptic membrane (i.e., axon terminus) and the postsynaptic membrane of a muscle fiber (i.e., sarcolemma).

Synapse is between two neurons (i.e., the space between is the synaptic cleft).

Presynaptic membrane of a neuromuscular junction releases the neurotransmitter acetylcholine (ACh) into the synapse from an action potential. ACh diffuses across the synapse and binds acetylcholine receptors on the sarcolemma.

Binding of ACh causes the postsynaptic membrane to depolarize and generate an action potential, which causes the sarcoplasmic reticulum to release calcium ions into the sarcoplasm (i.e., the cytoplasm of a muscle fiber), which leads to the shortening of the sarcomeres and the resulting muscle contraction.

A: *acetylcholine* synthesis is not affected by *myasthenia gravis.*

Neurons synthesize acetylcholine and independent of acetylcholine receptors on postsynaptic membranes.

Acetylcholine is a neurotransmitter in the autonomic nervous system (ANS).

Acetylcholine acts on the peripheral nervous system (PNS) and central nervous system (CNS) and is the *only neurotransmitter* used in the *motor division of the somatic nervous system.*

Acetylcholine

B: *muscle cells* store calcium in the *sarcoplasmic reticulum*, and the release of calcium is affected by *myasthenia gravis*.

30. D is correct.

Thick myosin and *thin actin filaments* are in skeletal, cardiac, and smooth muscle.

31. A is correct.

Na^+ and K^+ are the major *ions* involved in the action potential of a neuron.

Blocking Na^+ channels and preventing Na^+ from entering the cell inhibits the propagation of the action potential because the movement of Na^+ creates depolarization.

The –70mV (resting potential) becomes –40mV (threshold) for action potential propagation before the K^+ channels open to repolarize the neuron.

32. B is correct.

Glial cell is a non-neuronal cell that maintains homeostasis, forms myelin, and provides support and protection for neurons in the brain and peripheral nervous system

Oligodendrocyte is a glial cell that myelinates the axon of neurons in the CNS.

A: *astrocytes* are star-shaped glial cells in the brain and spinal cord and are the most abundant human brain cell.

They perform many functions, including biochemical support of endothelial cells that form the blood-brain barrier, facilitate nutrients to the nervous tissue, and maintain extracellular ion balance.

Following traumatic injuries, astrocytes enlarge and proliferate to form a scar and produce inhibitory molecules that inhibit the regrowth of a damaged or severed axon.

C: *Schwann cells* myelinate axons of neurons in the PNS.

D: *choroid plexus* is a plexus (i.e., branching network of vessels or nerves) in the ventricles of the brain where cerebrospinal fluid (CSF) is produced. There is a choroid plexus in each of the four ventricles within the brain.

33. D is correct.

Neurons do not produce *myelin sheaths* but are synthesized by *Schwann cells* for peripheral nerve cells (PNS) and *oligodendrocytes* for central nerve (CNS) cells.

Schwann cells and *oligodendrocytes* wrap the axon to create layers of insulating myelin (composed of lipids), preventing the passage of ions along the axon process and increasing the rate of depolarization along the axon.

A: *axon hillock* is a region in the cell body (i.e., soma) where membrane potentials propagated from synaptic inputs (temporal and spatial summation) are aggregated (i.e., summed) before being transmitted to the axon.

In its resting state, a neuron is polarized, with its inside at about –70 mV relative to the outside.

The axon hillock "sums" depolarization events to determine if a sufficient magnitude of depolarization is achieved.

Once threshold is reached (between –50 and –40 mV), the *all or none* action potential is propagated along the axon.

C: *nodes of Ranvier* are openings along the axons that permit depolarization of the membrane and give rise to saltatory conduction to increase the transmission rate along the nerve fiber.

34. A is correct.

Resting muscle is not entirely relaxed but experiences a slight contraction known as tonus.

B: *tonus* is the partial sustained contraction in relaxed muscles.

C: *isometric contractions* involve a constant length and increased muscle tension.

D: *isotonic contractions* involve the shortening of the muscle while the tension remains constant.

35. A is correct.

Organs are recognizable structures (e.g., heart, lungs, liver) performing specific physiological functions.

36. C is correct.

Na^+/K^+-ATPase pump moves *K^+ into* cells.

K^+ is *positively charged,* which causes the inside of the membrane to be more positive.

Resting potential (i.e., –70mV) of the neuron is measured with respect to the inside.

37. B is correct.

Na^+ / K^+ ATPase maintains the asymmetric concentration gradient of Na^+ and K^+ across the membrane.

38. D is correct.

Insulin binds to the receptor on the extracellular surface of the cell.

Insulin receptor (IR) is a tyrosine kinase transmembrane receptor activated by insulin, IGF-I, and IGF-II.

Ligand binding (e.g., insulin) to the α-chains of the IR domain induces a conformational change within the receptor and autophosphorylation of tyrosine residues within the intracellular TK domain of the β-chain.

Tyrosine kinase (e.g., insulin) receptors mediate their activity by adding a phosphate group to tyrosine on specific cellular proteins.

39. A is correct.

During an action potential, *Na^+ flows in,* and *K^+ flows out.*

Na^+ flows into the cell (down its electrochemical gradient) during an action potential to depolarize (make the voltage less negative) the cell membrane.

K^+ flows *out* (down electrochemical gradient) to repolarize the cell and restore the resting potential of –70mV.

When this outflow is excessive, the membrane becomes hyperpolarized due to the slow closing of K+ channels (e.g., the temporary value of –90mV), known as overshoot.

40. C is correct.

Folic acid (or vitamin B_9) is a water-soluble vitamin.

Folic acid is not biologically active, but its derivatives have high biological importance. Folate is a naturally occurring vitamin in food, while folic acid is synthetically produced.

Folic acid (or folate) is essential for numerous bodily functions. Humans cannot synthesize folate *de novo*, so it must be supplied through the diet.

Folate is needed to synthesize, repair, and methylate DNA and function as a cofactor in specific biological reactions. It is vital in rapid cell division and growth (e.g., infancy and pregnancy).

Children and adults require folic acid to produce healthy red blood cells and prevent anemia.

A: vitamin B_6 is a water-soluble vitamin.

Pyridoxal phosphate (PLP) is the active form and a cofactor in many reactions of amino acid metabolism (e.g., transamination, deamination, and decarboxylation).

PLP is necessary for the enzymatic reaction to release glucose from glycogen.

B: *calcium* is an essential component of a healthy diet and a mineral necessary for life.

Approximately 99 % of the Ca^{2+} is stored in bones and teeth. It has important uses, such as exocytosis, neurotransmitter release, and muscle contraction.

In heart muscles, Ca^{2+} replaces Na^+ as the mineral that depolarizes the cell to proliferate action potentials.

D: vitamin B_{12} (or *cobalamin*) is a water-soluble vitamin with a critical role in the ordinary functioning of the brain and nervous system and the formation of blood. It is involved in the metabolism of every cell, primarily affecting DNA synthesis and regulation, fatty acid synthesis, and energy production.

Fungi, plants, and animals are not capable of producing vitamin B_{12}. Bacteria and archaea produce it with enzymes required for its synthesis.

Many foods are a natural source of B_{12} because of bacterial symbiosis. This vitamin is the largest and most structurally complicated vitamin produced industrially only through bacterial fermentation synthesis.

41. D is correct.

Local anesthetics dissolve into the hydrophobic membrane and inhibit membrane-bound proteins.

The Na^+ voltage-gated channel is essential for nerve conduction but is inhibited by the local anesthetics in a nonspecific process that blocks nerve conduction.

42. D is correct.

Enzymes are not a class of molecules used as neurotransmitters.

43. D is correct.

Cell surface receptors (i.e., transmembrane receptors) are specialized integral membrane proteins facilitating communication between the cell and the outside world.

Extracellular signaling molecules (e.g., hormones, neurotransmitters, cytokines, growth factors) attach to the extracellular receptor, which triggers changes in the function of the cell.

Signal transduction occurs when the binding of the ligand outside the cell initiates a chemical change on the intracellular side of the membrane.

44. A is correct.

Piloerection is when the hair stands on its end and is a sympathetic nervous system *fight-or-flight* response (i.e., parasympathetic is associated with *rest* and *digestion*).

Sensory neurons bring information *toward* the central nervous system from sensory receptors, while motor neurons carry signals *to effector cells from the central nervous system*.

For piloerection, a signal from the CNS is relayed to effector cells, which involves a motor neuron.

45. A is correct.

Cytoplasm includes the cytosol, a watery fluid inside the cell.

46. B is correct.

Ca^{2+} binds troponin C on the actin (thin) filament.

Ca^{2+} binds, and tropomyosin changes its conformation to expose the myosin (thick filament) binding sites on the actin filament.

When myosin binds the myosin-binding sites on actin, the myosin head undergoes a *power stroke,* and the actin-myosin filaments slide past each other as the muscle contracts.

Plasma Ca^{2+} levels are tightly regulated by *calcitonin* and *parathyroid hormone* (PTH).

PTH raises calcium levels by stimulating osteoclasts, while calcitonin lowers plasma calcium levels by stimulating osteoblasts.

47. C is correct.

Myelinated axons exhibit greater conduction velocity than non-myelinated axons.

Myelin sheath, composed of lipids, is deposited by Schwann cells for peripheral nerve cells and oligodendrocytes for central nerve cells.

Myelin sheath covers the axon and increases conduction velocity (i.e., permits saltatory conduction by preventing (via insulation) the passage of ions during depolarization, except at the nodes of Ranvier).

48. A is correct.

Axon hillock is a specialized part of the cell body (or soma) of a neuron that connects to the axon and where membrane potentials propagated from synaptic inputs are summated before being transmitted to the axon.

The axon hillock is the *accounting center*, where a graded potential is summed (spatial or temporal summation) to be sufficient to reach the threshold.

Inhibitory postsynaptic potentials (IPSPs) and *excitatory postsynaptic potentials* (EPSPs) are summed in the axon hillock.

Once a triggering threshold is exceeded, an action potential propagates – all or none – through the axon.

Glial cell is a non-neuronal cell in the central nervous system involved in depositing myelin around axons.

49. D is correct.

Myelin acts as an *insulator*, preventing ions from passing through the axon membrane and allowing axons to conduct impulses faster.

Ions can only permeate through *nodes of Ranvier*, which are channels as small gaps in the myelin sheath.

Action potentials *skip* (i.e., saltatory conduction) from node to node and is much faster than conduction through a non-myelinated neuron because the area requiring depolarization to permit Na^+ in / K^+ out is smaller.

A: *action potentials* are initiated by graded stimuli that cause depolarization of the axon hillock.

B: pumping of Na^+ *out* of the cell is achieved by the Na^+/K^+ pump.

C: *resting potential* is achieved by the Na^+/K^+ pump.

50. D is correct.

Epithelial tissue forms coverings, linings, and glands.

51. C is correct.

Nodes of Ranvier are unmyelinated regions along the axon process between Schwann cells, depositing myelin.

Myelin sheath is a lipid that increases propagation speed for the action potential to travel from the cell body to the axon terminal.

Electrical impulses move by depolarization of the plasma membrane at the unmyelinated (nodes of Ranvier) and "jump" from one node to the next (i.e., *saltatory conduction*).

Acetylcholine receptors are on the dendrite of a postsynaptic neuron.

52. A is correct.

Organs are usually made of several tissues and many types of cells.

53. C is correct.

Purkinje fibers in cardiac tissue have large diameters and short axons.

Conduction velocity is related to diameter and inversely related to length.

Large diameter axons have more volume for action potentials to depolarize membranes, and more ions migrate.

Increasing the *diameter* or decreasing *axon length* increases the conduction velocity.

Cardiac Purkinje cell conduction is fast and Na^+ channel-dependent because conduction is channel-dependent.

54. B is correct.

Four primary *tissue* types are *connective*, *muscle*, *nervous* and *epithelial*.

55. C is correct.

Release of neurotransmitter requires the influx of Ca^{2+} and occurs at the *axon terminus*.

A: Na^+ influx causes neuron depolarization.

B: K^+ efflux (not influx) determines the neuron's resting potential and may cause hyperpolarization.

D: Cl^- ions are inside neurons and contribute to the negative resting potential (i.e., –70mV).

56. D is correct.

Adipose tissue (along with cartilage, bone, and blood) is connective tissue, mainly beneath the skin and around internal organs.

In adipose tissue, glucose is transformed and stored as *fat*.

Fatty acids are an essential energy source, ideal for an organism to store fat in the adipose tissue when a large quantity of energy needs to be stored for later use (e.g., hibernating bear).

57. B is correct.

Cells use Na^+ channels to maintain osmotic gradients and prevent lysis.

Skeletal, cardiac, smooth muscle and nerve cells are Na^+ dependent excitable cells producing action potentials when *depolarized* by Na^+ entering the cell.

Endothelial cells line luminal structures (e.g., gastrointestinal tract, blood vessels, excretory system).

Endothelial cells are *non-excitable* because they do not undergo depolarization.

58. B is correct.

Simple squamous epithelium comprises the cells lining the air sacs in the lungs.

Notes for active learning

Genetics – Detailed Explanations

1. A is correct.

Model organism for *genetic studies* (e.g., pea plants, Drosophila, zebrafish) has common features.

Organism must be bred in *large numbers*, and *ease of cultivation* favors viable offspring that *transmit genetic information* between generations.

Genetic studies rely upon statistics that favor *large sample numbers*. Therefore, a *short generation time* (i.e., the span between birth and fecundity) is preferred.

There should be *discreet phenotypic differences* among alleles (alternative forms of the gene).

For example, among the seven traits, Mendel (1822-1884) observed, he inventoried tall *vs.* short plants, round *vs.* smooth seeds, and green *vs.* yellow seeds.

Mendel controlled the crosses by manually transferring pollen from the anther of a mature pea plant of one variety to the stigma of a separate mature pea plant of the second variety.

The organism should have a *well-characterized genome* (gene identity and function have been studied).

Increasing the *number of chromosomes* increases the genes that can influence the observable phenotypes.

An organism with fewer chromosomes makes statistical analysis direct and supports causation when the genome is manipulated.

2. C is correct.

People with a *sex-linked genetic disease*, hemophilia, suffer from excessive bleeding because their blood will not clot. Tom, Mary, and their four daughters do not exhibit symptoms of hemophilia.

However, their son exhibits symptoms of hemophilia because Mary is heterozygous.

3. B is correct.

r/K selection refers to selecting traits in a species, whereby the parental investment is related to the quantity/quality of offspring.

A higher quantity of offspring with decreased parental investment, or a lower quantity of offspring with increased parental investment, promotes reproductive success in different environments.

r-selected species emphasize *high growth rates and typically exploit less-crowded ecological niches*.

r-selected species produce many offspring, which may die before adulthood (i.e., high r, low K).

This strategy is better in an environment with *density-independent factors* (e.g., harsh environment, short seasons).

The species withstand predation better because of more offspring than needed for population survival.

continued...

K-selected species display traits associated with living at *densities close to carrying capacity* and are typically strong competitors in crowded niches. They invest heavily in *fewer offspring*, most of which will mature (i.e., low r, high K).

K-strategists fare better with *density-dependent factors* (e.g., limited resources) and exploit limited resources by specializing.

Species that use r-selection are *opportunistic,* while K-selected species are described as *equilibrium.*

4. C is correct.

Eye color is sex-linked in *Drosophila*.

Determine the phenotype of the parents. A red-eyed fly with red-eyed and sepia-eyed parents must be heterozygous because a sepia-eyed parent only contributes the recessive sepia allele.

When the heterozygous (Rr) red-eyed fly is crossed with a homozygous recessive (rr) sepia-eyed fly, ½ of the offspring are red-eyed (Rr) because of the dominant (red) allele from the heterozygous fly.

Punnett square:

Sepia eyed Parent	Red eyed parent: R	Red eyed parent: r
r	Rr (red)	rr (sepia)
r	Rr (red)	rr (sepia)

Since the question does not assign the gender to the sepia and red-eyed parents, the Punnett squares for two combinations for sex-linked traits are:

Sepia eyed male (♂)	Red eyed female (♀): R	Red eyed female (♀): r
r	Rr (red)	rr (sepia)
y	Ry (red)	ry (sepia)

Sepia eyed female (♀)	Red eyed male (♂): R	Red eyed male (♂): y
r	Rr (red)	ry (sepia)
r	Rr (red)	ry (sepia)

5. D is correct.

Color blindness pertains to cone photoreceptors in retinas, as the cones can detect the color frequencies of light. About 8 percent of males, but 0.5 percent of females, are colorblind, whether it is one color, a color combination, or another mutation.

Males are at a greater risk of inheriting an *X-linked mutation* because males have one X chromosome (XY) while females have two (XX). Men lack a second X chromosome to compensate for the X chromosome that carries the gene mutation.

If a woman inherits a typical X chromosome in addition to the one that carries the mutation, she does not display the mutation.

6. D is correct.

The decimating fire was a random event unrelated to the apparent fitness of the fly in its typical environment.

Genetic drift is the *random change over time in allele frequency* within a population, such as the one caused by the decimating fire in the loss of allele(s) for the altered structure.

A: *reproduction* is not involved in the loss of the advantageous modification.

B: *natural selection* is not the cause since the death of the flies was unrelated to their fitness, and a decimating fire would likely have killed all flies, regardless of their advantageous modification.

C: *Hardy-Weinberg equilibrium* describes ideal circumstances which do not apply to this situation.

7. C is correct.

Microscopy is the laboratory technique of magnifying objects that cannot be seen with the unaided eye.

Gregor Mendel (1822-1884) performed cross-breeding experiments with pea plants to study inheritance patterns and introduced the terms *dominant* and *recessive* for phenotypic traits (or *alleles*).

8. B is correct.

AAbbCc produces 2 gametes:

AbC and Abc = 1/2

AaBbCc produces 8 gametes:

ABC, ABc, AbC, Abc, aBC, aBc, abC, abc = 2/8 possible = 1/4

From probability: 1/2 × 1/4 = 1/8

	ABC	ABc	AbC	Abc	aBC	aBc	abC	abc
AbC	X	X	X	X	X	**Yes**	X	X
Abc	X	X	X	X	**Yes**	X	X	X

9. B is correct.

Afflicted children are aa = 1 of 4 possibilities = ¼ or 25%.

	A	a
A	AA	Aa
a	Aa	**aa**

10. B is correct.

If the four criteria are met, gene frequencies remain constant. If a criterion is not met, gene frequencies (and allele frequencies) change, and evolution occurs.

Hardy-Weinberg law states that the *gene ratios* (P + Q =1) and the *allelic frequencies* ($p^2 + 2pq + q^2 = 1$) remain constant between generations in a non-evolving population.

The Hardy-Weinberg law requires four criteria:

1) a large population,

2) random mating,

3) no migration into or out of the population, and

4) no mutations.

All four conditions are required for the gene frequency to remain constant. If one (or more) four conditions are not satisfied, the gene frequencies change over the generations, and the population evolves.

11. C is correct.

Tumor suppressor gene protects a cell from aberrant cell cycles.

When this gene's function is lost or reduced due to mutation, the cell can progress to cancer (usually combined with other genetic mutations).

The loss of the *tumor suppressor* gene may be more critical than proto-oncogene/oncogene activation to form many kinds of human cancer cells.

Both alleles of the tumor suppressor gene encoding a particular protein must be affected before an effect is manifested. If one allele is damaged, the second can produce the correct protein.

12. D is correct.

Color blindness is a *sex-linked trait* because the gene is on the X chromosome.

Mother is a carrier (not afflicted with the condition) and is heterozygous for the recessive allele (color blindness).

Father has the allele on his X chromosome (Y chromosome lacks the gene).

Genotype and *phenotype* of an XY son depend entirely on the mother (afflicted vs. carrier) since the afflicted father transmits the gene on his X.

The mother is heterozygous; a son has a 50% probability of receiving the color-blindness allele from his mother.

13. B is correct.

If two strains of true-breeding plants with different alleles are crossed, their progeny are the F_1 generation.

14. C is correct.

AaBbCcDdEe × AaBbCcDdEe

Probability: $\frac{1}{2} \times \frac{1}{2} \times \frac{1}{2} \times \frac{1}{2} \times \frac{1}{2} = 1/32$

15. A is correct.

Autosomal recessive inheritance is the product of mating two carriers (i.e., heterozygous parents). In the mating of two heterozygotes for an autosomal recessive gene, there is a:

1) 25% (1/4) probability of a homozygous unaffected child

2) 25% (1/4) probability of a homozygous affected child

3) 50% (1/2) probability of a heterozygous (carrier) child

Overall, 75% of children are phenotypically normal (25% AA and 50% Aa).

Of all children, 50% are phenotypically normal but carry the mutant gene (Aa).

16. D is correct.

If the dominant allele frequency is three times that of the recessive allele, $p = 3q$.

Hardy-Weinberg equilibrium:

$$p + q = 1$$

so

$$3q + q = 1$$

Solving for q,

$$4q = 1;\ q = 0.25 \text{ and } p = 0.75$$

Allele frequency:

$$p^2 + 2pq + q^2 = 1$$

Heterozygote allele = 2pq

Substituting for p and q,

$$2(0.75)\cdot(0.25) = 0.375 \text{ or } 37.5\%$$

17. D is correct.

Loss of heterozygosity is a chromosomal event resulting from losing the gene and surrounding region.

Diploid cells (e.g., human somatic cells) contain *two copies* of the genome, one from each parent.

Each copy contains approximately 3 billion bases, and for the majority of positions in the genome, the base is consistent between individuals. However, a small percentage may contain different bases.

These positions are *single nucleotide polymorphisms* (or SNP). The region is *heterozygous* when the genomic copies from each parent have different bases.

Most chromosomes within somatic cells are paired, allowing SNP locations to be potentially heterozygous.

One parental copy of a region can be lost, resulting in the region with just one copy. If the copy lost contained the dominant allele of the gene, the remaining recessive allele would appear in a phenotype.

18. A is correct.

Maternal inheritance involves all progeny exhibiting the phenotype of the *female* parent.

B: not maternal inheritance because the progeny exhibits the phenotype of the *male* parent.

C and D: Mendelian 1:1 segregation and not maternal inheritance.

Maternal inheritance is uniparental when all progeny have the genotype and phenotype of the female parent.

19. A is correct.

Gene is a fundamental physical and functional unit of heredity transferred from a parent to offspring and determines some offspring characteristics.

Genes are DNA sequences encoding proteins.

Alleles are forms of the same gene with slight differences in their sequence of DNA bases.

Genome is a complete set of genetic information of an organism.

A genome has the genetic information needed for an organism and allows it to develop, grow and reproduce.

20. B is correct.

GC base pairs converted to AT base pairs in the promoter will likely lose gene function completely.

21. A is correct.

Mutations affect proteins but not lipids or carbohydrates.

In proteins, the effects on the protein are no change (i.e., silent mutation), abnormal protein production, loss of protein (enzyme) function, or gain of protein (enzyme) function.

Loss of function of a gene product may result from mutations encoding a regulatory element or the loss of critical amino acid sequences.

Gain-of-function mutations are changes in the amino acids resulting in enhancement of the protein function.

There may be an increase in the level of protein expression (affecting the operator region of genes) or an increase in each protein molecule's ability (change in the protein's shape) to perform its function.

22. A is correct.

The desired phenotype is green smooth peas, and green and smooth are dominant phenotypes. Therefore, the genotypes selected for the cross must avoid the two recessive alleles (g and s).

For GgSs × GGSS, one parent (GGSS) is a double dominant, and therefore all offspring have the dominant phenotype (G and S) regardless of the other parent's genotype.

B: Gg × gg yields 1/2 yellow (g) phenotype offspring

C: ss × Ss yields 1/2 wrinkled (s) phenotype offspring

D: Gg × Gg yields 1/4 yellow (g) phenotype offspring

23. C is correct.

Retinoblastoma (Rb) is a rapidly developing cancer in the immature cells of a retina, the light-detecting tissue of the eye. It is a common malignant tumor of the eyes in children. A single allele is inherited (i.e., dominant) for the phenotype.

24. A is correct.

Phenotype of the first child does not influence the probability of the second child.

For example, the probability of getting a tail on the first toss of a coin does not influence the probability of getting a head on the second toss.

Punnett square determines possible gametes and their combinations.

If ½ of the woman's gametes carry the trait and ½ of the father's gametes carry the trait, the probability of a child receiving the allele from each parent is $\frac{1}{2} \times \frac{1}{2} = \frac{1}{4}$.

25. C is correct.

Cross of spherical-seeded and wrinkled-seeded pea plants in Mendel's experiment inherited alleles (or *gene variants*) from each parent.

However, only spherical-seeded plants resulted from the cross.

The wrinkled-seed gene is a recessive allele compared to the spherical seed (i.e., the dominant gene).

Dominant allele is a genetic variant expressed more strongly than other variants (or alleles) of the gene (i.e., recessive) for many reasons.

26. B is correct.

Notation 2N indicates that a given cell line is diploid, two homologous versions of each chromosome.

Human somatic cells are diploid with 23 different chromosome pairs (N = 23) for 46 chromosomes (2N = 46).

Gamete cells (eggs and sperm) are haploid (i.e., 1N).

Mitosis is the mode of cell division used by somatic cells, resulting in two diploid daughter cells genetically identical to the diploid parent cell.

27. C is correct.

Probability (p) of rolling a number (e.g., 4) on a 6-sided die is 1/6; 6 sides and one side carries a number 4.

$$p \text{ (of a 4)} = 1/6$$

Using two dice, what is the probability of rolling a pair of 4s?

Multiply the individual probabilities.

Probability of a 4 appearing on both dice is:

$$p \text{ (of two 4s)} = 1/6 \times 1/6 = 1/36$$

28. D is correct.

Degree of genetic linkage measures the physical distance of two genes on the same chromosome.

Probability of crossover and corresponding exchange between gene loci (location on the chromosome) is generally proportional to the distance between the loci.

Pairs of genes far apart on a chromosome are more likely to be separated during crossover than genes physically close. Thus, the frequency of genetic recombination between two genes is related to their distance.

Recombination frequencies are used to construct genetic maps.

One map unit (Morgan units) is a 1 percent recombinant frequency.

Recombination frequencies are roughly additive but are a good approximation for small percentages.

Percentage of recombinants cannot exceed 50%, resulting when two genes are at opposite ends of the chromosome.

Crossover events result in an exchange of genes.

However, an odd number of crossover events (a 50% probability between an even and an odd number of crossover events) results in a recombinant product.

29. A is correct.

Epigenetic inheritance results from changes in gene activity, which are *not* caused by changes in the DNA sequence. It studies stable, long-term alterations in the transcriptional potential that are not necessarily heritable.

Unlike simple genetics based on changes to the DNA sequence (genotype), the changes in gene expression or cellular phenotype of epigenetics have other causes.

An example of an epigenetic change in eukaryotes is *cellular differentiation*.

During *morphogenesis*, totipotent (i.e., all potent) stem cells become pluripotent (i.e., highly potent, but limited determinate potential) cells of the embryo, which become fully differentiated cells.

As a single fertilized egg cell (zygote) divides, the resulting daughter cells change into the different cell types in an organism (e.g., neurons, muscle cells, epithelium, endothelium of blood vessels) by activating some genes while inhibiting the expression of others.

30. C is correct.

Female children receive one X from their mother and one X from their father.

The X from the father must carry the color-blindness allele because the father is colorblind.

The X from the mother has a wild-type and a color blindness allele because she is heterozygous recessive.

50% of female children are homozygous colorblind, and 50% are heterozygous carriers.

31. D is correct.

True breeding means that the organism is homozygous (e.g., AA or aa) for the trait.

All progeny are *heterozygous* Aa (below) and exhibit the *dominant* phenotype.

	A	A
a	Aa	Aa
a	Aa	Aa

32. C is correct.

	A	A
a	Aa	Aa
a	Aa	Aa

	A	a
A	AA	Aa
a	Aa	aa

F_1: all tall F_2: ¾ are tall, and ¼ is short

33. B is correct.

Frameshift mutation is when 1 or 2 base pairs are added or deleted. A 3 base pair addition or deletion causes an *in-frame* mutation because 3 nucleotides encode each codon.

Frameshift mutation (i.e., addition/deletion of other than multiples of 3 nucleotides) causes the ribosome to read all downstream codons in the wrong frame. They usually result in truncated (i.e., *nonsense* mutation) or non-functional proteins (i.e., *missense* mutation).

An altered base pair (i.e., *point* mutation) is not a frameshift mutation because it substitutes (not adds or deletes) and does not cause the ribosome to read codons out of frame.

Point mutations can result in nonsense (i.e., premature stop codon) or missense (i.e., improperly folded protein) mutations.

Base pair additions/deletions (other than in multiples of 3) cause frameshift mutations.

34. D is correct.

Mendel's *law of independent assortment* states that the probability of a cross resulting in a genotype equals the *product* of individual probabilities.

Crosses by two heterozygous individuals for the three genes (A, B, and C) produce homozygous dominant offspring for each trait.

Each parent is heterozygous for A, genotype = Aa.

Ratio of offspring equals 1/4 AA, 1/2 Aa, and 1/4 aa; a typical 1:2:1 ratio for heterozygous crosses.

Parents are heterozygous for genes B and C, the probability of offspring being BB is 1/4, and CC is 1/4.

Probability that offspring are genotype AABBCC = *product of individual probabilities*:

$$1/4 \times 1/4 \times 1/4 = 1/64$$

35. B is correct.

Nonsense mutation is a DNA point mutation resulting in a premature stop codon in the transcribed mRNA and a truncated (i.e., incomplete) protein, usually nonfunctional.

Missense mutation is a point mutation where a nucleotide is changed and substitutes for a different amino acid.

Genetic disorders (sickle cell anemia, thalassemia, Duchenne muscular dystrophy) result from nonsense mutations.

36. B is correct.

Recessive trait is expressed when present in both copies or is the single copy (i.e., allele) of the gene.

A human Y chromosome confers maleness.

Recessive (single copy) alleles on the X are expressed (e.g., hemophilia).

Recessive X-linked allele is expressed in unaffected females with two (homozygous) alleles.

37. B is correct.

Mendelian *Laws of inheritance* explain patterns of disease transmission.

The inheritance patterns of single-gene diseases are *Mendelian* after Augustinian friar Gregor Mendel (1822-1884), who first reported the different patterns of gene segregation for specific traits of garden peas.

Mendel calculated *probabilities* of inheritance for traits in the next generations.

Most genes have more versions (i.e., alleles) because of mutations or polymorphisms.

Individuals can carry a normal, mutant, or rare allele, depending on mutation/polymorphism and allele frequency within a population.

Single-gene diseases are usually inherited in a pattern depending on gene location and whether one or two regular copies of the gene are needed for the disease to manifest (i.e., affected individuals).

Expression of the mutated allele is characterized as dominant, co-dominant, or recessive.

Five basic *patterns of inheritance for single-gene diseases*:

Autosomal dominant:

each affected person has an affected parent

manifests in each generation

Autosomal recessive:

parents of an affected person are carriers (i.e., unaffected)

typically, NOT seen in each generation

X-linked dominant:

females affected more frequently

can affect males and females in the same generation

X-linked recessive:

males affected more frequently

often affects males in each generation

Mitochondrial:

males and females can be affected but passed by females

can appear in each generation

Accurate family history is essential to determine an inheritance pattern when a family is affected by a disease.

38. A is correct.

Two traits are *unlinked* when inherited on separate chromosomes or because the genes are greater than 50 centimorgans. At large distances, double-crossing over occurs, and the genes appear unlinked.

39. B is correct.

Transduction involves a virus and is one of three methods (*conjugation* and *transformation*) that bacterial cells use to introduce genetic variability into their genomes.

Transduction is when a virus introduces novel genetic material while infecting its host.

Mitosis occurs in somatic cells for growth and repair, producing two identical diploid (2N) daughter cells.

40. D is correct.

Let T = tall and t = short; B = brown eyes and b = blue eyes.

Father is *homozygous tall* and *blue-eyed*; his genotype is TTbb.

Mother is *heterozygous tall* and *heterozygous brown-eyed*; her genotype is TtBb.

Determine the probability that parents produce a tall child with blue eyes (T_bb).

The genes for height and eye color are unlinked.

Father (TTbb) contributes T and b alleles, so his gametes have T and b alleles.

Mother (TtBb) contributes T or t and B or b, so her gametes are (in equal amounts): TB, tB, Tb, or tb.

Genotypes of the offspring: TTBb, TTbb, TtBb, Ttbb.

Half the offspring are tall and brown-eyed (T_B_), and half are tall and blue-eyed (T_bb).

Therefore, the probability of a tall child with blue eyes is ½.

A faster method is calculating phenotype ratios for height and eye color separately and then combining them.

Mating TT × Tt = 100% tall.

Mating Bb × Bb = ½ blue and ½ brown.

Multiplying 1 tall × ½ blue = ½ tall blue.

41. A is correct.

Recombination is the exchange of genetic information between homologous chromosomes and occurs during prophase I of meiosis.

Crossing over between non-sister homologs in meiosis results in a new combination of alleles (e.g., AB / ab can yield Ab / aB).

Recombination occurs in eukaryotes during mitosis but between sister chromatids which are copies (replicated during the S phase) and therefore do not lead to novel genotypes.

Recombination is a DNA repair mechanism between homologous chromosomes.

Research supports that recombination is not a random event.

Recombination *hotspots* include chromosome regions with high GC content and particular architecture (e.g., genome size, haploid chromosome number, chromosome size, and chromosome rearrangements).

Enzymes catalyze recombination (e.g., rec A, rec B, rec C, and rec D) by initiating and facilitating strand invasion and strand transfer during recombination.

High recombination frequency means the genes are *farther apart.*

Each percent frequency of recombination equals one map unit between the genes. So, 2.5% recombination frequency equals genes 2.5 map units apart.

Largest recombination frequency is 50% as if the genes were on different chromosomes (consistent with Mendel's Law of Independent Assortment).

Recombination frequency would be the same for *cis*- and *trans*-heterozygotes because the distance would be the same between the genes regardless of whether they are on the same chromosome (i.e., *cis*) or homologous chromosomes (*trans*).

B: *recombination frequency* is not a completely random event.

Specific regions within the chromosome have differences in the propensity to undergo recombination; the presence of *hotspots* and architectural features (e.g., histones) increase or decrease recombination frequencies.

C: recombination frequency increases (not decreases) with distance.

D: genes have different distances. Therefore, with different distances, the recombination frequency changes.

42. C is correct.

There are two possible alleles for each of the three genes.

If the genes assort independently (not linked), there are $2^3 = 8$ combinations.

43. A is correct.

Each affected person has an affected parent in the *autosomal dominant* inheritance pattern.

Autosomal dominant inheritance is a way a genetic trait can be passed from parent to child.

One copy of a mutated (changed) gene from one parent can cause the genetic condition. A child who has a parent with the mutated gene has a 50% chance of inheriting that mutated gene.

Men and women are equally likely to have mutations, and sons and daughters are equally likely to inherit them.

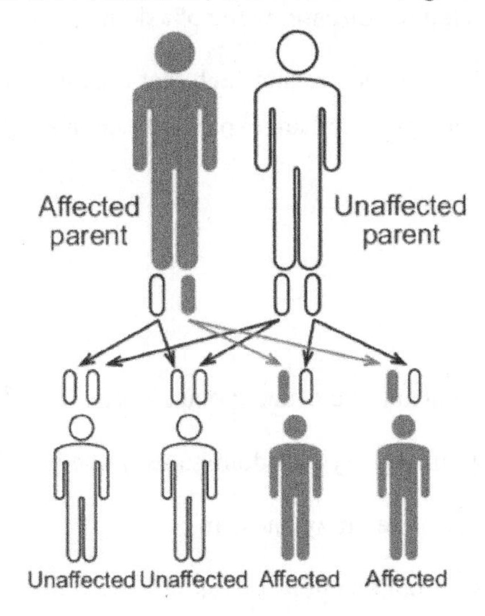

Autosomal dominant inheritance pattern with presence in each generation

44. C is correct.

Parents are Aa × Aa (carriers but not afflicted with the disease). Progeny could be AA, Aa, Aa, or aa.

From the Punnett square, eliminate aa because this is the disease state.

The question asks the probability that she is heterozygous (Aa) but not homozygous (AA) = 2/3.

45. C is correct.

Anticipation is associated with an earlier onset of symptoms and an increase in disease severity each generation.

Anticipation is observed in autosomal dominant diseases by trinucleotide repeat expansion (e.g., Huntington's disease, myotonic dystrophy) because triple repeats of increased length are unstable during cell division.

A: *codominance* is when a gene has more than one dominant allele. In the ABO blood group system, the I^A and I^B alleles are codominant.

Heterozygous individual for *two codominant alleles* expresses the phenotypes associated with both alleles.

Heterozygous individuals for the I^A and I^B alleles express the AB blood group phenotype, A- and B-type antigens are on the surface of red blood cells.

Codominance occurs at the locus for the beta-globin component of hemoglobin.

continued...

Three molecular phenotypes of Hb^A/Hb^A, Hb^A/Hb^S, and Hb^S/Hb^S are detectable by protein electrophoresis.

B: *penetrance* is the proportion of individuals carrying the variant of a gene (allele or genotype) and expressing the trait (phenotype).

In medical genetics, the penetrance of a disease-causing mutation is the proportion of individuals with the mutation who exhibit clinical symptoms.

For example, if a mutation in the gene responsible for an autosomal dominant disorder has 95% penetrance, 95% of those with the mutation develop the disease, while 5% do not.

D: *gain of function mutations* change the gene product such that it gains a new and abnormal function. These mutations usually have dominant phenotypes and are expressed with a single allele.

46. B is correct.

Hardy-Weinberg equation:

$$p^2 + 2pq + q^2 = 1$$

where p equals gene frequency of dominant allele, and q equals gene frequency of recessive allele

Hence, p^2 is the frequency of homozygous dominants in the population,

$2pq$ is the frequency of heterozygotes, and

q^2 is the frequency of homozygous recessives.

For a trait with two alleles, $p + q$ must equal 1 since the combined frequencies of the alleles = 100%.

If the frequency of the recessive allele for a trait is 0.6, $q = 0.6$.

Since $p + q = 1$

$p = 0.4$

To calculate the frequency of individuals expressing the dominant phenotype (not the dominant genotype), determine the number of individuals homozygous for the dominant trait (p^2) and add the number of heterozygotes ($2pq$) exhibiting the dominant phenotype:

$$p^2 = (0.4) \times (0.4)$$

$$p^2 = 0.16$$

$$2pq = 2 \times (0.6) \times (0.4)$$

$$2pq = 0.48$$

So, $p^2 + 2pq = 0.16 + 0.48$

$$p^2 + 2pq = 0.64$$

A: 0.48 = frequency of *heterozygous* individuals.

C: 0.16 = frequency of *homozygous dominant* individuals.

D: 0.36 = frequency of *homozygous recessive* individuals.

47. C is correct.

Maximum recombination frequency between two genes is 50%.

48. B is correct.

For a recessive trait to appear in a phenotype of an offspring (e.g., long hair), offspring inherit a recessive allele (Mendel called it *traits*) from each parent (i.e., two copies of the recessive gene).

Short-haired parents carry one copy (i.e., heterozygous) of the recessive long-haired allele (or *gene*).

Combined with the second copy from the other long-haired parent, it produced the long-haired offspring.

49. D is correct.

Meiosis in males produces four haploid (1N) unique cells genetically different from the parental cell.

50. C is correct.

The 3 pyrimidines are cytosine, and thymine (uracil replaces thymine in RNA).

The word pyrimidine contains "**y**" as do the nucleotides, pyrimidines.

Pyrimidines (longer word than purine) are one-ring structures, while purines (shorter word) are adenine and guanine, larger structures with two rings.

51. D is correct.

Point mutations occur when a single nucleotide base (A, C, G, T) is substituted by another.

Silent mutation is a point mutation that 1) occurs in a noncoding region or 2) does not change the amino acid sequence due to the degeneracy of the genetic code.

Frameshift mutation is an insertion or deletion of some nucleotides. These mutations severely affect the coded protein since nucleotides are read as triplets.

The addition or loss of nucleotides (except in multiples of three) changes the reading frame of the mRNA and often gives rise to premature polypeptide termination (i.e., nonsense mutation).

Missense mutation results from the insertion of a single nucleotide that changes the amino acid sequence of the specified polypeptide.

52. D is correct.

Two reciprocal crossing-over events appear in the progeny at an approximate ratio of 1:1.

53. C is correct.

EEBB × eebb produces offspring of single genotype EeBb, as determined by the Punnett square for the cross between a homozygous dominant by a homozygous recessive.

54. D is correct.

Mutations may cause premature translation termination (i.e., *nonsense* mutation) and nonfunctional protein.

55. D is correct.

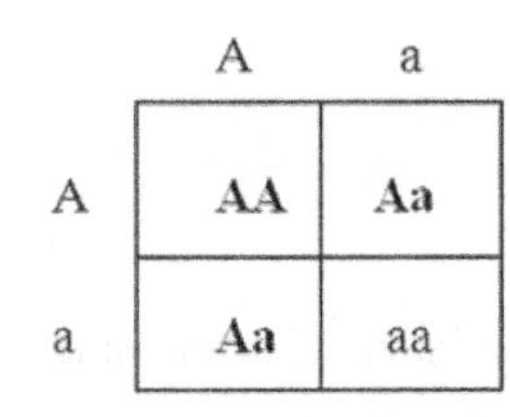

	A	a
A	AA	Aa
a	Aa	aa

Afflicted children are AA, Aa or Aa (not aa) = 3 of 4 possibilities = ¾ or 75%.

56. D is correct.

Recombinant frequencies of linked genes map the relative locations of genes on a single chromosome.

Recombinant frequencies are determined by crossing individuals that differ in alleles for the genes in question and then determining the genotypes of their progeny.

Recombinant frequencies equal frequencies of nonparent genotypes since these genotypes arise by crossover.

Mapping is based on the *probability* of a crossover between two points; the probability of crossover *increases* as the distance between the genes *increases.*

Farther away, genes have a *greater* recombinant frequency.

The probability that two genes are inherited together (i.e., linked) *decreases* as the distance between them on a chromosome *increases.*

One map unit = 1% recombination frequency, and recombinant frequencies are (roughly) additive.

However, if the genes are far apart, the recombination frequency reaches a maximum of 50%, at which point the genes are considered to be sorted independently.

There are four genes (D, E, F, and G), and the recombinant frequencies between each pair are given.

To construct the map, start with the allele pair with the highest recombinant frequency: between G and E (23%), which means that G and E are 23 map units apart and on the two ends.

Determine the intervening genes by finding the genes closest to the two endpoints.

G and D are 8 map units apart, closest to G. Thus, D must be next to G.

Genes on this chromosome must be G, D, F, and E by elimination.

EFDG is equally correct if the map started from the opposite direction, but this is not an answer choice.

To verify, D and E are 15 map units apart because the distance from G to D, which is 8, plus the distance from D to E, which is 15, is the distance from G to E, which equals 23.

G and F are 15 map units apart, while F and E are 8 units apart.

The numbers add, whereby the distance from G to E equals G to D + the distance from D to E.

The observed numbers may be off by one or two map units (not a mistake) because map distances are roughly additive (i.e., based on rounding for the probabilities).

Questions **57** through **63** are based on the following:

The pedigree illustrated by the schematic shows the inheritance of albinism, a homozygous recessive condition manifested in a total lack of pigment. Specify the genotypes using *A* and *a* to indicate dominant and recessive alleles.

Note: solids are albino individuals.

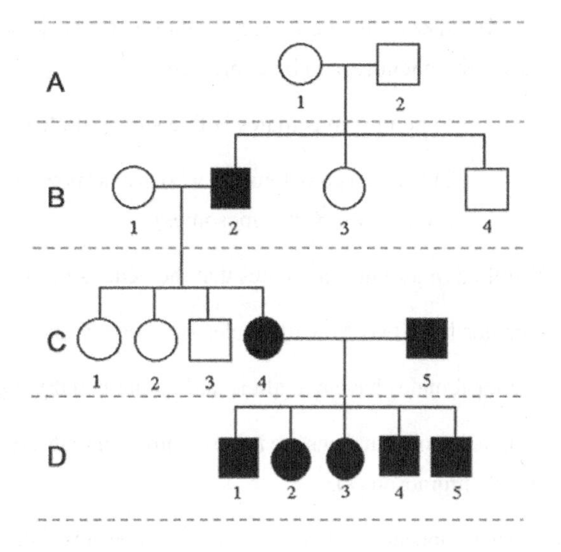

57. C is correct.

Individual A-1 in the pedigree is *Aa.*

58. C is correct.

Individual A-2 in the pedigree is *Aa.*

59. C is correct.

Individual B-1 in the pedigree is *Aa.*

60. B is correct.

Individual B-2 in the pedigree is *aa.*

61. C is correct.

Individual C-3 in the pedigree is *Aa.*

62. B is correct.

Individual C-4 in the pedigree is *aa.*

63. B is correct.

Individual D-4 in the pedigree is *aa.*

64. B is correct.

BBss × bbss produces gametes Bbss.

Crossed:

Bbss × Bbss and produce the four gametes:

BBss, Bbss, bBss and bbss

Phenotypically,

¾ (BBss, Bbss, bBss) are black and spotted

¼ (bbss) is red and spotted

65. A is correct.

X-linked recessive inheritance is a mode of inheritance whereby a mutation in a gene on the X chromosome causes the phenotype to be expressed

1) hemizygous males with a single allele of the mutation because they have one X chromosome and

2) homozygous females who are homozygous for the mutation (i.e., a copy of the gene mutation on each of two X chromosomes).

X-linked inheritance indicates that the gene is on the X chromosome.

Females have two X, while males have one X and one Y.

Carrier females have one allele and do not usually express the phenotype.

X-linked gene mutations are more common in males (i.e., a single allele of the X chromosome) than in females (i.e., two X chromosomes).

The gene appears to *alternate generations* because heterozygous phenotypically normal females transmit it.

Affected males transmit the gene to their daughters, carriers for the trait.

There is no father-to-son transmission because the sons inherit the father's Y chromosome.

Males carrying the mutant gene show the trait.

66. C is correct.

X-inactivation (i.e., lyonization) is when one of two X chromosomes in female mammals is inactivated.

Inactive X chromosome is silenced by transcriptional inactivity within heterochromatin (i.e., condensed DNA).

Females have two X chromosomes, and X-inactivation prevents them from having twice as many X chromosome gene products as males (XY) for dosage compensation of the X chromosome.

The choice of which X chromosome becomes inactivated is random in humans.

Once an X chromosome is inactivated, it remains inactive throughout life and in descendants.

Calico and tortoiseshell-colored cats are phenotypic examples of X-inactivation because the alleles for black and orange fur coloration reside on the X chromosome.

Inactivation of an X chromosome carries one gene resulting in the fur color of the allele for the active gene.

Calico cats are almost always female because the X chromosome determines the color of the cat, and female cats (like all female mammals) have two X chromosomes.

Male mammals have one X and one Y chromosome.

Y chromosome does not have color genes; there is no probability that a male cat could have orange and non-orange.

One prominent exception is when, in rare cases, a male has XXY chromosomes (Klinefelter syndrome).

67. D is correct.

Autosomal dominance is typical Mendelian inheritance.

Individuals need a single copy of the mutant gene to exhibit the disease for *autosomal dominant* traits.

Autosomal dominance usually,

equal numbers of males and females affected

traits do not skip generations

father-to-son transmission

68. B is correct.

Deleting a portion of the Y chromosome containing the testis-determining factor results in some XY individuals being phenotypically female.

69. B is correct.

Catastrophic events do *not* cause significant genetic drift to large homogeneous populations.

Emigration, selective predation, and mutation affect the Hardy-Weinberg equilibrium.

70. C is correct.

Inbreeding exposes recessive alleles by increasing *homozygosity* by one allele from each parent.

Closely related individuals are likely to carry alleles of recessive genes and have an increased probability of passing recessive alleles to their offspring.

71. D is correct.

Polyploidy refers to a numerical change in a full set of chromosomes.

Most eukaryotic organisms are diploid (2N) with two sets of chromosomes – one set inherited from each parent.

Polyploid cells and organisms contain more than two paired (i.e., homologous) sets of chromosomes.

If crossing two species is not possible because of differences in ploidy level, polyploids can be used as a bridge for gene transfer.

Additionally, polyploidy reduces fertility due to meiotic errors, allowing the cultivation of seedless varieties.

Polyploidy is in some organisms and is especially common in plants.

In addition, polyploidy occurs in some tissues of animals that are otherwise diploid (e.g., human muscle tissues).

72. C is correct.

Transgenesis introduces an exogenous gene (or *transgene*) into an organism to exhibit a new characteristic transmitted to its offspring.

Hybrid typically refers to the offspring of distinct species from interbreeding between two animals (or plants).

73. A is correct.

Genetic marker is a gene or DNA sequence with a known location on a chromosome used to identify individuals. It can be a variation that results from mutation or alteration in the genomic loci.

A genetic marker may be a short DNA sequence, such as a sequence surrounding a single base-pair change (single nucleotide polymorphism – SNP) or a long one (e.g., minisatellites).

74. D is correct.

Plasmid is a small circular DNA molecule separate from chromosomal DNA within a cell and can replicate independently.

In nature, plasmids carry genes that may benefit the organism's survival (e.g., antibiotic resistance in bacteria) and can be transmitted among bacteria, even of another species.

Artificial plasmids are commonly used as vectors in molecular cloning to confer antibiotic resistance and drive the replication of recombinant DNA sequences within host organisms.

75. C is correct.

Transformation is "horizontal gene transfer" when foreign genes transfer among bacteria.

In transformation, foreign DNA is taken *from the medium* and incorporated directly through the cell membrane.

Transformation depends on the recipient bacterium, which must be in a state of natural or artificial competence to take up exogenous genetic material.

Two other mechanisms for *horizontal gene transfer* are *conjugation* (i.e., genetic material between bacteria in direct contact) and *transduction* (i.e., injection of exogenous DNA by a bacteriophage into the host bacterium).

76. D is correct.

Plasmid is a small circular DNA separate from chromosomal DNA within a cell and replicates independently.

Commonly as small, circular, double-stranded DNA molecules in bacteria, plasmids are sometimes in archaea and eukaryotic organisms.

In nature, plasmids carry genes that may benefit the organism's survival (e.g., antibiotic resistance in bacteria) and can be transmitted among bacteria, even of another species.

Artificial plasmids are commonly used as vectors in molecular cloning to drive the replication of recombinant DNA sequences within host organisms.

77. B is correct.

Restriction enzymes are *endonucleases* that cut DNA at specific *internal sequences*, usually inverted repeat sequences (i.e., palindromes that read the same if the DNA strand is rotated 180°).

78. B is correct.

Restriction enzymes cut DNA at specific sequences.

In the examples, the endonuclease (i.e., enzyme cutting within the strand) cleaves double-stranded DNA (dsDNA) between the nucleotides adenosine (A) and guanine (G) palindrome sequences.

The sticky ends are overhangs of TTAA as reading 5' to 3' (by convention, reading top strand left to right).

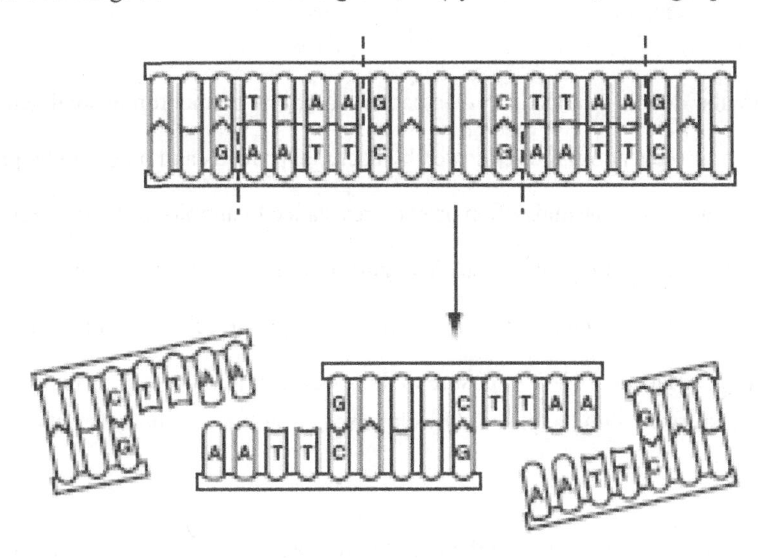

79. A is correct.

Recombinant DNA is nucleotides formed in the laboratory through genetic recombination (e.g., molecular cloning) to combine genetic material from multiple sources, creating sequences, not in biological organisms.

Recombinant DNA is possible because DNA molecules from organisms share the same chemical structure. They differ in the nucleotide sequence within that identical overall structure.

80. C is correct.

Yeasts are eukaryotic model systems for molecular biology studies as they exhibit fast growth and have dispersed cells. They have a well-defined genetic system and a versatile DNA transformation system that can be utilized for protein production.

Transformation is when exogenous DNA is introduced into a cell, resulting in an inheritable change or genetic modification, as first reported in *Streptococcus pneumoniae* by Griffith in 1928.

Principle of *DNA transformation* was demonstrated by Avery *et al.* in 1944.

Budding yeast *Saccharomyces cerevisiae* was first successfully transformed in 1978.

Plasmids are prokaryotic (i.e., bacteria) and do *not* undergo post-translational modification (i.e., removal of introns and ligating exons). Plasmids are smaller strands of nucleotides than eukaryotic chromosomes.

Yeast artificial chromosome (YAC) is a human-engineered DNA molecule used to clone deoxynucleic acid sequences in yeast cells.

YACs are engineered with DNA segments of one million base pairs used for mapping and sequencing genomes.

81. B is correct.

Transgenesis introduces an exogenous gene – a transgene – into an organism so that the organism develops a new characteristic and transmits it to offspring.

Hybrid in genetics has several meanings, the most common of which is the offspring resulting from the interbreeding between two animals or plants of distinct species.

82. A is correct.

Plasmids are small circular double-stranded DNA in bacteria carrying extrachromosomal genetic information.

Plasmids (with an origin of replication) are replicated by bacterial proteins and inherited by progeny.

The proteins encoded by genes on plasmids often provide resistance to antibiotics by degrading the antibiotic.

Through recombinant DNA technology, plasmids are engineered to carry other genes not typically in bacteria.

Plasmids are introduced by *transforming* bacterial cells (i.e., through the cell wall and plasma membrane.

After transformation (i.e., uptake of DNA), exposure to the specific antibiotic (e.g., penicillin) allows the selection of bacteria transformed with the plasmid by clone selection (i.e., antibody-resistant clones).

83. D is correct.

Dolly, the sheep, was cloned in 1996 by fusing the nucleus from a mammary gland cell of a Finn Dorset ewe into an enucleated egg cell from a Scottish Blackface ewe.

During gestation, Dolly was carried to term in the uterus of another Scottish Blackface ewe.

She was a genetic copy of the Finn Dorset ewe from the somatic mammary gland cell.

Dolly's creation showed that somatic (i.e., body cell) cell DNA in a differentiated (*vs. pluripotent* or *totipotent*) could be induced through nuclear transfer (i.e., transplantation) to expand developmental fate (e.g., like a germ cell) in progression from a zygote.

84. C is correct.

Transformation (i.e., introducing foreign DNA into cells) is successful when foreign DNA is integrated into another organism's genome.

Once integrated, it replicates and divides with the host cell.

85. C is correct.

Disease- and drought-resistant plants require fewer environmental resources (e.g., water, fertilizer) and fewer pesticides. Increased supply of food with reduced cost and longer shelf life.

The potential development of allergens and toxicity in GM-related crops is GMO risks for humans. However, studies show GM crops have increased yield and nutritional value.

86. A is correct.

Gene therapy focuses on genetically modifying cells to produce a therapeutic effect (or the treatment of disease) by repairing or reconstructing defective genetic material.

87. B is correct.

DNA profiling (or *genetic fingerprinting*) is a laboratory technique to identify individuals by their DNA profiles.

DNA profiles are deoxyribose nucleotide bases (i.e., DNA used for identification.

Genetic fingerprinting (or DNA *profiling*) is used in paternity testing and criminal investigation.

It differs from complete genome sequencing (e.g., human genome project).

About 99.9% of human DNA sequences are the same.

DNA profiling distinguishes individuals with a high probability of certainty unless they are monozygotic (i.e., identical twins).

Notes for active learning

Genetics and Reproduction – Detailed Explanations

1. B is correct.

Gametes form via *meiosis* and are double-stranded haploids. A single chromosome consists of two hydrogen-bonded complementary DNA strands.

2. A is correct.

Oogenesis produces one viable egg and (up to) three polar bodies resulting from the cytoplasm's unequal distribution during meiosis.

Gametes (e.g., egg and sperm) become haploid (1N) through reductive division (i.e., meiosis), in which a diploid cell (2N) gives rise to four haploid sperm or one haploid egg and (up to) three polar bodies.

B: *interstitial cells* are stimulated by luteinizing hormone (LH) to produce testosterone which, along with FSH, stimulates sperm development within the seminiferous tubules.

C: follicle-stimulating hormone (FSH) stimulates the eggs to develop in follicles within the ovaries.

D: follicle-stimulating hormone (FSH) is involved in gamete production for males and females.

3. C is correct.

Let C designate wild-type and c designate the color bind allele.

Mother is Cc, and the father is CY (a normal allele with a single copy of the X gene).

From mating, the mother's gamete (as a carrier due to her dad) is C or c, with a 50% probability of the gamete inheriting the C or c allele.

Assuming a boy (i.e., the father transmits Y and not X), the father's allele of Y (boy) is 100%, and the probability of the mother passing a c (colorblind) is 50%.

Probability of a son being color blind is 50% or ½.

If the question had asked, "what is the probability that they will have a color-blind child?" the analysis changes to determine the probability for all children (not just boys in the original question).

Gametes produced by the mother are C and c with a 50% probability each.

Affected child is a boy.

What is the probability that the father passes the X or Y gene to the offspring? Here, the probability is 50%.

Individual event probabilities are multiplied to determine the overall probability:

$$\frac{1}{2} \times \frac{1}{2} = \frac{1}{4}$$

4. C is correct.

Primary oocytes are arrested in meiotic prophase I from birth until ovulation within the ovaries.

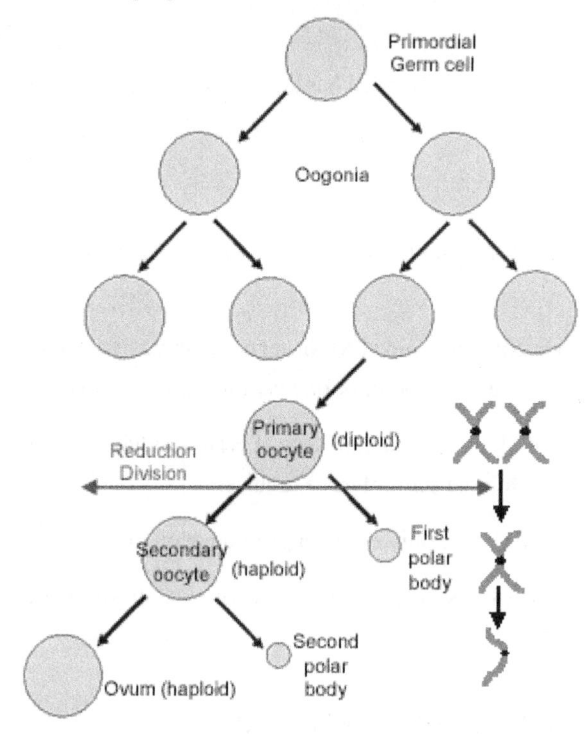

Diploid primordial germ cell undergoes two rounds of meiosis to form haploid ovum and polar bodies

5. C is correct.

Seminiferous tubules are in the testes and are the site of sperm production.

Spermatozoa are the mature male gametes in many sexually reproducing organisms.

Spermatogenesis is how spermatozoa are produced from male primordial germ cells through mitosis and meiosis.

The initial cells in this pathway are spermatogonia, which yield 1° spermatocytes by mitosis.

The 1° spermatocyte divides via meiosis into two 2° spermatocytes.

Meiosis converts 1° spermatocyte (2N) into four spermatids (1N).

2° spermatocytes complete meiosis by dividing into two spermatids as mature spermatozoa (i.e., sperm cells).

1° spermatocyte gives rise to two 2° spermatocytes that, by further meiosis, produce four spermatozoa.

Seminiferous tubules are in the testes and the location of meiosis and subsequent creation of gametes (e.g., spermatozoa for males or ova for females).

The epithelium of the tubule consists of Sertoli cells whose primary function is to nourish the developing sperm cells through the stages of spermatogenesis.

Sertoli cells act as phagocytes, consuming the residual cytoplasm during spermatogenesis.

Spermatogenic cells differentiate between the Sertoli cells, which differentiate through meiosis into sperm cells.

6. C is correct.

Human cell after the first meiotic division is 1N with 2 chromatids.

7. D is correct.

Anterior pituitary secretes *follicle-stimulating hormone* (FSH) and *luteinizing hormone* (LH), influencing the maturation of follicles.

Follicle-stimulating hormone (FSH) stimulates the maturation of gametes (e.g., ova and spermatids).

Follicle-stimulating hormone (FSH) stimulates estrogen production, which aids in maturing the primary follicle.

Luteinizing (LH) stimulates ovulation and development of the corpus luteum; the mature corpus luteum secretes progesterone, causing the uterine lining to thicken and become vascular in preparation for implantation of the fertilized egg (i.e., zygote).

8. D is correct.

Genetic recombination is when two DNA strand molecules exchange genetic information (i.e., a base composition within the nucleotides), resulting in new combinations of alleles (i.e., alternative forms of genes).

In eukaryotes, the natural process of genetic recombination during meiosis (i.e., the formation of gametes – eggs and sperm) results in genetic information passed to progeny.

Genetic recombination in eukaryotes involves pairing homologous chromosomes (i.e., a set of maternal and paternal chromosomes), which may involve nucleotide exchange between the chromosomes.

The information exchange may occur without physical exchange when a section of genetic material is duplicated without a change in the donating chromosome or by breaking and rejoining the DNA strands (i.e., forming new molecules of DNA).

Mitosis may involve recombination, where two sister chromosomes form after DNA replication. New combinations of alleles are often not produced because the sister chromosomes are usually identical.

In meiosis and mitosis, recombination occurs between similar DNA molecules (homologous chromosomes or sister chromatids, respectively).

In meiosis, non-sister (i.e., same parent) homologous chromosomes pair with each other, and recombination often occurs between non-sister homologs.

For somatic cells (i.e., undergo mitosis) and gametes (i.e., undergo meiosis), recombination between homologous chromosomes or sister chromatids is a common DNA repair mechanism.

9. C is correct.

Primary oocytes (2N cells) are arrested in prophase I of meiosis I until puberty. There is additional development into secondary oocytes that occurs prior to ovulation.

After ovulation, the oocyte is arrested in *metaphase of meiosis II* until fertilization.

10. B is correct.

Pseudoautosomal regions are named because any genes within them are inherited, like autosomal genes. Pseudoautosomal regions allow males to pair and segregate X and Y chromosomes during meiosis.

Males have two copies of genes: one in the pseudoautosomal region of their Y chromosome and the other in their X chromosome's corresponding portion.

Typical females possess two copies of pseudoautosomal genes, as each X chromosome contains pseudoautosomal regions.

Crossing over (during prophase I) between X and Y chromosomes is usually restricted to pseudoautosomal regions.

Pseudoautosomal genes exhibit an *autosomal*, rather than sex-linked, inheritance pattern.

Females can inherit an allele initially on the Y chromosome of their father, and males can inherit an allele initially on the X chromosome of their father.

11. B is correct.

Primary spermatocytes have completed synthesis (S phase) of interphase but not the first meiotic division and are diploid (2N) with 46 chromosomes (i.e., 23 pairs).

12. B is correct.

Chromosomes (not chromatids) segregate during mitosis to produce identical somatic (body) 2N (diploid) cells from the parental cell. Meiosis is the process for germline cells (i.e., egg, sperm).

Mutations are inheritable changes in the cell's genetic (DNA) material; recombination occurs during prophase I (at the chiasma of the tetrad) of meiosis, and homologous chromosomes segregate during meiosis I.

During meiosis I, homologous chromosomes are separated. Subsequently, during meiosis II, the sister chromatids separate to produce four 1N (haploid) products, each with half the number of chromosomes as the original cell.

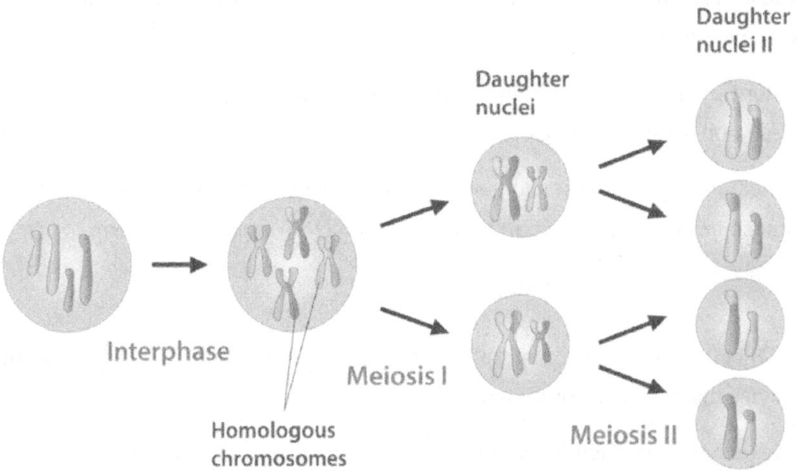

Chromosomes replicate in S phase of mitosis to produce homologous chromosomes. Meiosis I daughter cells are diploid (2N), while the gametes formed from meiosis II (reductive phase) are haploid (1N).

13. C is correct.

In females, *secondary oocytes are haploid* (i.e., a single copy of 23 chromosomes, each with a pair of chromatids). They do not complete meiosis II (i.e., haploid with a single chromatid) until fertilized by a sperm.

Each month during puberty, *one primary oocyte* (i.e., diploid, each with a pair of chromatids) completes meiosis I to produce a *secondary oocyte* (1N) and a *polar body* (1N).

1N secondary oocyte (i.e., 23 chromosomes each with a pair of chromatids) is expelled as an ovum from the follicle during ovulation, but meiosis II does not occur until fertilization.

A: *menarche* is marked by the onset of menstruation and signals the possibility of fertility.

B: *menstruation* is sloughing off the endometrial lining of the uterus during the monthly hormonal cycle.

D: *menopause* is when menstruation ceases.

14. D is correct.

Klinefelter syndrome describes the symptoms from additional X genetic material in males.

A: *Turner syndrome* is the condition in females with a single X (monosomy X) chromosome.

B: *XYY syndrome* is a genetic condition in which a human male has an extra male (Y) chromosome, giving 47 chromosomes instead of 46.

47 XYY is not inherited but usually occurs during the formation of sperm cells.

Nondisjunction error during anaphase II (meiosis II) results in sperms with an extra Y chromosome.

If an atypical sperm contributes to genetic makeup, the child has an extra Y chromosome in each somatic cell.

C: *Triple X syndrome* is not inherited but usually occurs during the formation of gametes (e.g., ovum and sperm) because nondisjunction in cell division results in reproductive cells with additional chromosomes.

During cell division, errors (non-disjunction) can result in gametes with additional chromosomes.

An egg or a sperm may gain an extra X chromosome due to non-disjunction, and if one gamete contributes to the zygote, the child will have an extra X chromosome in each cell.

15. C is correct.

In males, diploid spermatogonia (2N) cells undergo meiosis I to produce 1° diploid spermatocyte (2N), which undergoes meiosis II to yield 2° haploid spermatocytes (1N).

2° spermatocytes undergo meiosis II to produce four spermatids (1N) that mature into spermatozoa (i.e., sperm).

In females, 1° oocyte is (2N), whereby the 2° oocyte undergoes the second meiotic division to produce two (1N) cells – a mature oocyte (i.e., ovum – female gamete) and another polar body.

A: *primary oocyte* is diploid (2N).

During fertilization, a (1N) ovum and a (1N) sperm fuse to produce a (2N) zygote.

B: *spermatogonium* is a diploid (2N) cell.

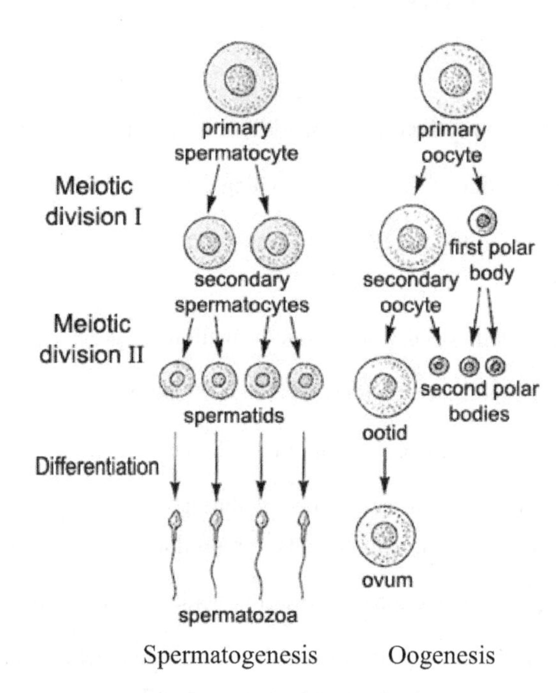

Diploid primary oocytes and oocytes undergo two rounds of meiosis forming haploid spermatozoa and ovum

16. D is correct.

The probability that a child will be male (or female) is ½.

Each event is *independent*; the first (or second or third) child does *not* affect future events.

The probability for 4 children is:

$$\tfrac{1}{2} \times \tfrac{1}{2} \times \tfrac{1}{2} \times \tfrac{1}{2} = 1/16$$

The same probability would be that the first and third child is female, with the second and fourth as male (or another combination).

17. D is correct.

Unequal division of cytoplasm occurs during the meiotic process of oogenesis (i.e., production of an egg cell). Meiotic divisions occur in two stages.

First stage produces precursor (2N) cells when a daughter cell (precursor egg) receives most of the cytoplasm; the other is devoid of sufficient cytoplasm (but genetically identical) and a nonfunctioning polar body.

In the second division of oogenesis, the large (2N) daughter cell divides again, and again one (1N) daughter cell receives the most cytoplasm (i.e., putative *ovum*).

The other daughter eggs become small nonfunctional (1N) *polar bodies.*

The polar body (from meiosis I) may divide (via meiosis II) to form two nonfunctional (1N) polar bodies. The result is a potential of four (1N) cells.

However, only one—the one with a greater amount of cytoplasm during each meiotic division—becomes a functional egg (i.e., ovum) cell along with (up to) three (1N) polar bodies.

A: *bacterial cells* divide for reproduction, and cytoplasmic division is equal.

B: *mitosis of kidney* cells distributes cytoplasm equally.

C: *spermatogenesis* is when one (2N) precursor cell forms four functional (1N) sperm cells because both meiosis divisions are equal and contain an equal amount of cytoplasm.

18. B is correct.

Dyneins are motor proteins (or *molecular motors*) using ATP to perform movement as *retrograde transport.*

Dynein transports cellular contents by *walking* along cytoskeletal microtubules towards the minus-end of the microtubules, usually oriented towards the cell center (i.e., *minus-end directed motors.*)

Kinesins are motor proteins that move toward the *plus-end* of the microtubules (i.e., *plus-end directed motors*).

Ovulation is the phase of the female menstrual cycle. A partially mature ovum that has yet to complete meiosis II is released from the ovarian follicles into the Fallopian tube (i.e., oviduct).

After ovulation, the egg can be fertilized by sperm during the *luteal phase.*

Ovulation is determined by circulating hormone levels and is not affected by a defect in dynein motor proteins.

A: *lungs* require cilia to remove bacteria and other particulates.

C: a male with Kartagener's syndrome would be *infertile due to sperm immobility.*

D: *ova* would not typically enter the Fallopian tubes (i.e., oviduct) because of the lack of cilia, which would cause an increased risk of ectopic pregnancy.

19. D is correct.

DNA replication occurs during the synthesis (S) phase of interphase (i.e., G1, S, G2) to form sister chromatids joined by the centromere.

Replication occurs during the S phase (i.e., interphase) of the cell cycle.

Transcription (in the nucleus) and *translation* (in the cytoplasm) occur during the S phase.

20. A is correct.

During meiosis, the gamete (e.g., ovum and sperm) reduces its genetic component from diploid (2N) to haploid (1N) with half the typical chromosome number for somatic (i.e., body cells).

When a haploid egg and sperm unite, they form a diploid zygote.

Ova contains an X chromosome, while sperm contains an X or a Y chromosome.

Gametes form in meiosis (i.e., two reduction divisions) without intervening chromosome replication.

During prophase I of meiosis I, tetrads form, and sister chromatids (i.e., a chromosome replicated in a prior S phase) undergo homologous recombination as *crossing over*.

Crossing over increases genetic variance within the progeny and is a driving force in the evolution of a species.

21. C is correct.

X-linked dominance is a mode of inheritance whereby a dominant gene is on the X chromosome.

X-linked dominant is less common than X-linked recessive.

For X-linked dominant inheritance, one allele is sufficient to cause the disorder when inherited from a parent who has the disorder.

X-linked dominant traits do not necessarily affect males more than females (unlike X-linked recessive traits).

An affected father has all affected daughters but no affected sons (unless the mother is also affected).

22. B is correct.

Meiosis is cell division in sexually reproducing eukaryotes (animals, plants, and fungi), whereby the chromosome number is reduced by half, resulting in four genetically distinct haploid daughters.

DNA replication is followed by mitosis and *two rounds of cell division* in meiosis to produce four (1N) cells.

The two rounds of meiotic divisions are Meiosis I and Meiosis II.

Meiosis I is a *reductive division*, as the cells are reduced from diploid (2N) to haploid (1N).

Meiosis II (only G phase separates I and II) is an *equational division*, as the cells begin and end as haploids.

23. C is correct.

During prophase I, the *chromatin condenses* into chromosomes, the centrioles migrate to the poles, the spindle fibers begin to form, and the nucleoli and nuclear membrane disappear.

Homologous chromosomes physically pair and intertwine in the process of *synapsis*.

During prophase I, chromatids (i.e., a strand of the replicated chromosome) of homologous chromosomes break and exchange equivalent pieces of DNA via crossing over.

A: in anaphase I, homologous chromosomes separate and are pulled by the spindle fibers to opposite cell poles.

Disjunction (i.e., separation of homologous chromosomes) is essential for segregation, as described by Mendel.

B: in telophase I, a nuclear membrane forms around each new nucleus, and chromosomes consist of sister chromatids joined at the centromere.

Cells divide into two daughter cells, each receiving a haploid nucleus (1N) of chromosomes.

D: in metaphase I, homologous pairs align at the equatorial plane, and each pair attaches to a separate spindle fiber by its kinetochore (i.e., protein collar around the centromere of the chromosome).

24. D is correct.

Crossing over occurs during prophase I of meiosis.

Recombination occurs at the chiasma (physical contact) of the tetrad (two sets of sister chromatids).

Homologous chromosomes segregate during meiosis I.

25. A is correct.

In prophase I, *tetrads form*, genetic recombination occurs, and the spindle apparatus forms.

Chromosomes migrate to the poles of the cell during anaphase from the splitting of the centromere.

26. A is correct.

Spermatogenesis and *oogenesis* are *gametogenesis*.

Haploid (1N) gametes (i.e., ova and sperm) are produced by diploid (2N) cell reductive divisions (i.e., meiosis).

Spermatogenesis occurs in the gonads, whereby the cytoplasm equally divides during meiosis with the production of four viable sperm 1N cells.

Oogenesis occurs in the gonads, whereby the cytoplasm divides unequally. One 1N ovum (e.g., egg) receives the bulk of the cytoplasm and (up to) three additional 1N polar bodies.

The polar bodies contain a 1N genome (like sperm and egg) but lack sufficient cytoplasm for a viable gamete.

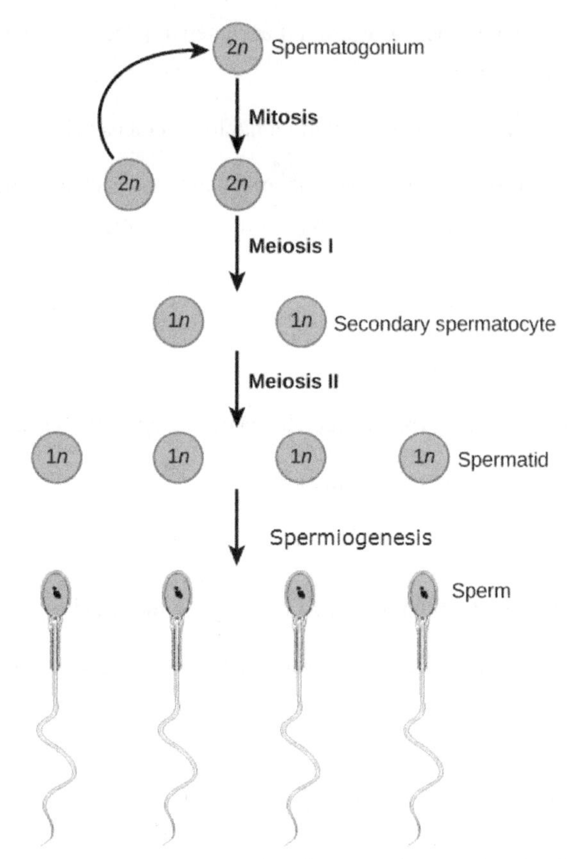

Diploid primary oocytes and oocytes undergo two rounds of meiosis forming haploid spermatozoa and ovum

27. B is correct.

Barr body is the inactive X chromosome in a female somatic cell rendered inactive by *lyonization* for species in which sex is determined by the Y chromosomes (i.e., humans and other species).

Lyon hypothesis states that cells with multiple X chromosomes inactivate all but one X randomly during mammalian embryogenesis.

In humans with more than one X chromosome, the number of Barr bodies visible at interphase is one less than the total number of X chromosomes.

For example, a man with Klinefelter syndrome of 47, XXY karyotype has a single Barr body.

A woman with a 47, XXX karyotype has two Barr bodies.

28. A is correct.

Polar bodies form in females as 1N, nonfunctional cells during meiosis.

Meiosis is a two-stage process whereby a 2N cell undergoes a reduction division to form two 1N cells.

Each 1N cell forms two 1N cells for four 1N cells from a parental 2N germ cell in the *second meiotic* division.

For sperm cells, four functional, unique 1N gamete sperm cells form.

For egg cells, the first meiotic division involves an *unequal division of cytoplasm* that results in one large cell and one small cell (i.e., the first polar body).

The large cell divides (second meiotic division) to generate *one functional egg* (1N ovum containing most of the cytoplasm) and another polar body.

First polar body divides again to form two other polar bodies. One large ovum (i.e., functional egg cell) and three polar bodies form during a female meiotic division.

Polar bodies form in mitosis, which is how somatic (i.e., body cells) cell divisions occur; equal cells do not form gametes (i.e., germline cells).

29. A is correct.

Turner syndrome (i.e., 45, X) describes several conditions in females, of which monosomy X (i.e., the absence of the entire sex (X) chromosome, the Barr body) is the most common.

Turner syndrome is a chromosomal abnormality when all or part of a sex chromosome is absent or abnormal.

Notes for active learning

Development – Detailed Explanations

1. A is correct.

Respiratory exchanges during fetal life occur through the *placenta*.

Placenta connects the developing fetus to the uterine wall and allows nutrient uptake, waste elimination, and gas exchange via the mother's blood supply.

Umbilical cord connects the developing embryo (or fetus) and the placenta. During prenatal development, the umbilical cord is physiologically and genetically part of the fetus and contains two arteries (the umbilical arteries) and one vein (the umbilical vein).

Umbilical vein supplies the fetus with oxygenated, nutrient-rich blood from the placenta. Conversely, the fetal heart pumps deoxygenated, nutrient-depleted blood through the umbilical arteries back to the placenta.

Fetal circulatory systems change at birth as the newborn uses its lungs. After the infant's first breath, the newborn's cardiovascular system constricts the *ductus arteriosus* (i.e., connects the pulmonary artery to the aorta) and converts it to the ligamentum arteriosum. Resistance in the pulmonary blood vessels decreases, increasing blood flow to the lungs.

At birth, umbilical blood flow ceases, and blood pressure in the inferior *vena cava* decreases, causing a decrease in pressure in the *right atrium*. The *left atrial pressure* increases due to increased blood flow from the lungs. Increased left atrial pressure, coupled with decreased right atrial pressure, causes *closure* of the *foramen ovale*.

Ductus venosus, which shunts blood from the left umbilical vein directly to the inferior vena cava to allow oxygenated blood from the placenta to bypass the liver, completely closes within three months after birth.

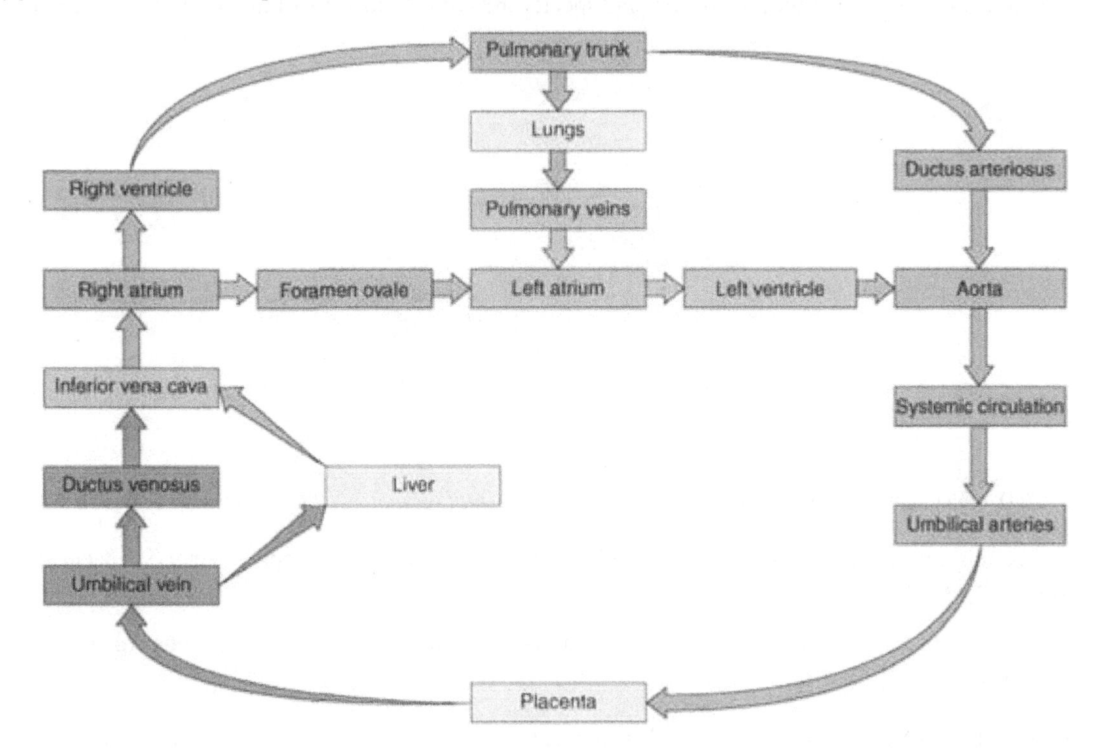

Adult and fetal circulatory system with ductus arteriosus and ductus venosus providing shunt pathways

2. D is correct.

Indeterminate cleavage results in cells that maintain the ability to develop into a complete organism.

A: *zygote implantation* into the uterus causes cell migration transforming the blastula from a single-cell layer into a three-layered gastrula (i.e., ectoderm, mesoderm, and endoderm).

B: *blastulation* begins when the morula develops the blastocoel as a fluid-filled cavity that (by the fourth day) becomes the blastula as a hollow sphere of cells.

C: *determinate cleavage* results in cells whose differentiation potentials are determined early in development.

3. B is correct.

Mutations in *Drosophila,* transforming one body segment into a different one, are in homeotic genes.

Homeotic genes encode the related homeodomain protein involved in developmental patterns and sequences.

Hox genes are *homeotic transcription factors* that play a crucial role in controlling the body plan along the *anterior-posterior axis* (i.e., craniocaudal axis) and specify the segment identity of tissues within the embryo.

Homeotic genes influence the development of specific structures in plants and animals, such as the Hox and ParaHox genes, which are essential for segmentation.

Homeotic genes determine where, when, and how body segments develop. For example, alterations in homeotic genes in laboratory flies cause changes in patterns of body parts, sometimes producing dramatic effects, such as legs growing in place of antennae or an extra set of wings.

Hox genes are *homeotic transcription factors* that play a crucial role in controlling the body plan along the *anterior-posterior axis* (i.e., craniocaudal axis) and specify the segment identity of tissues within the embryo.

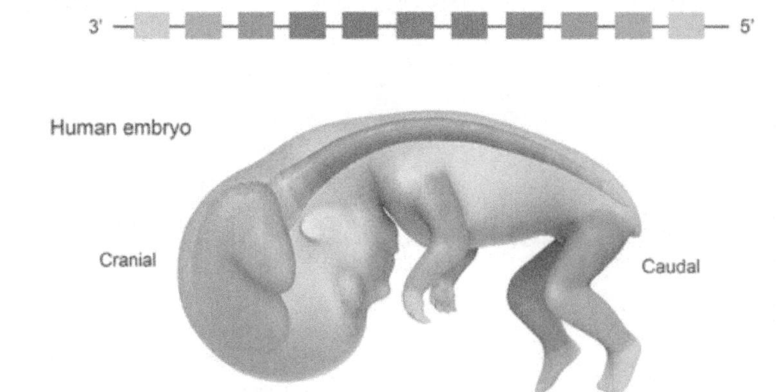

HOX genes encode homeodomain proteins as developmental regulators of the anterior-posterior axis

Homeodomain is a protein structural domain that binds DNA or RNA and is a transcription factor (i.e., facilitates polymerase binding and activation).

Homeodomain proteins fold with a 60-amino acid helix-turn-helix structure in which the short loop regions connect three alpha-helices.

N-terminus of the two helices is *antiparallel*, and the longer C-terminal helix is roughly perpendicular to the axes established by the first two. The third helix functions as a *transcription factor* and interacts directly with DNA.

4. B is correct.

Ectoderm gives rise to the hair, nails, skin, brain, and nervous system.

Ectoderm forms "*outer linings*," including the epidermis (i.e., outermost skin layer) and hair.

Ectoderm is the precursor to *mammary glands* and *central* (CNS) and *peripheral nervous systems* (PNS).

Connective tissue is derived from *mesoderm.*

Rib cartilage is derived from *mesoderm.*

Epithelium of the digestive system is derived from *endoderm.*

5. D is correct.

Chorion is a membrane between the developing fetus and mother in humans and most mammals.

Chorion consists of two layers: an outer layer formed by the *trophoblast* and an inner layer formed by the *somatic mesoderm* (in contact with the amnion).

6. A is correct.

The embryo does *not* support the maintenance of the corpus luteum when an embryo lacks synthesis of human chorionic gonadotropin (hCG).

Human chorionic gonadotropin interacts with a receptor on the ovary, which results in progesterone secretion; progesterone creates a thick lining of blood vessels and capillaries on the uterus that can sustain the fetus; thus, the corpus luteum is supported during pregnancy.

7. C is correct.

Mesoderm develops into the circulatory, musculoskeletal and excretory systems, outer coverings of internal organs, gonads, and various types of muscle tissue.

Ectoderm develops into the brain and nervous system, hair and nails, lens of the eye, inner ear, sweat glands, the lining of the nose and mouth, and skin epidermis.

Endoderm develops into the epithelial lining of the digestive tract, respiratory tracts, lining of the liver, bladder, pancreas, thyroid, and alveoli of the lungs.

Epidermis is not an embryonic germ layer but the layer of the skin covering the dermis.

8. B is correct.

Gastrulation is a phase early in the embryonic development of animals, during which the single-layered blastula is reorganized into a trilaminar (*three-layered*) structure of the gastrula.

Three germ layers are the *ectoderm, mesoderm,* and *endoderm.*

Gastrulation occurs after cleavage, the formation of the blastula, and primitive streak, followed by organogenesis when individual organs develop within the newly formed germ layers.

Following gastrulation, cells are organized into sheets of connected cells (as in epithelial) or mesh of isolated cells (i.e., *mesenchyme*). Each germ layer gives rise to *specific tissues and organs* in the developing embryo.

Ectoderm gives rise to the epidermis and other tissues that will form the nervous system.

Mesoderm is between the ectoderm and the endoderm. It gives rise to somites that form muscle, cartilage of the ribs and vertebrae, dermis, notochord, blood and blood vessels, bone, and connective tissue.

Endoderm gives rise to the epithelium of the respiratory system, digestive system, and organs associated with the digestive system (e.g., liver and pancreas).

Gastrulation occurs when a blastula of one-layer folds inward and enlarges to create the *three primary germ layers* (i.e., endoderm, mesoderm, and ectoderm).

Archenteron gives rise to

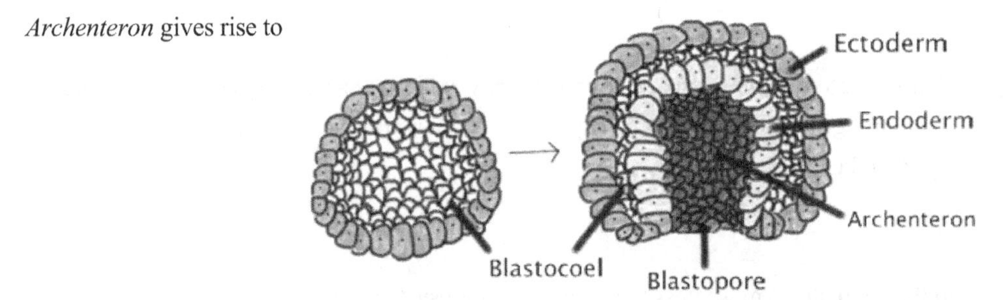

Blastula (left) becomes the gastrula (right) with the formation of the three primary germ layers

9. A is correct.

During the first *eight weeks* of development, myelination of the spinal cord does not occur.

Myelination of the *corticospinal tract* starts around 36 weeks and finishes around two years. Most major developmental milestones before two years are due to myelination of nerve fibers.

10. A is correct.

Ectoderm germ layers give rise to the skin epidermis and the nervous system.

Endoderm germ layer gives rise to the lining of the digestive system, its associated glands, organs (e.g., liver and pancreas), and the lungs.

Mesoderm gives rise to most organs and systems, including excretory, reproductive, muscular, skeletal, and circulatory systems. If tissue is not specifically endoderm or ectoderm, it is likely to *be mesoderm derived.*

The incorrect choices are *mesoderm-derived* tissues or structures.

11. C is correct.

Fate mapping traces the embryonic origin of tissues in the adult by establishing the correspondence between individual cells (or groups of cells) at one stage of development and their progeny at later stages.

When carried out at single-cell resolution, this process is *cell lineage tracing.*

A: *phylogenetic tree* (i.e., an *evolutionary tree*) is a branching diagram showing the inferred evolutionary relationships (phylogeny) among biological species or other entities based upon similarities and differences in their physical or genetic characteristics.

Taxa joined in the tree are implied to have descended from a *common ancestor.*

A pedigree presents family information in an easily readable chart.

Pedigrees use *standardized symbols*: *squares* represent males and *circles* females.

Pedigree construction is *family history*; details about an earlier generation may be uncertain as memories fade.

For unknown sex, a diamond is used. Phenotype in question is represented by a filled-in (darker) symbol.

Heterozygotes are indicated by a shaded dot inside a symbol or a half-filled symbol.

Linkage map is a genetic relationship of an experimental population that shows the relative position of its genes or genetic markers based on recombination frequency rather than the physical distance along each chromosome.

Genetic linkage is the tendency of genes proximal on a chromosome to be inherited together during meiosis.

Genes whose loci (i.e., position) are closer are less likely to be separated onto different chromatids during chromosomal crossover (i.e., during prophase I) and are genetically *linked.*

12. A is correct.

Hyaline cartilage tissue is the precursor of long bones in the embryo.

Fibrous cartilage is in intervertebral discs.

Dense fibrous connective tissue generally forms *tendons* and *ligaments.*

Elastic cartilage provides internal support to the external ear and epiglottis due to recoil properties.

13. D is correct.

Gene expression changes as development proceeds; different proteins are encoded by expressed genes.

During development, cells change in their ability to respond to signals from other tissues and in their ability to induce changes in other cells. These changes during development are inherited by daughter cells (i.e.., progeny).

Microtubules participate in mitosis but do not change during development.

Somatic cells have the same genes (exceptions include gametes and B and T cells).

14. C is correct.

Acrosome is at the tip of the sperm and contains specialized secretory molecules.

Acrosomal reaction is due to a signaling cascade involving the glycoproteins on the egg's surface.

Acrosin digests the zona pellucida and membrane of the oocyte.

Part of the sperm cell membrane fuses with the egg cell's membrane, and the contents of the head enter the egg fused with the plasma membrane. This allows the sperm to release its degradation enzymes, penetrate the egg's tough coating, and bind and fuse.

A *pronucleus* is the nucleus of a sperm or an egg cell after the sperm enters the ovum but before they fuse.

15. D is correct.

Three primary germ layers form during gastrulation in embryogenesis: *ectoderm*, *mesoderm,* and *endoderm.*

Ectoderm is the external germ layer giving rise to the skin, fingernails, and nervous system (including the eye).

Mesoderm is the middle germ layer and gives rise to most organ systems, including the musculoskeletal, cardiovascular, reproductive, and excretory systems.

Endoderm is the innermost germ layer and gives rise to the gallbladder, liver, pancreas, and epithelial lining of luminal structures and accessory digestive organs.

16. D is correct.

Ductus arteriosus is a blood vessel connecting the pulmonary artery to the proximal descending aorta in the developing fetus. It allows most of the blood from the right ventricle to bypass the fetus's fluid-filled non-functioning lungs. Upon closure at birth, the *ductus arteriosus* becomes the *ligamentum arteriosum.*

Ligamentum teres (i.e., round ligament) refers to several structures:

ligamentum teres *uteri* (i.e., round ligament of the uterus),

ligamentum teres *hepatis* (round ligament of the liver), and

ligamentum teres *femoris* (i.e., ligament of head of the femur).

17. C is correct.

During gastrulation, invagination of the blastula forms the mesoderm as the third primary germ layer.

18. C is correct.

Homeotic genes encode homeodomain proteins involved in developmental patterns and sequences.

Homeodomain is a protein structural domain that binds DNA or RNA and is often in transcription factors.

Homeodomain protein folding consists of a 60-amino acid helix-turn-helix structure in which short loop regions connect three alpha-helices. The N-terminus of the two helices is antiparallel, and the longer C-terminal helix is roughly perpendicular to the axes established by the first two.

The third helix functions as a transcription factor and interacts directly with DNA.

19. D is correct.

Neurulation and *organogenesis* follow gastrulation.

Mitosis continues throughout development, but *cleavage* is a specific term reserved for *the first few cell divisions* when the *zygote* becomes the *morula.*

During *cleavage*, no growth occurs, and the morula is the same approximate size as the zygote.

Blastula formation precedes gastrulation.

Blastocoel is the fluid-filled central region of a blastula and forms early after fertilization when the zygote divides into many cells.

20. A is correct.

Trophoblast cells give rise to the outer layer of a blastocyst, provide nutrients to the embryo, and develop into a large part of the placenta.

Trophoblasts form during the first stage of pregnancy and are the first cells to differentiate from the fertilized egg.

21. B is correct.

Placenta connects the developing fetus to the uterine wall and allows nutrient uptake, waste elimination, and gas exchange via the mother's blood supply.

Umbilical cord connects the developing embryo (or fetus) and the placenta.

During prenatal development, the *umbilical cord* is physiologically and genetically part of the fetus and contains two arteries (the *umbilical arteries*) and one vein (the *umbilical vein*).

Umbilical veins supply the fetus with oxygenated, nutrient-rich blood from the placenta.

The *fetal heart* pumps deoxygenated, nutrient-depleted blood through the umbilical *arteries* to the placenta.

22. C is correct.

For vertebrates, induction is how a group of cells cause *differentiation* in another group of cells.

For example, cells that form the notochord induce neural tube formation.

For example, induction in vertebrate development is eye formation, where the optic vesicles induce the ectoderm to thicken and form the lens placode (i.e., thickened portion of ectoderm becoming lens), which induces the optic vesicle to form the optic cup, which induces the lens placode to form the cornea.

A: *neural tube* does develop into the nervous system but is not induced by another group of cells or tissue.

B: *thyroxin stimulating hormone* (TSH) does stimulate the secretion of thyroxine but is not induction.

D: *neurons synapse* with other neurons via neurotransmitters (i.e., chemical messenger), but they do not induce changes in other tissues as does induction.

23. D is correct.

Acrosomal reaction by the sperm is hydrolytic enzymes degrading the plasma membrane.

Acrosome is at the tip of the sperm and contains specialized secretory molecules.

Acrosomal reaction is due to a signaling cascade involving the glycoproteins on the egg's surface.

Acrosin digests the zona pellucida and membrane of the oocyte, and the sperm releases its degradation enzymes to penetrate the egg's tough coating and allow the sperm to bind and fuse with the egg.

24. C is correct.

A: *endoderm* is the innermost germ layer and gives rise to the inner lining of the respiratory and digestive tracts and associated organs.

B: *blastula* refers to a hollow ball of embryonic cells arising from the morula. The blastula is *not* a germ layer.

D: *ectoderm* is the outermost germ layer and gives rise to the hair, nails, eyes, skin, and central nervous system.

25. B is correct.

Inner cell mass is the cells inside the primordial embryo that forms before implantation and gives rise to the definitive structures of the fetus.

Primitive streak is a structure that forms in the blastula during the initial stages of embryonic development.

The presence of the primitive streak establishes bilateral symmetry, determines the site of gastrulation, and initiates germ layer formation.

26. D is correct.

Fetal circulatory system changes as newborns begin using their lungs at birth.

Resistance in the pulmonary blood vessels decreases, causing an increase in blood flow to the lungs.

Umbilical blood flow ceases at birth, and blood pressure in the inferior vena cava decreases, which causes a decrease in pressure in the right atrium.

In contrast, the left atrial pressure increases due to increased blood flow from the lungs.

Increased left atrial pressure, coupled with decreased right atrial pressure, causes closure of the foramen ovale.

Ductus arteriosus (i.e., connects the pulmonary artery to the aorta) constricts and subsequently is sealed.

Ductus venosus, which shunts blood from the left umbilical vein directly to the inferior vena cava to allow oxygenated blood from the placenta to bypass the liver, completely closes within three months after birth.

The fetus produces adult hemoglobin a few weeks before birth (2 α and 2 β chains; alpha and beta) though lower amounts of fetal hemoglobin continue until the production completely stops.

After the first year, low fetal hemoglobin levels (2 α and 2 γ chains; alpha and gamma) are in the infant's blood.

27. B is correct.

Homeotic genes encode the related homeodomain protein involved in developmental patterns and sequences.

Homeobox is a stretch of DNA about 180 nucleotides long that encodes a homeodomain (i.e., protein) in vertebrates and invertebrates.

Exons (expressed sequences) are retained during RNA processing of the primary transcript (hnRNA) into mRNA for translation into proteins.

28. A is correct.

Somatic cells have the same genome, but individual cells express different genes.

Differences in expression are *spatial* (i.e., cell type) or *temporal* (i.e., stages of development).

Ectoderm tissue arises after gastrulation as a primary germ layer. Each germ layer retains its *determination.*

Somatic cells have identical genomes compared to their parents.

Gametes (via segregation and recombination during prophase I) have unique 1N genomes compared to their parents.

29. C is correct.

Yolk sac in humans gives rise to *blood cells* and *gamete-forming cells.*

Chorion is a double-layered membrane formed by trophoblast and extra-embryonic mesoderm. It gives rise to the fetal part of the placenta.

Luteal placental shift (7-9 weeks) is when the placenta develops enough to produce hormones that sustain a pregnancy. Before this shift, the *placenta secretes progesterone* instead of the corpus luteum.

In humans, waste goes to the placenta and is received by the mother.

Non-placental organisms use the allantois to collect wastes.

30. A is correct.

Trophoblast is primarily responsible for forming placental tissue. They give rise to the outer layer of a blastocyst, provide nutrients to the embryo, and develop into a large part of the placenta.

Trophoblasts form during the first stage of pregnancy and first cells to *differentiate* from the fertilized egg.

31. C is correct.

Spina bifida is a bone abnormality that arises from the embryonic mesoderm germ layer.

A lesion to the mesoderm affects development of other structures based on different connective tissue (e.g., blood, blood vessels, muscles, and connective tissue of organs).

Thus, this lesion affects the development of blood vessels and muscles.

I: *intestinal epithelium* develops from the *endoderm.*

II: skin, hair, and the nervous system develop from the *ectoderm.*

32. B is correct.

Homeotic genes participate in developmental patterns and sequences.

Homeotic genes encode the related homeodomain protein involved in developmental patterns and sequences.

For example, homeotic genes determine where, when, and how body segments develop.

Alterations in these genes cause changes in body parts and structure patterns, sometimes resulting in dramatic effects.

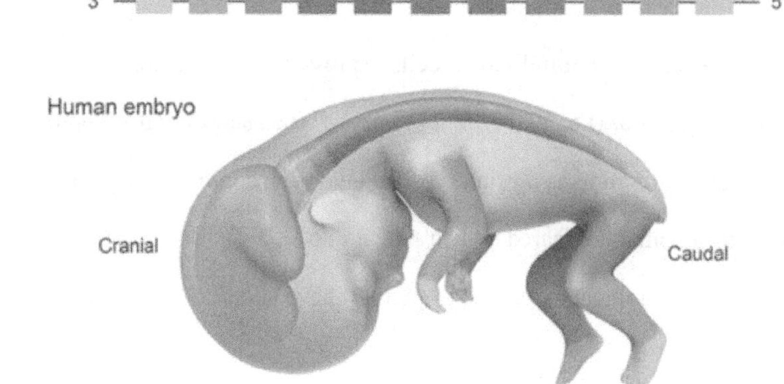

HOX genes encode homeodomain proteins as developmental regulators of the anterior-posterior axis. The linear sequence of genes on the chromosome corresponds to the cranial-caudal orientation

Homeodomain is a protein structural domain that binds DNA or RNA and is a transcription factor (i.e., facilitates polymerase binding and activation).

33. D is correct.

Mesoderm forms muscles, blood, bone, reproductive organs, and kidneys.

34. C is correct.

Primitive streak is a transitional structure formed at the onset of gastrulation.

Inner cell mass is converted into the trilaminar embryonic disc comprised of the three germ layers: ectoderm, mesoderm, and endoderm.

Primitive streak formation is not part of implantation but an early process of embryonic development.

35. A is correct.

During labor, the *oxytocin* hormone stimulates contractions of uterine smooth muscle.

36. D is correct.

Ectoderm cells are determined but not differentiated because they have the potential to develop into more than one type of tissue, but not any type.

Experimentally, ectoderm development was influenced (i.e., induced) by changing locations within the developing embryo.

The underlying *mesoderm* differentiated because it released the molecular inducers as signals to the overlying ectoderm (undifferentiated).

A: *ectoderm* cell *location* is essential because their development (i.e., differentiation into specific tissue/structures) is induced by the underlying mesoderm cells that send chemical substances (i.e., inducers) specific to the position of the mesoderm.

Mesoderm, not ectoderm, determines cellular differentiation at this stage of development.

B: *differentiated fate* of the cells has not yet been determined because the transplanted cells would develop into wing feathers instead of claws.

C: *ectoderm cells* cannot develop into any tissue because the location influences the development of the transplanted ectoderm cells.

37. D is correct.

Recognition of the sperm by the *vitelline envelope* (i.e., a membrane between the outer zona pellucid and inner plasma membrane) triggers the cortical reaction, transforming it into the hard *fertilization membrane* as a physical barrier to other spermatozoa (i.e., *slow block to polyspermy*).

Cortical reaction within the egg is analogous to the acrosomal reaction within the sperm.

38. C is correct.

Polyspermy in humans results in a nonviable zygote.

39. C is correct.

Mesoderm germ layer gives rise to many tissues.

A: *intestinal mucosa* is derived from the endoderm

B: *nerve* is derived from the ectoderm.

D: *lung epithelium* is derived from the endoderm.

40. C is correct.

Genomic imprinting is *epigenetic* (i.e., heritable change) when specific genes are expressed in a parent-of-origin-specific manner.

Genomic imprinting is an epigenetic process involving *DNA methylation* and *histone modulation* to achieve single allelic gene expression without altering the original genetic sequence.

41. C is correct.

Embryos require a *greater protein translation rate* using ribosomes to read mRNA transcripts.

42. C is correct.

Zygote (i.e., fertilized egg) is the first structure to form during fertilization in humans that undergo rapid cell divisions without significant cellular growth to produce a cluster of cells of the same total size as the original zygote.

Cells derived from cleavage are *blastomeres* and form a solid mass known as a *morula.*

Cleavage ends with the formation of the *blastula.*

> Ovulation → fertilization (sperm and oocyte) → diploid zygote (undergoes cleavage) → morula (solid ball of cells) → blastocoel (undergoes invagination) → blastopore (ectoderm and endoderm)

43. A is correct.

Capacitation is the final step in the maturation of spermatozoa. It is required for them to be competent to fertilize an oocyte.

Capacitation destabilizes the acrosomal sperm head membrane, allowing greater binding between sperm and oocyte by removing steroids (e.g., cholesterol) and non-covalently bound glycoproteins, which increases membrane fluidity and Ca^{2+}permeability.

Ca^{2+} influx produces intracellular cAMP levels and increased sperm motility.

44. C is correct.

Endoderm develops into the *epithelial linings* of the digestive and respiratory tracts, parts of the liver, thyroid, pancreas, and bladder lining.

45. C is correct.

Homeotic genes influence the development of specific structures in plants and animals, such as the Hox and ParaHox genes, which are essential for segmentation.

Homeotic genes determine where, when, and how body segments develop in organisms.

Alterations in these genes cause changes in patterns of body parts, sometimes causing dramatic effects, such as legs growing in place of antennae or an extra set of wings.

B: *loss-of-function* mutations result in the gene product with less or no function. When the allele has a complete loss of function (i.e., null allele), it is an *amorphic* (i.e., complete loss of gene function) mutation.

Phenotypes associated with such mutations are often recessive.

Exceptions are haploid or *haploinsufficiency* (i.e., a diploid organism has a single copy of the functional gene) when the reduced dosage of a normal gene product is not enough for a typical phenotype.

46. A is correct.

Cells can assume several different fates and are not yet terminally differentiated.

B: *gastrula cells* influenced by their surroundings are *competent.*

C: *ectoderm layer* gives rise to the eye, among other structures.

D: cells can become other ectoderm tissue (e.g., gills).

47. B is correct.

Proteases and *acrosin* enzymes degrade the protective barriers around the egg and allow the sperm to penetrate.

Acrosomal reaction by the sperm is hydrolytic enzymes degrading the plasma membrane.

Acrosome is at the tip of the sperm and contains specialized secretory molecules.

Acrosomal reaction is due to a signaling cascade involving the glycoproteins on the egg's surface.

Acrosin digests the zona pellucida and membrane of the oocyte, and the sperm releases its degradation enzymes to penetrate the egg's tough coating and allow the sperm to bind and fuse with the egg.

48. A is correct.

Human blastocyst implants in the uterine wall about a week after fertilization.

49. B is correct.

The *ectoderm* develops into the nervous system, the epidermis, the eye lens, and the inner ear.

I: *endoderm* develops into the lining of the digestive tract, lungs, liver, and pancreas.

III: *mesoderm* develops into the connective tissue, muscles, skeleton, circulatory system, gonads, and kidneys.

50. A is correct.

After the infant's first breath, the newborn's cardiovascular system constricts the *ductus arteriosus* (i.e., connects the pulmonary artery to the aorta) and converts it to the *ligamentum arteriosum.*

Fetal circulatory systems change at birth as the newborn uses its lungs. Resistance in the pulmonary blood vessels decreases, increasing blood flow to the lungs.

At birth, umbilical blood flow ceases, and blood pressure in the inferior vena cava decreases, which causes a decrease in pressure in the right atrium.

In contrast, the left atrial pressure increases due to increased blood flow from the lungs. Increased left atrial pressure, coupled with decreased right atrial pressure, causes *closure* of the *foramen ovale.*

Ductus venosus, which shunts blood from the left umbilical vein directly to the inferior vena cava to allow oxygenated blood from the placenta to bypass the liver, completely closes within three months after birth.

diagram below

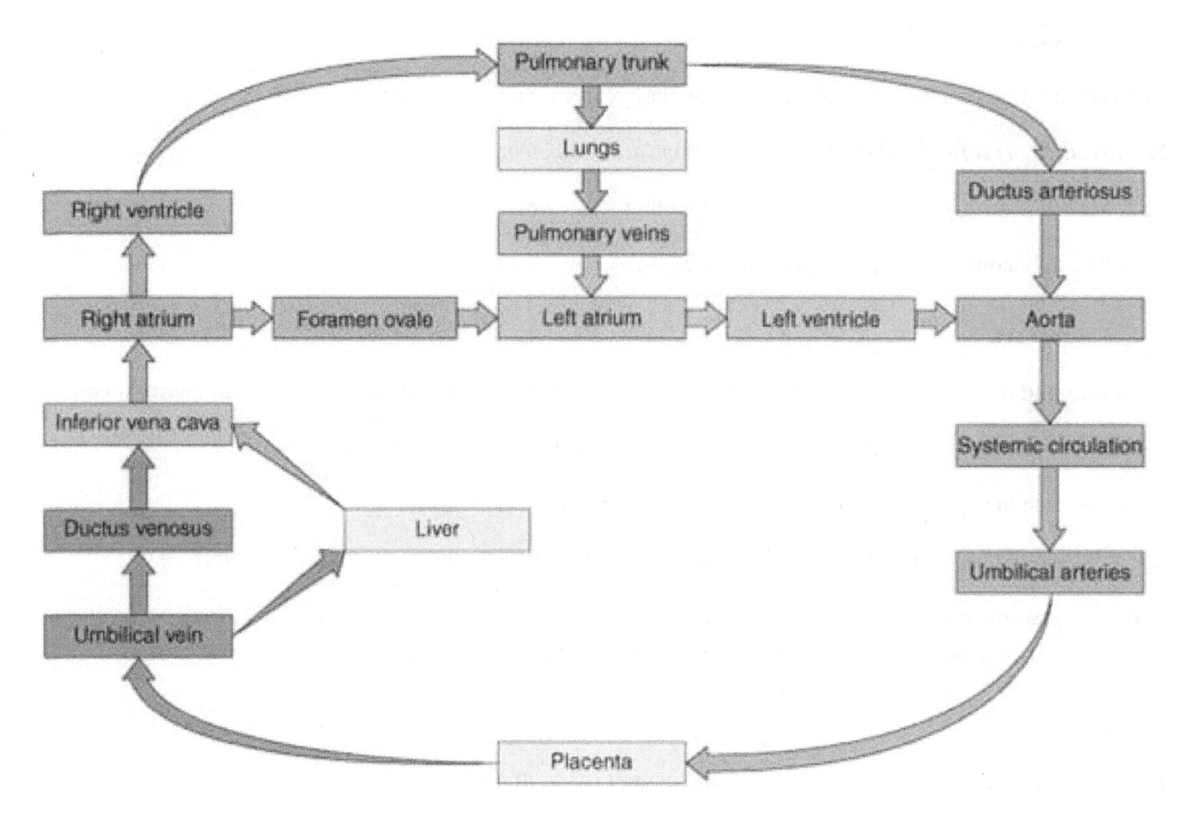

Adult and fetal circulatory system with ductus arteriosus and ductus venosus providing shunt pathways

51. C is correct.

Genomic imprinting is an epigenetic (i.e., heritable changes in gene activity) process involving DNA methylation and histone remodeling for monoallelic (i.e., single allele) gene expression without altering the genetic sequence within the genome.

Epigenetic changes are established in the germline (i.e., cells that give rise to gametes of egg/sperm) and can be maintained through mitotic divisions.

52. A is correct.

Amniotic fluid, surrounded by the amnion, is a liquid environment around the egg that protects it from shock.

Embryonic membranes include:

1) *chorion* lines the inside of the shell and permits gas exchange;

2) allantois is a saclike structure developed from the digestive tract and functions in respiration, excretion, and gas exchange with the external environment;

3) amnion encloses *amniotic fluid* as a watery environment for embryogenesis and shock protection;

4) yolk sac encloses the yolk and transfers food to the developing embryo.

53. A is correct.

Mesoderm gives rise to the entire circulatory system, muscle, and most other tissue between the gut and skin (excluding the nervous system).

B: *ectoderm* gives rise to skin, the nervous system, retina, and lens.

C: *differentiated endoderm* has a restricted fate that does not include heart tissue.

D: *endoderm* gives rise to the inner lining of the gut.

54. C is correct.

At the end of the *first trimester*, an ultrasound can determine the sex of the fetus.

55. C is correct.

The egg is viable and able to be fertilized 12-24 hours after ovulation.

56. B is correct.

Blastulation begins when the *morula* develops a fluid-filled cavity (i.e., blastocoel). By the fourth day, it becomes a hollow sphere of cells (i.e., blastula).

A: *gastrula* is the embryonic stage characterized by the three primary germ layers (i.e., endoderm, ectoderm, and mesoderm), the blastocoel, and the archenteron.

Early gastrula is two-layered (i.e., ectoderm and endoderm), and shortly afterward, a third layer (i.e., mesoderm) develops.

Gastrulation is followed by organogenesis when individual organs develop within newly formed germ layers.

C: *morula* is the solid ball of cells from the early cleavage stages in the zygote.

D: *zygote* is the (2N) cell formed by the fusion of two (1N) gametes (e.g., ovum and sperm).

57. B is correct.

Proteases and *acrosin* enzymes degrade the protective barriers around the egg and allow the sperm to penetrate.

Acrosomal reaction by the sperm is hydrolytic enzymes degrading the plasma membrane.

Acrosome is at the tip of the sperm and contains specialized secretory molecules.

Acrosomal reaction is due to a signaling cascade involving *glycoproteins* on the egg's surface.

Acrosin digests the *zona pellucida* and membrane of the oocyte, and the sperm releases its degradation enzymes to penetrate the egg's tough coating and allow the sperm to bind and fuse with the egg.

58. C is correct.

Regarding fertilization, the vagina's acidic environment destroys millions of sperm cells.

59. B is correct.

Zygote is a fertilized egg undergoing rapid cell divisions without significant cellular growth to produce a cluster of cells of the same total size as the original zygote.

The cells derived from cleavage are *blastomeres* and form a solid mass known as a *morula*.

Cleavage ends with the formation of the *blastula*.

Among species, depending mainly on the amount of yolk in the egg, cleavage is:

holoblastic (i.e., total or entire cleavage) or

meroblastic (i.e., partial cleavage).

Egg pole with the highest yolk concentration is the *vegetal pole*, while the opposite is the *animal pole*.

Humans undergo *holoblastic cleavage* (i.e., total cleavage).

Notes for active learning

Notes for active learning

Molecular Biology of Eukaryotes – Detailed Explanations

1. A is correct.

5'-CCCC-3' and 5'-AAAA-3'primers should be used to amplify the DNA shown via PCR.

```
5' AAAA                    GGGG 3'
   ------------------------->
   <-------------------------
3' TTTT                    CCCC 5'
```

Polymerase chain reaction (PCR) requires the sequence at the ends of the fragment to be amplified.

From the ends, primers use complementary base pairing to anneal the target fragment and permit amplification.

Regions between ends are not required as the parent strands are the template used by the DNA polymerase.

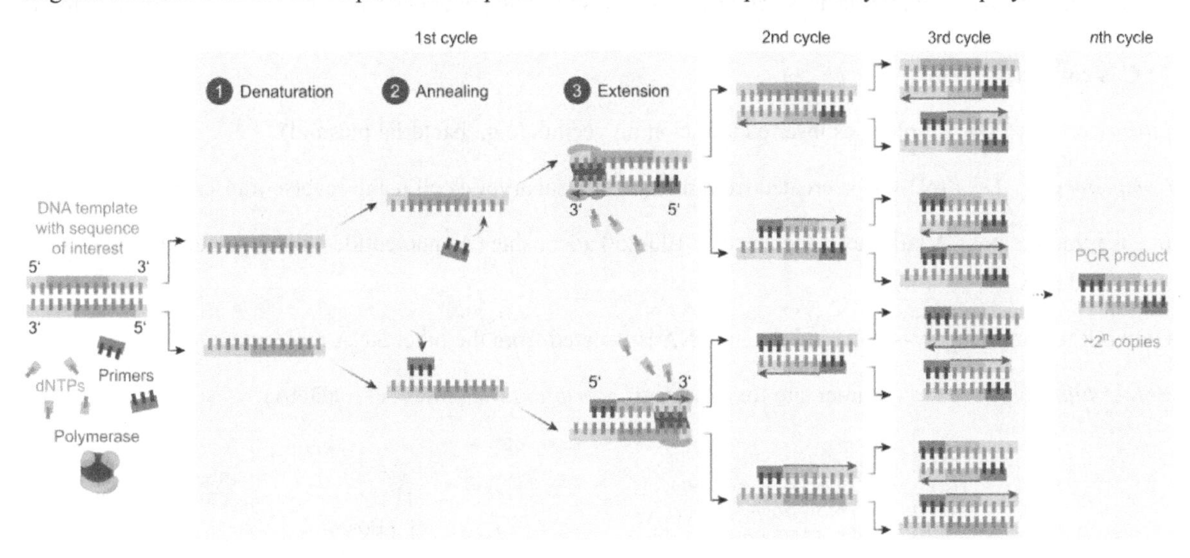

Polymerase chain reaction (PCR) with exponential product amplification during each cycle. Step one heats DNA to separate the two strands of the double helix. Step 2 cools the sample for annealing by complementary primers. Step 3 is chain elongation for the synthesis of DNA by polymerase anchored to the primers.

2. A is correct.

Proteins are the major phenotypic expression of a genotype.

3. C is correct.

Dideoxy (without ~OH at 2' and 3' positions) cytosine is used in DNA sequencing to cause termination when the template strand is G.

4. A is correct.

Adding a 3' poly-A tail to mRNA (not proteins) is a *post-transcription* event.

Post-transcription events include adding a 5' cap and splicing exons (removing introns) from RNA molecules.

5. C is correct.

Centromeres are chromosomal regions of highly coiled DNA (i.e., *heterochromatin*) at the point of attachment of the sister chromatids, replicated during the S phase of interphase.

6. D is correct.

Genes provide hereditary information for the organism, but the environment (to a degree) influences the phenotypic pattern of proteins resulting from gene expression.

Genetic and environmental factors interact to produce the phenotype. These are examples of the environment affecting gene activation.

D: *shivering* is an example of a change in the environment causing a physiological (i.e., behavioral) change to maintain homeostasis. Homeostasis is achieved because shivering generates heat when muscles contract rapidly.

7. C is correct.

Library refers to DNA molecules inserted into cloning vectors (e.g., bacterial plasmid).

Complementary DNA (cDNA) is created from mRNA in a eukaryotic cell using reverse transcriptase.

In eukaryotes, a poly-A tail (i.e., a sequence of 100-250 adenosine (A) nucleotides) distinguishes mRNA from tRNA and rRNA.

Only mRNA has the poly-A tail bind (i.e., mRNA is isolated from the other RNA molecules).

Poly-A tail can be used as a primer site for *reverse transcription* (i.e., mRNA → cDNA).

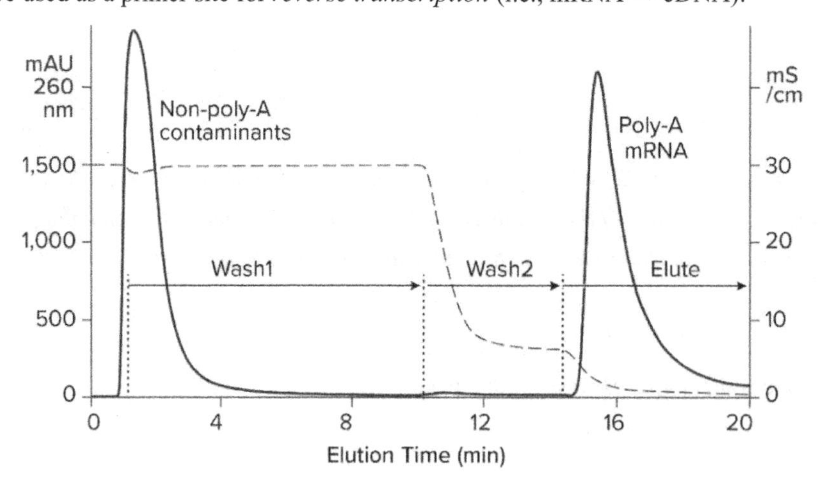

mRNA is purified by column chromatography using oligomeric dT nucleotide resins

mRNA is isolated by oligo-dT and used as a complementary primer to bind the poly-A tail and extend the primer molecule by reverse transcriptase to create the cDNA strand.

The original mRNA templates are removed using RNAse, leaving a *single-stranded* cDNA (sscDNA).

cDNA is converted into double-stranded DNA by DNA polymerase for double-stranded cDNA.

cDNA is cloned in bacterial plasmids.

8. A is correct.

Quaternary protein structure requires two or more polypeptide chains whereby different genes specify each polypeptide.

Complex polysaccharides are linked to monomers of sugar. Complex polysaccharides include sugar monomers such as lactose (e.g., glucose and galactose).

The presence of more than one monomer requires additional genes.

9. A is correct.

Genomic library is a set of clones representing a given organism's entire genome. Among the tools making recombinant DNA technology possible are *restriction enzymes.*

Restriction endonucleases (i.e., *restriction enzymes*) cut DNA at specific sequences, often inverted repeat sequences (i.e., palindromes that read the same if the DNA strand is rotated 180°).

After cutting, the ends of some restriction-digested double-stranded DNA fragments have several nucleotide overhangs of single-stranded DNA as "sticky ends."

Restriction enzymes cut similarly, so the sticky end from one fragment anneals via hydrogen bonding with the sticky end from another fragment cut by the same enzyme.

After annealing, DNA ligase covalently closes the plasmid into circular DNA for transformation into bacteria.

10. D is correct.

Attachment of glycoprotein side chains is a post-translational modification.

Rough endoplasmic reticulum (RER) and the *Golgi apparatus* are two organelles modifying proteins as a post-translational event.

Lysosomes are organelles with low pH that function to digest intracellular molecules.

11. A is correct.

Telomerase (i.e., enzyme ending in *~ase*) restores the ends of the DNA in a chromosome.

Telomeres are maintained by *telomerase*, an enzyme that (during embryogenesis) adds repeats to chromosomal ends. A measure of telomerase activity in adults indicates one marker for cancer activity (i.e., uncontrolled cell growth) within the cell.

DNA polymerase cannot fully replicate the 3' DNA end, resulting in shorter DNA with each division.

The new strand synthesis mechanism prevents the loss of the DNA coding region.

New strand synthesis prevents the loss of the terminal DNA at the coding region during replication and represents telomere function.

Telomeres are at chromosomal ends and consist of nucleotide repeats that provide stability and prevent the loss of the ends of the DNA coding region during DNA replication.

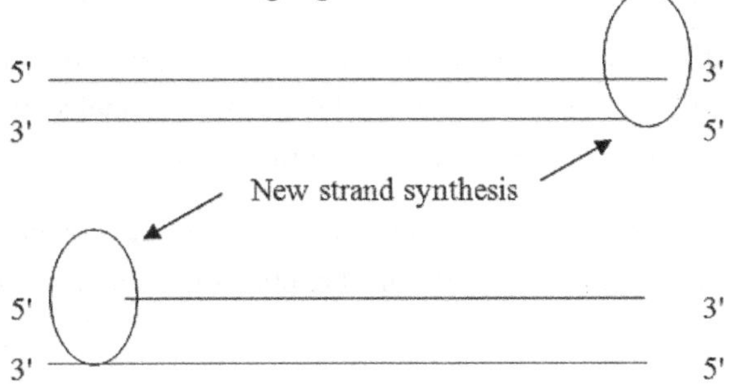

12. B is correct.

Unlike a genomic library that reflects the entire DNA of the organism, a *cDNA library* uses mRNA from *expressed genes after processing* (i.e., removal of introns and ligating of exons).

13. C is correct.

Central dogma of molecular biology proposes that information flow in the cell is unidirectional.

Schematically,

DNA → RNA → protein

14. C is correct.

Alternative splicing occurs in the nucleus with three stages of RNA processing:

1) adding a G-modified cap to the 5' end of the primary transcript,

2) adding a 3' polyA tail, and

3) removing introns (intervening sequences) and ligating exons (expressed sequences).

This process cleavages hnRNA to make corresponding mRNAs transported in the cytoplasm.

15. D is correct.

Ribosomal RNA (rRNA) binds the small and large ribosomal subunits (i.e., 30S & 50S in prokaryotes and 40S & 60S in eukaryotes) to create the functional ribosome (i.e., 70S in prokaryotes and 80S in eukaryotes).

Ribosomes are complex assemblies of RNA molecules and several associated proteins. rRNAs are the only RNA molecules (others being mRNA and tRNA) synthesized in the nucleolus (within the nucleus).

16. A is correct.

E. coli RNA polymerase synthesizes RNA in the 5' to 3' direction and copies a DNA template.

17. B is correct.

Introns (intervening sequences) vary in size and number among different genes.

18. C is correct.

I: eukaryotes *splice* hnRNA (*primary transcript*) by removing introns (intervening sequences) and ligating exons (expressed sequences) in the nucleus before exporting the modified mRNA transcript to the cytoplasm for translation.

II: after protein synthesis in the ER, they may be modified in the Golgi apparatus (e.g., glycosylation), but this is different from the required splicing of mRNA molecules (i.e., removal of introns) before the mRNA can pass through the nuclear pores and enter the cytoplasm.

III: prokaryotic ribosomes (30S small & 50S large subunit = 70S complete ribosome) are smaller than eukaryotic ribosomes (40S small & 60S large subunit = 80S complete ribosome).

19. C is correct.

Deacetylation of histones associated with the retrotransposon and methylation of retrotransposon DNA decreases the transcription of retrotransposons.

20. B is correct.

Central dogma of molecular biology refers to the direction of genetic information flow.

DNA → RNA → protein

The central dogma of molecular biology is violated by retroviruses with RNA genomes and reverse transcriptase to copy viral RNA into DNA within the infected host cell.

21. A is correct.

miRNA is generated from the cleavage of double-stranded RNA. miRNA (or *interference RNA*) is a small non-coding RNA molecule (about 22 nucleotides) in plants, animals, and some viruses, which functions in transcriptional and post-transcriptional regulation of gene expression.

miRNA hybridizes to mRNA and inactivates its ability as a template for translation into protein.

22. C is correct.

DNA polymerase cannot fully replicate the 3' DNA end, resulting in shorter DNA with each division. The new strand synthesis mechanism prevents the loss of the DNA coding region.

The process of new strand synthesis prevents the loss of the terminal DNA at the coding region during replication by *telomeres*. Telomeres are at chromosomal ends and consist of nucleotide repeats that provide stability and prevent the loss of the ends of the DNA coding region during DNA replication.

Telomeres are generated by *telomerase*, an enzyme that (during embryogenesis) adds repeats to chromosomal ends. A measure of telomerase activity in adults indicates one marker for cancer activity (i.e., uncontrolled cell growth) within the cell.

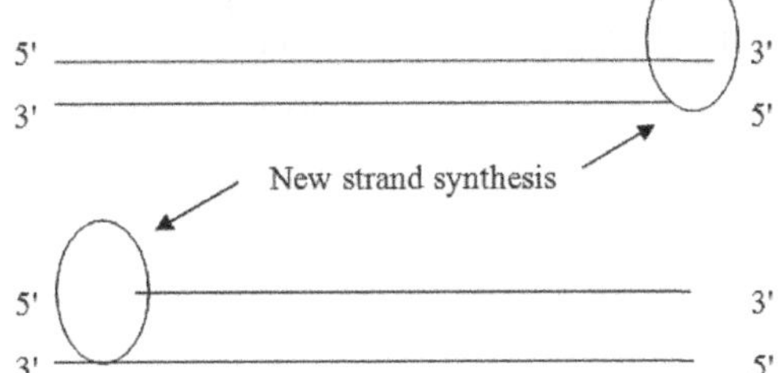

A: *kinetochore* is a protein collar around the centromere on the chromosome as the site of attachment of the spindle fiber to the chromosome during cell division.

Kinetochore attaches to the spindle fibers (microtubulin) and is anchored to chromosomes by centromeres. The other end of the spindle fibers is attached at the poles (centromere region) of the cell to the centrioles.

B: *centrosome* (*~some* means body) is a region at the poles of the cell giving rise to the asters (microtubules projecting past the centrioles) of the centrioles.

D: *centromeres* are on the chromosomes consisting of highly coiled DNA (i.e., heterochromatin) at the point of attachment of the sister chromatids.

23. B is correct.

Core particle of 8 histones is the *nucleosome* (i.e., octamer).

24. C is correct.

miRNA (or *interference RNA*) is a small non-coding RNA molecule (~22 nucleotides) in plants, animals, and some viruses, which functions in transcriptional and post-transcriptional regulation of gene expression.

miRNA hybridizes to mRNA and inactivates its ability to be used as a template for protein translation.

25. A is correct.

Promoter is the region of DNA in prokaryotes to which *RNA polymerase binds* most tightly.

Promoter is a region of 100–1000 base pairs long on the DNA that initiates gene transcription.

Promoters are nucleotides near the genes they transcribe, on the same strand, and upstream on the DNA (towards the 3' region of the antisense strand – template and non-coding strands).

Promoters contain specific DNA sequences and response elements that provide a secure initial binding site for RNA polymerase and transcription factors proteins.

Transcription factors have specific activator (or repressor) sequences of nucleotides that attach to specific promoters and regulate gene expressions.

In bacteria, the promoter is recognized by RNA polymerase and an associated sigma factor (i.e., a protein needed only for initiation of RNA synthesis), which are often brought to the promoter DNA by an activator protein's binding to its own nearby DNA binding site.

In eukaryotes, the process is complicated, and at least seven factors are necessary for binding an RNA polymerase II to the promoter.

26. D is correct.

Genomic libraries reflect the entire DNA of the organism and, unlike a cDNA library, do not use mRNA, which corresponds to expressed genes after processing (i.e., removal of introns).

Retrotransposons are genetic elements that can amplify themselves in a genome and are ubiquitous components of the DNA of many eukaryotic organisms.

27. D is correct.

tRNA has a *cloverleaf secondary structure* and is the smallest single-stranded RNA.

tRNA contains the *anticodon* and delivers individual amino acids to the growing peptide chain based on the *codon* specified by mRNA.

A: hnRNA (*heteronuclear RNA* or *primary transcript*) has not yet undergone post-transcriptional modification (i.e., 5' Guanine cap, removal of introns and ligation of exons, and the addition of a 3' poly-A tail).

Once three modifications occur, the hnRNA becomes a mature mRNA and is transported through the nuclear pores (in the nuclear envelope). The mRNA enters the cytoplasm for translation into proteins.

B: mRNA is a single-stranded RNA molecule from its genesis and is shorter than hnRNA (i.e., the primary transcript before post-transcriptional processing).

mRNA does not contain introns (exons are joined) and has a 5' G-cap and a 3' poly-A tail.

C: rRNA is synthesized in the *nucleolus* (organelle within the nucleus) and is the most abundant single-stranded RNA molecule.

rRNA (and associated proteins) are necessary for *ribosome* assembly in protein synthesis (i.e., translation).

28. B is correct.

Inversion is a chromosomal rearrangement when a chromosome segment is reversed and occurs when a single chromosome undergoes breakage and rearrangement.

Inversions do not cause abnormalities if rearrangement is balanced with no extra or missing DNA.

Heterozygous individuals for an inversion have increased production of abnormal chromatids resulting from crossing over within inversion spans.

Heterozygous inversions lead to *lowered fertility* due to the production of *unbalanced gametes*.

29. D is correct.

Nucleolus is the organelle within the nucleus responsible for synthesizing ribosomal RNA (rRNA).

A: *Golgi apparatus* is the organelle responsible for processing, packaging, and distributing proteins.

B: *lysosomes* are organelles with low pH that digest intracellular molecules.

C: *mitochondrion* is a double-membraned organelle where the Krebs (TCA) cycle, electron transport, and oxidative phosphorylation occur.

30. D is correct.

AG mutant flowers not having reproductive organs supports that the AG gene is vital for forming reproductive flower organs in *Arabidopsis*.

31. C is correct.

Glycocalyx refers to extracellular material, such as glycoprotein produced by bacteria, endothelial, epithelial, and other cells. It consists of several carbohydrate moieties of membrane glycolipids and glycoproteins.

Glycocalyx is composed of a *negatively charged* network of proteoglycans, glycoproteins, and glycolipids on the apical surface of endothelial cells.

Carbohydrate portions of glycolipids on plasma membrane surfaces contribute to cell-cell recognition, communication, and intracellular adhesion.

Glycocalyx plays a significant role in endothelial vascular tissue, including the modulation of red blood cell volume in capillaries and a principal role in the vasculature to maintain plasma and vessel wall homeostasis.

Glycocalyx is on the apical surface of vascular endothelial cells that line the lumen and includes a wide range of enzymes and proteins that regulate leukocyte and thrombocyte adherence.

32. A is correct.

Chromatin (comprising chromosomes) is the combination of DNA and proteins that comprise the genetic contents within the nucleus of a cell.

Primary functions of *chromatin*:

1) package DNA into a smaller volume;

2) strengthen DNA for mitosis;

3) prevent DNA damage,

4) control gene expression (i.e., RNA polymerase binding) and DNA replication.

Three levels of *chromatin organization*:

1) DNA wraps around histone proteins, forming nucleosomes (i.e., *beads on a string*) in uncoiled euchromatin DNA;

2) multiple histones wrap into a 30 nm fiber consisting of nucleosome arrays in their most compact form (i.e., heterochromatin);

3) higher-level DNA packaging of the 30 nm fiber into the metaphase chromosome (during mitosis and meiosis).

Tandem repeats occur in DNA when a pattern of nucleotides is repeated, and the repetitions are adjacent. An example would be ATCCG ATCCG ATCCG, whereby the sequence ATCCG is repeated three times.

Tandem repeats may arise from errors during DNA replication whereby the polymerase retraces its path (over a short distance) and repeats the synthesis of the same template region of DNA.

33. A is correct.

DNA topoisomerases regulate DNA supercoiling.

Gyrase (a subset of topoisomerase II) creates double-stranded breaks between the DNA backbone and relaxes DNA supercoils by unwinding the nicked strand around the other.

B: *helicase* unwinds DNA and induces severe supercoiling in the double-stranded DNA when hydrolyzing the hydrogen bonds between the complementary base pairs and exposing the bases for replication.

C: *DNA polymerase I* is in prokaryotes and participates in excision repair with 3'-5' and 5'-3' exonuclease activity and processing of Okazaki fragments generated during lagging strand synthesis

D: *DNA polymerase III* is in prokaryotes and is the primary enzyme in DNA replication.

34. B is correct.

The 3' OH of cytosine attacks the phosphate group on the guanine.

35. A is correct.

Introns are intervening sequences in the primary transcript but are excised when RNA is processed into mRNA.

Processed mRNA consists of *exons ligated* (i.e., joined).

C: *lariat structures* are the protein scaffolding used for the splicing of the hnRNA (i.e., primary transcript) into mRNA as the introns are removed and the exons are ligated.

36. B is correct.

Histone H1 is not in the eight-particle core of a *nucleosome*. It is in the linker regions of about 50 nucleotides between the nucleosomes.

Nucleosome is an *octamer* of the core histones: two H2A, two H2B, two H3, and two H4 histones.

37. A is correct.

Cellulose comprises the plant cell wall and is not a chemical component of a bacterial cell wall (*peptidoglycan*).

38. D is correct.

Combinatorial control of gene transcription in eukaryotes is when the presence (or absence) of combinations of transcription factors is required.

39. D is correct.

Once synthesized via transcription, RNA molecules undergo three steps for post-transcriptional processing:

1) 5' G cap increases RNA stability and resistance to degradation in the cytoplasm;

2) 3' poly-A-tail functions as a *molecular clock*, and

3) introns (i.e., non-coding regions) are removed, and exons (i.e., coding regions) are spliced (joined).

40. B is correct.

The second round of transcription can begin before the initial transcript is completed.

41. A is correct.

SP1 is a *transcription factor* that binds nucleic acids.

Therefore, SP1 binds RNA and DNA. Select an organelle that lacks RNA or DNA.

Golgi apparatus is the organelle responsible for processing, packaging, and distributing proteins. It is not composed of nucleic acids, nor does it process them.

Since no nucleic acids exist within the Golgi apparatus, the transcription factor SP1 would not bind to it.

B: *mitochondrion* is the organelle bound by a double membrane, where the Krebs cycle, electron transport, and oxidative phosphorylation occur.

Mitochondria are the site of most ATP molecules produced during aerobic respiration. The mitochondria (via the endosymbiotic theory) contain DNA (similar in size and composition to bacterial DNA), and the SP1 transcription factor would bind.

C: *nucleolus* is an organelle within the nucleus where rRNA synthesis occurs. Thus, SP1 would bind to a nucleic acid (rRNA) within the nucleolus.

D: *ribosomes* contain rRNA and assembled proteins as the translation site (mRNA is converted into proteins).

42. A is correct.

Spliceosome is a large and complex molecular apparatus assembled from snRNP and protein complexes.

Spliceosomes remove introns from pre-mRNA primary transcript (i.e., heteronuclear RNA or hnRNA); catalyzes the removal of introns and ligation of exons.

snRNA is a component of the snRNP and provides specificity by *recognizing* the sequences of critical splicing signals at the 5' and 3' ends and branch-site of introns.

Each spliceosome comprises five small nuclear RNAs (snRNA) and a range of associated protein factors.

The spliceosome occurs anew on each hnRNA (pre-mRNA).

hnRNA contains specific sequence elements recognized during spliceosome assembly; the 5' end splice, the branch point sequence, the polypyrimidine (i.e., cytosine and uracil) tract, and the 3' end splice site.

43. B is correct.

Polynucleotides (e.g., DNA) are the only of the four macromolecules (i.e., nucleic acids, proteins, lipids, carbohydrates) repaired rather than degraded.

DNA repair is essential for maintaining cell function and is performed by biological repair systems (i.e., p53 tumor repressor protein).

Uncontrolled cell growth via disruption to the cell cycle regulation may occur by somatic cell mutations.

44. D is correct.

Poly-A tail of RNA is enzymatically added soon after transcription (DNA → hnRNA) is completed.

45. D is correct.

H1 histones are in about 50 nucleotides between the nucleosomes in the linker regions.

Nucleosome is an *octamer* of the core histones: two H2A, two H2B, two H3, and two H4 histones.

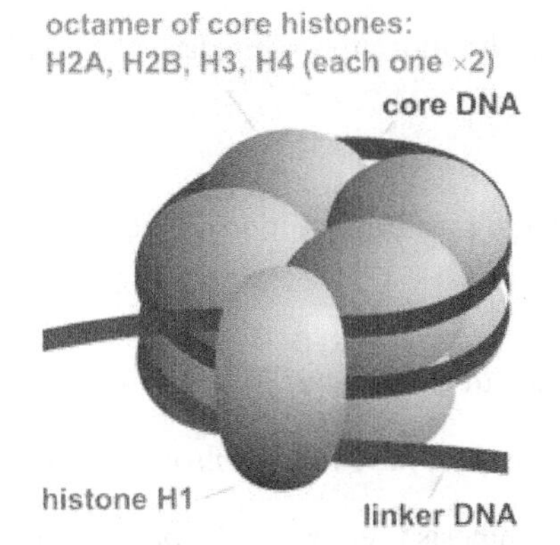

Nucleosome of 8 histones joined by a linker region with histone H1 permit efficient coiling of DNA

46. B is correct.

Splicing process involves snRNA which consists of sugar ribose (like other RNA molecules).

RNA is labile (unstable) and can function as a nucleophile because of the 2'–OH.

47. C is correct.

Chromatin is composed of DNA and histone proteins.

DNA has an overall negative charge because of the negative oxygen (i.e., single-bonded with seven valence electrons) attached to the phosphate group attached to the deoxyribose sugar.

For electrostatic interactions, histones must be *positively charged.*

Histones have a high concentration of basic (positive charge) amino acids (e.g., lysine and arginine).

48. C is correct.

Nucleic acids (e.g., DNA, RNA) elongate via *nucleophilic attack* by 3'–OH of nascent (i.e., growing) strand.

3'–OH undergoes nucleophilic attack on the phosphate group closest to the sugar in the incoming nucleotide.

2'–OH is in RNA (i.e., ribose) compared to a 2'–H for DNA (i.e., deoxyribose, where *deoxy* signifies the absence of O as in OH).

49. A is correct.

Heterochromatin is tightly packed DNA. Heterochromatin consists of genetically inactive satellite sequences (i.e., tandem repeats of noncoding DNA).

Euchromatin is loosely coiled regions of DNA actively engaged in gene expression because RNA polymerase binds the relaxed region of DNA.

Centromeres and *telomeres* are *heterochromatic.*

Barr body of the second inactivated X-chromosome in females is *heterochromatic.*

50. D is correct.

RNA of the prokaryote does *not* undergo post-transcriptional modifications:

5' cap,

removal of introns and ligation of exons, and

addition of a 3' poly-A tail), as does hnRNA (*primary transcript*) in eukaryotes.

Prokaryotes lack a nucleus, so RNA synthesis (i.e., *transcription*) coincides with protein synthesis (i.e., *translation*) in the cytosol.

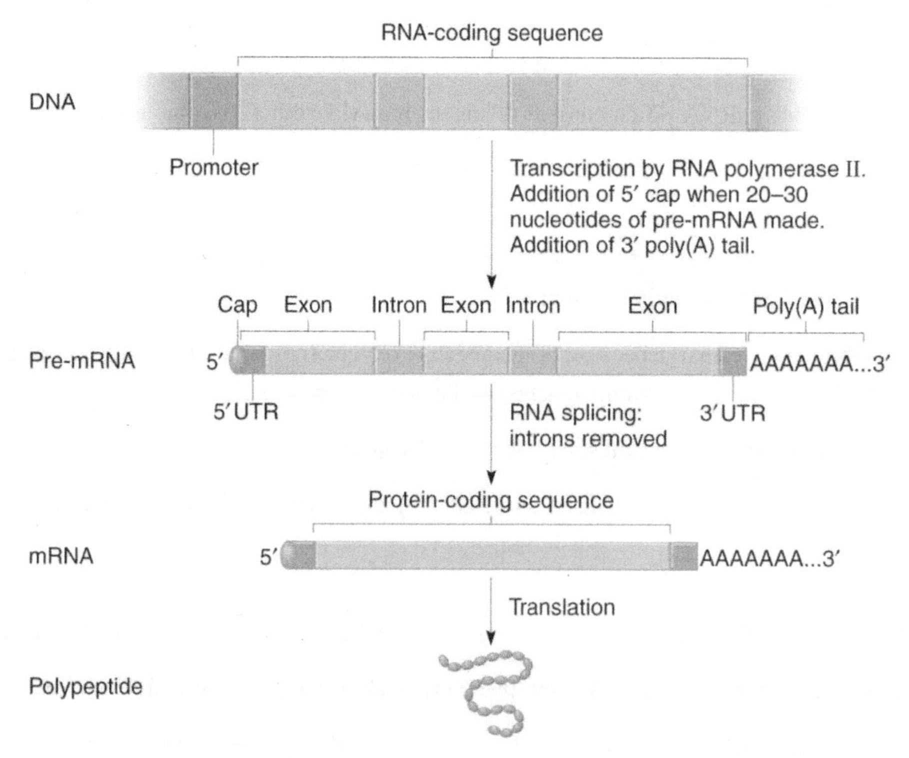

Gene expression with transcription, RNA processing, and mRNA translation into protein. Nucleotide sequences on chromosomes are transcribed and processed into mRNA by joining exons (removing introns), adding a 5' cap and a poly-A tail.

Notes for active learning

Notes for active learning

DNA and Protein Synthesis – Detailed Explanations

1. D is correct.

Histones are basic (i.e., positively charged) proteins associated with nuclei DNA to condense chromatin.

Nuclear DNA does not appear in free linear strands; instead, it is highly condensed and wrapped around histones (i.e., positively charged proteins) to fit inside the nucleus and form chromosomes.

Three major types of RNA participate in gene expression:

1) *messenger* RNA (mRNA) molecules carry the coding sequences (i.e., "blueprints") for protein synthesis and are transcripts;

2) *ribosomal* RNA (rRNA) forms the core of a cell's ribosomes (i.e., macromolecular cellular particles where protein synthesis takes place);

3) *transfer* RNA (tRNA) molecules transport amino acids (i.e., protein building blocks) to the ribosomes during protein synthesis.

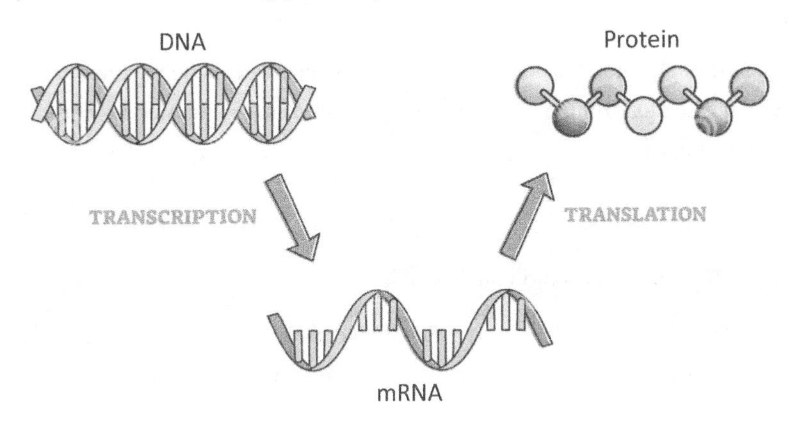

Gene expression with DNA transcribed into mRNA, which is translated into protein

2. D is correct.

Frederick Griffith reported an early experiment (1928) suggesting that bacteria transfer genetic information through *transformation.*

Griffith observed a *transforming principle*, where heat-killed S (smooth) bacteria was destroyed, and (now known) its DNA survived the process and was incorporated by R (rough) strain bacteria.

S genetic fragments protected R strain bacteria from host immunity and killed the host.

3. D is correct.

Depurination is the hydrolysis of the glycosidic bond of DNA and RNA purine nucleotides guanine or adenine.

Nucleotides have sugar, phosphate, and base (A, C, G, T or U).

For DNA, the sugar is deoxyribose, while RNA contains ribose.

Glycosidic bonds are hemiacetal groups of a saccharide (or an amino acid) and the hydroxyl group of an organic compound (e.g., alcohol).

Glycosidic bond formation from the nucleophilic attack of alcohol on the anomeric carbon of a hemiacetal

4. A is correct.

Unequal crossing over is a gene duplication (or deletion) event that deletes a sequence in one strand of the chromatid. It replaces it with duplication from its sister chromatid in mitosis, or homologous chromosomes recombine during prophase I in meiosis.

5. D is correct.

Sulfur is in the amino acid cysteine but is absent in nucleic acids.

Hershey-Chase experiment (i.e., *blender*) in 1952 used radiolabeled molecules of phosphorus (^{32} P for nucleic acids) and sulfur (^{35}S for proteins) to determine whether nucleic acids (phosphorus) or protein (sulfur) carried the genetic information.

Nucleic acids contain C, H, O, N and P and are polymers of *nucleotide* subunits.

Nucleic acids (e.g., DNA, RNA) encode cellular information for protein synthesis and replication.

6. D is correct.

mRNA is the subclass of RNAs molecule translated into proteins.

7. A is correct.

Aging of normal cells is associated with a loss of *telomerase activity*.

8. C is correct.

Translation is initiated on ribosomes within the cytoplasm.

A: *transcription* (not translation) occurs in the nucleus.

B: *Golgi* receives proteins from the rough endoplasmic reticulum for processing and sorting.

Golgi modifies (e.g., adds carbohydrate groups) and sorts proteins in the *secretory pathway*.

D: proteins destined for the *lumen of the rough endoplasmic reticulum* have at their amino terminus a particular sequence of amino acids referred to as a *leader sequence* (about 6 to 10 amino acids).

This sequence is recognized by the *signal recognition protein* (SRP) that binds a receptor on the rough ER, attaching the ribosome and the nascent polypeptide to the endoplasmic reticulum membrane.

9. D is correct.

When a gene is duplicated by crossing over between chromatids, the gene on the other chromatid is deleted.

Unequal crossing over is a gene duplication (or deletion) event that deletes a sequence in one strand of the chromatid. It replaces it with duplication from its sister chromatid in mitosis, or homologous chromosomes recombine during prophase I in meiosis.

10. C is correct.

To show that DNA, not RNA, protein, or other cell components, was responsible for transformation, Avery, MacLeod, and McCarty (1944) used several biochemical tests.

Trypsin, chymotrypsin, and ribonuclease (enzymes digesting proteins or RNA) did not affect the transforming agent causing the disease.

DNase treatment degrades DNA and destroys the extract's ability to cause disease.

Streptococcus pneumoniae (i.e., pneumococcus) is a Gram-positive pathogenic bacterium.

S. pneumoniae was recognized as a major cause of pneumonia in the late 19th century and has been the subject of numerous humoral immunity (i.e., antibody-mediated) studies.

11. B is correct.

Western blotting separates proteins by electrophoresis and is commonly used to identify the presence of HIV antibodies (proteins).

Blotting techniques rely on gel electrophoresis to separate DNA, RNA, or proteins based on size.

After resolution (i.e., separation) by electrophoresis, the gel (containing resolved products) is blotted (i.e., transferred to nitrocellulose).

After transferring the macromolecules (DNA, RNA, or proteins) from the gel to the blotting paper by capillary action, the blotting paper is probed by specific markers that hybridize with complementary sequences fixed on the blotting paper.

A: *Eastern blotting* does not exist.

C: *Northern blotting* uses RNA in gel electrophoresis.

D: *Southern blotting* uses DNA in gel electrophoresis.

12. C is correct.

Position C represents the ribose sugar's 3' hydroxyl (~OH).

As in DNA, the 3' hydroxyl is the site of attachment.

RNA and DNA require a free 3' OH for the nucleic acid to increase length.

Position D contains a 2' hydroxyl (~OH) that distinguishes this sugar as ribose, as opposed to DNA which would lack the 2' hydroxyl (deoxyribose = without oxygen) at the 2' position of the sugar.

13. C is correct.

Adenine and guanine are *purines*.

Cytosine and thymine/uracil are *pyrimidines*; note the presence of *y* for pyrimidines.

A: DNA strands are *antiparallel*: one strand has a 5'→ 3' polarity, and its complementary strand 3' → 5'.

B: DNA consists of nucleotides, which have a phosphate group, a deoxyribose sugar, and a base (A, C, G, T).

D: cytosine binds guanine with *three* hydrogen bonds.

Adenine binds thymine (in DNA) or uracil (in RNA) with *two* hydrogen bonds.

14. C is correct.

Tumor suppressor gene protects a cell from aberrant cell cycles.

When this gene mutates to cause a loss (or reduction) in its function, the cell can progress to cancer, usually with other genetic changes.

Loss of genes may be more critical than proto-oncogene/activation for forming many human cancer cells.

Apoptosis is the process of programmed cell death (PCD) that may occur in multicellular organisms.

Biochemical events lead to characteristic cell changes (morphology) and death, including blebbing, cell shrinkage, nuclear fragmentation, chromatin condensation, and chromosomal DNA fragmentation.

In contrast to necrosis (i.e., traumatic cell death that results from acute cellular injury), apoptosis confers advantages during an organism's lifecycle.

For example, the separation of fingers and toes in a developing human embryo occurs because cells between the digits undergo apoptosis.

Unlike necrosis, apoptosis produces cell fragments called *apoptotic bodies* that phagocytic cells can engulf and quickly remove before the cell contents spill onto surrounding cells and cause damage.

A: *telomerase* is an enzyme that adds DNA sequence repeats (i.e., TTAGGG) to the 3' end of DNA strands in the telomere regions at the ends of eukaryotic chromosomes.

This region of repeated nucleotides as telomeres with noncoding DNA hinders the loss of essential DNA from chromosome ends. When the chromosome is copied, 100–200 nucleotides are lost, causing no damage to the coding region of the DNA.

Telomerase is a reverse transcriptase that carries its RNA molecule used as a template when it elongates telomeres that have been shortened after each replication cycle.

Embryonic stem cells express telomerase, allowing them to divide repeatedly.

In adults, telomerase is highly expressed in cells that divide regularly (e.g., male germ cells, lymphocytes, and specific adult stem cells). Telomerase is not expressed in most adult somatic cells.

15. B is correct.

Aminoacyl tRNA synthetase (enzyme) uses energy from ATP to attach a specific amino acid to tRNA.

16. C is correct.

DNA was the transforming principle verified in experiments by Avery, MacLeod, and McCarty (1944) and Hershey and Chase (1952).

17. D is correct.

There are 4 different nucleotides (adenine, cytosine, guanine, and thymine/uracil).

Each codon is composed of 3 nucleotides.

Therefore, there must be 64 (4^3) possible variations of codons to encode for the 20 amino acids.

Genetic code is *degenerate* (i.e., redundant) because several codons encode for the same amino acid.

61 codons encode for amino acids and 3 stop codons that terminate translation.

18. C is correct.

Signal sequence at the N-terminus of the polypeptide targets proteins to organelles (e.g., chloroplast, mitochondrion).

19. C is correct.

Adenine pairs with thymine *via* 2 hydrogen bonds, while guanine pairs with cytosine *via* 3 hydrogen bonds.

Treatment of DNA with 2-aminopurine causes the adenine-thymine (A-T) base pair to be replaced with a guanine-thymine (G-T) base pair (before replication).

Thymine is replaced by cytosine: G-C base pair after replication.

This single-point mutation is incorporated into future generations.

If the mutation had been corrected before replication (via proofreading mechanisms during replication), there would be no change in the DNA base sequence.

20. D is correct.

Codons with two bases would be insufficient because the four bases in a two-base codon would form $4^2 = 16$ pairs, less than the 20 combinations needed to specify the amino acids.

A triplet is sufficient because four bases in a three-base codon can form $4^3 = 64$ pairs, enough to encode the 20 amino acids.

21. B is correct.

After one replication, the DNA was at an intermediate density between ^{14}N and ^{15}N.

After two replications, there were two densities – one band in the centrifuge tube was an intermediate between the ^{14}N and ^{15}N, while the other consisted of ^{14}N.

The *semiconservative* DNA replication model was one of three tested by the Meselson-Stahl (1958) experiment.

- ***Semiconservative replication*** would produce two copies containing one original and one new strand.
- ***Conservative replication*** would leave the two original template DNA strands in a double helix and produce a copy composed of two new strands containing all the new DNA base pairs.
- ***Dispersive replication*** would produce two copies of the DNA, each containing distinct regions of DNA composed of either original or new strands.

In the Meselson-Stahl (1957-58) experiments, *E. coli* were grown for several generations in a medium with ^{15}N.

When DNA was extracted and separated by centrifugation, the DNA separated according to density.

The E. coli cells with ^{15}N in their DNA were transferred to a ^{14}N medium and divided.

The DNA of the cells grown in ^{15}N medium had a higher density than cells grown in a normal ^{14}N medium.

Since conservative replication would result in equal amounts of DNA of the higher and lower densities (but no intermediate density), conservative replication was excluded.

This result was consistent with semiconservative and dispersive replication.

Semiconservative replication yields one double-stranded DNA with one with^{15}N DNA and one with ^{14}N DNA.

Dispersive replication would result in double-stranded DNA, with both strands having mixtures of ^{15}N and ^{14}N DNA, which would have appeared as DNA of an intermediate density.

22. C is correct.

DNA microarray (or *DNA chip*) collects microscopic DNA spots attached to a solid surface. DNA microarrays measure the expression levels of many genes or genotype multiple genome regions.

Each DNA spot contains picomoles (10^{-12} moles) of a specific DNA sequence.

These short sections of a gene (or other DNA element) hybridize cDNA *probes*.

An array simultaneously uses tens of thousands of probes; microarrays evaluate many genetic tests in parallel.

23. B is correct.

Avery, MacLeod, and McCarty (1944) demonstrated that DNA was the *transforming principle* for nonvirulent strains of pneumococcus.

Enzymes that destroyed nucleic acids destroyed the transforming activity, strengthening their hypothesis.

24. A is correct.

Codon-anticodon hybridization (i.e., bonding interaction) occurs between mRNA (*codon*) and tRNA (*anticodon*) during translation for protein synthesis.

25. B is correct.

Northern blot is a molecular biology technique to study gene expression by detecting RNA expression levels. Northern blotting uses electrophoresis to separate RNA samples by size. It involves the capillary transfer of RNA from the electrophoresis gel to the blotting membrane. It uses a hybridization probe via complementary hydrogen bonding to target expressed RNA fragments (i.e., expressed genes).

Eukaryotic mRNA is isolated using oligo (dT) cellulose chromatography to hybridize mRNA with a poly-A tail. The sample is resolved (i.e., separated) by gel electrophoresis.

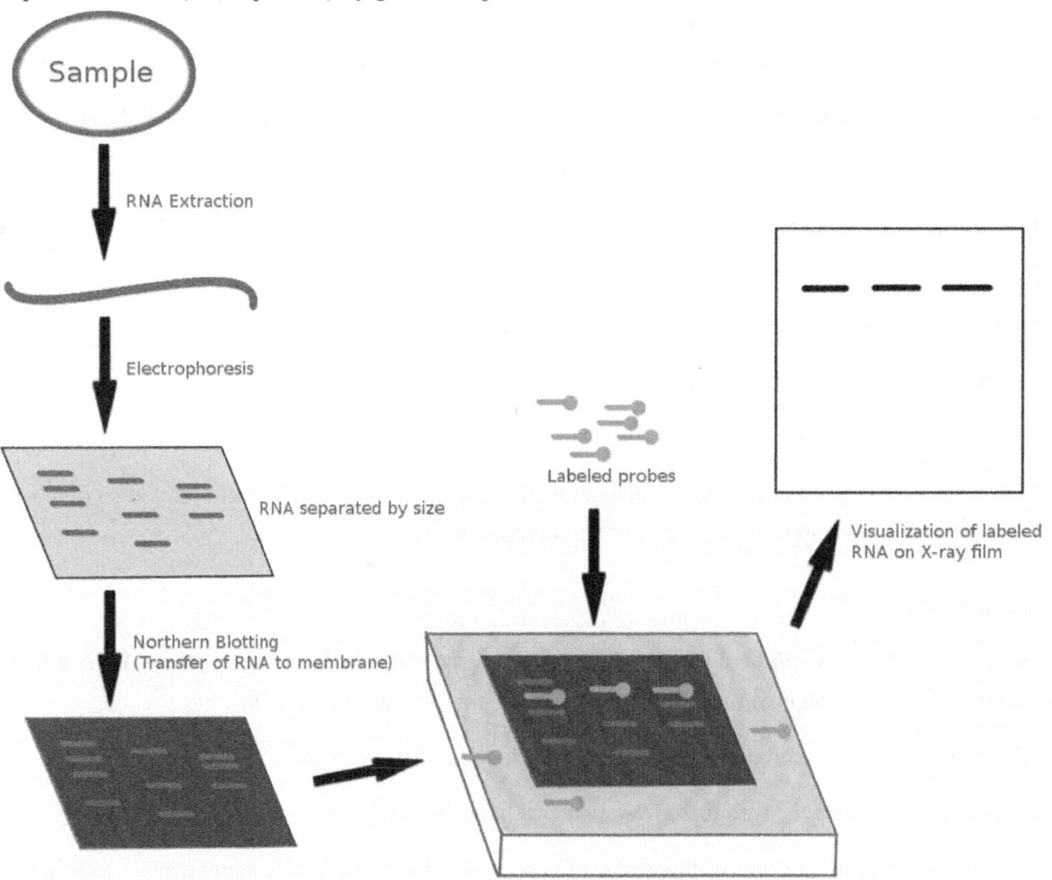

Northern blot uses RNA resolved by electrophoresis to evaluate gene expression using specific probes

Electrophoresis gels are fragile, and probes cannot enter the gel matrix. After resolution by electrophoresis, the size-separated RNA sample is transferred to a positively charged nylon (or nitrocellulose) membrane through capillary blotting. The negatively-charged mRNA adheres to the positive charge on the nylon.

In situ hybridization uses labeled probes of complementary DNA (cDNA) or RNA to localize a specific DNA or RNA sequence in a tissue section (*in situ*). Probes hybridize to the target sequence at an elevated temperature, and the excess probe is washed away.

26. B is correct.

Chromosomes replicate during the synthesis (S) phase of interphase.

27. B is correct.

DNA contains T, which is replaced with U in RNA.

28. B is correct.

Duplicated genes are closely related but diverged in sequence and function over evolutionary time.

29. D is correct.

Hershey and Chase showed in 1952 that when bacteriophages (i.e., viruses), composed of DNA and protein, infect bacteria, their DNA enters the host bacterial cell while their protein does not.

Hershey and Chase grew separate populations of viruses and incorporated radioactive sulfur (^{35}S to label protein) or phosphorus (^{32}P to label DNA) into the bacteriophages.

Two groups of viral progeny contained either ^{32}P or ^{35}S radioactive isotopes.

Separate aliquots of the labeled progeny were allowed to infect unlabeled bacteria. The viral ^{35}S protein coats remained outside the bacteria, while the ^{32}P DNA entered the bacteria.

Centrifugation separated the phage protein coats from the bacteria.

Bacteria were lysed to release the phages. The experiment demonstrated that the DNA, not protein, was the *transforming* molecule that entered the bacteria from a viral infection.

30. C is correct.

Replication forks open double-stranded DNA by disrupting hydrogen bonds between complementary nucleotide base pairs (e.g., A bonded to T and C bonded to G).

Gyrase cuts one strand of the DNA backbone and relaxes the positive supercoil that accumulates as helicase separates the two strands of DNA.

Ligase seals the backbone of DNA (i.e., joins Okazaki fragments) by forming phosphodiester bonds between deoxynucleotides in DNA.

31. A is correct.

Four atoms in the peptide bond are in the box.

Note that the oxygen on the carbonyl is oriented 180° from the H (antiperiplanar) on the nitrogen because the lone pair on the nitrogen participates in resonance and the peptide bond is rigid (i.e., double-bond-like character).

```
     H  O      H |O     | H  O
     |  ||     | ||     | |  ||
[ -N-Cα-C-N-Cα-|C-N|-Cα-C- ]
   |  |     |  |   |  |  |
   H  R1    H  R2  |  H  | R3
```

32. D is correct.

DNA and ribozymes of RNA (discovered in 1982) are capable of self-replication.

Protein functions include:

1) peptide hormones as chemical messengers transported within the blood,

2) enzymes that catalyze chemical reactions by lowering the energy of activation,

3) structural proteins for physical support within the cells, tissues, and organs,

4) transport proteins as carriers of essential materials, and

5) immune system antibodies bind foreign particles (i.e., antigens).

33. B is correct.

Eukaryote RNA polymerase needs transcription factors to bind the promoter and initiate basal-level transcription.

34. B is correct.

The percent of adenine cannot be determined because RNA is a single-stranded molecule.

Base-pairing rules for DNA (i.e., Chargaff's rule) are for double-stranded DNA but *not* single-stranded RNA.

35. A is correct.

I: AUG sequences are not only the initial start codon and downstream of the initial *start codon* (AUG). If this sequence is not the start codon, this change could result in a stop codon (UAA).

II: *genetic code* is read 5′ to 3′ and AUG (encoding methionine) is a start codon. A change in the start sequence in the mRNA (AUG to AAG) causes a failure in initiating translation.

III: changes in the first, second, or third amino acid may change U to A in the resultant amino acid.

The third position of the codon is the *wobble position* because the specified amino acid often does not change.

There are nucleotide changes that do not change the specified amino acid because the genetic code is redundant (i.e., most amino acids are encoded by more than one codon).

For example, AUU and AUA codons both encode isoleucine. The genetic code is *degenerate*, whereby changing a nucleotide (often in the 3rd position) does not change the amino acid encoded by the triplet codon.

Each codon (three nucleotides) encodes for one amino acid, and there is no ambiguity in the genetic code.

36. B is correct.

Genetic code (mRNA into protein) has several amino acids specified by more than one codon, three stop codons, and each is 3 nucleotides (bases) long.

37. D is correct.

Polymerase I (Pol I) adds nucleotides at the RNA primer-template junction (i.e., the origin of replication) and is involved in excision repair with 3'-5' and 5'-3' exonuclease activity and processing of Okazaki fragments generated during lagging strand synthesis.

B: *primase* adds the first two RNA primers at the start of DNA replication because the DNA polymerase must bond to double-stranded molecules.

RNA primer is removed by DNA polymerase I after the newly synthesized DNA strand has been replicated via DNA polymerase III.

a: *template strand* of parental DNA

b: *leading strand* of newly synthesized DNA

c: *lagging strand* (Okazaki fragments) of newly synthesized DNA

d: *replication fork* with helicase opening and unwinding the double-stranded DNA

e: *RNA primer* synthesized by primase

f: *direction* of DNA strand synthesis

DNA replication

38. C is correct.

Okazaki fragments are associated with the lagging DNA strand and (like all DNA) are synthesized in a 5'→ 3' direction by DNA polymerase III.

A: DNA polymerase I removes the short sequence RNA primers deposited by primase needed for the anchoring of the polymerase III to DNA for the synthesis of DNA in a 5'→ 3' direction.

B: Okazaki fragments are used to replicate the lagging strand and are covalently linked by *DNA ligase* (not DNA polymerase I), forming a continuous DNA strand.

D: Okazaki fragments are not synthesized to fill in gaps after removing the RNA primer by DNA polymerase I.

diagram below

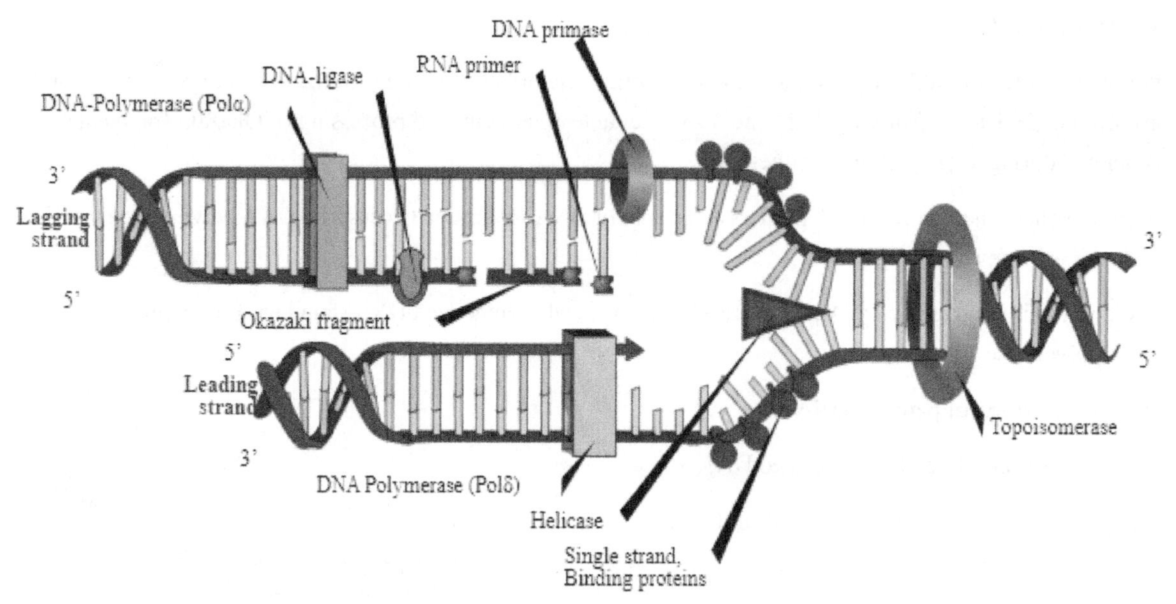

DNA semiconservative replication with associated proteins for leading and lagging strands. DNA polymerase proceeds from 5' to 3' along parental strands.

39. C is correct.

Ribosomal RNAs form a *large* subunit and a *small* subunit.

During translation, mRNA is between the small and large subunits, and the ribosome catalyzes the formation of a peptide bond between the two amino acids held by the rRNA.

A single mRNA can be translated simultaneously by multiple ribosomes.

Ribosomes catalyze the formation of a *peptide bond* between two amino acids tethered by rRNA.

A ribosome has three binding sites: A, P, and E.

Peptidyl transferase catalyzes this reaction.

The A site binds an aminoacyl-tRNA (i.e., a tRNA bound to an amino acid).

The amino (NH_2) group of the aminoacyl-tRNA, with the new amino acid, attacks the ester linkage of peptidyl-tRNA (in the P site), the last amino acid of the growing chain, forming a new peptide bond.

The tRNA holding the last amino acid moves to the E site, and the aminoacyl-tRNA is now the peptidyl-tRNA.

40. A is correct.

Protein synthesis does require energy.

B: rRNA is part of the ribosome and is necessary for proper binding of the ribosome to mRNA.

C: tRNA brings an amino acid to the ribosome, where it interacts with the mRNA of the proper sequence.

D: tRNA does have the amino acid bound to its 3' end.

41. B is correct.

Polymerase chain reaction (PCR) requires the sequence at the ends of the fragment to be amplified.

From the ends, primers use complementary base pairing to anneal the target fragment and permit amplification.

No knowledge of the region between the ends is required because the parent strands will be the template used by the DNA polymerase.

42. D is correct.

Shape of tRNA is determined primarily by *intramolecular base pairing*.

43. B is correct.

In prokaryotic cells, methylated guanine contributes to correcting mismatched pairs of bases.

44. A is correct.

Magnesium is a *divalent* mineral that DNA and RNA polymerases use as a cofactor (i.e., catalyst not consumed in the reaction) to stabilize interactions between polymerase and negative charge on the nucleic acid backbone.

45. C is correct.

Ribosome structure is created by the internal base-pairing of rRNA and ribosomal proteins.

46. A is correct.

Three types of RNA are mRNA, tRNA, and rRNA, which DNA encodes.

rRNA is synthesized in the nucleolus within the nucleus.

tRNA functions as a carrier of amino acid molecules.

Unlike mRNA, tRNA is a comparatively short ribonucleotide polymer of RNA subunits.

Although tRNA is single-stranded mainly, there are some double-stranded segments where the nucleotide chain loops back (i.e., hairpin turns) with hydrogen bonds between complementary base pairs; like DNA, two hydrogen bonds between A and U and three hydrogen bonds between C and G.

mRNA is the template for protein synthesis and has a poly-A tail, which functions as a *molecular clock* for mRNA degradation.

47. D is correct.

Phosphate group is the chemical group at the 5' end of a single polynucleotide strand.

48. C is correct.

Puromycin is an analog with a similar shape to tRNA.

Puromycin joins the ribosome, forms one peptide bond, and becomes covalently attached to the nascent protein.

However, since it lacks a carboxyl group, it cannot be linked to the next amino acid, and protein synthesis terminates prematurely.

Puromycin

A: *initiation* requires binding a single aminoacyl-tRNA (the initiator) to the ribosome and is unaffected.

B: *aminoacyl-tRNA* enters the large subunit of the ribosome at the A site during elongation.

D: *puromycin* lacks a carboxyl group and can only form one bond, so peptide synthesis stops prematurely.

49. C is correct.

In *E. coli* cells, DNA polymerase I degrades the RNA primer portion of Okazaki fragments.

50. D is correct.

DNA polymerase I proofreading increases replication fidelity by monitoring for mismatched pairs originating from the high processivity of polymerase III that rapidly replicates DNA.

Bacteria have a much lower DNA replication rate of about 1 in 1,000, increasing the mutation rate of bacteria.

51. C is correct.

DNA is a nucleotide polymer of deoxyribose sugar, phosphate group, and a nitrogenous base (e.g., A, C, G, T).

Phosphodiester bonds join nucleotides in DNA's backbone.

52. A is correct.

In *E. coli* cells, DNA polymerase III synthesizes most of the Okazaki fragments.

53. A is correct.

All the molecules, except cysteine, are nitrogenous bases – the component molecules of DNA and RNA (e.g., mRNA, rRNA & tRNA).

Nitrogenous bases guanine (G) and adenine (A) are purines, while cytosine (C) and thymine (T is in DNA) or uracil (U is in RNA) are pyrimidines.

Cysteine is an amino acid (not a nitrogenous base), and amino acids are the monomers for proteins.

54. A is correct.

Restriction enzymes (*restriction endonucleases*) cut DNA at specific nucleotide sequences (i.e., restriction sites).

Prokaryotes have endogenous restriction enzymes that selectively cleave foreign DNA.

Restriction enzymes are a defense mechanism against invading viruses in bacteria and archaea.

Host DNA is protected by a modification enzyme (i.e., *methylase*) that alters prokaryotic DNA and prevents cleavage by the endogenous restriction enzyme.

55. C is correct.

RNA polymerase is an enzyme that produces primary transcript RNA in transcription.

Molecule C has a phosphodiester bond from the 3' of the base to the 5' downstream base and a triphosphate at the 5' end of the molecule.

A: represents DNA because of the absence of hydroxyl at the 2' position of the sugar.

B: contains a monophosphate at the 5' position.

D: shows a phosphodiester bond at the 2' position (not the 3').

56. B is correct.

First step, two strands of DNA double helix are physically separated at an elevated temperature in DNA melting.

Second step, the temperature is lowered, and the two DNA strands become templates for DNA polymerase to amplify the target DNA selectively.

Third step, the reaction mechanism uses RNA polymerase to synthesize a complementary strand to the template.

The selectivity of PCR results from using primers complementary to the DNA region targeted for amplification under specific thermal cycling conditions.

The process continues for 30 to 40 cycles, doubling the amount of DNA each cycle.

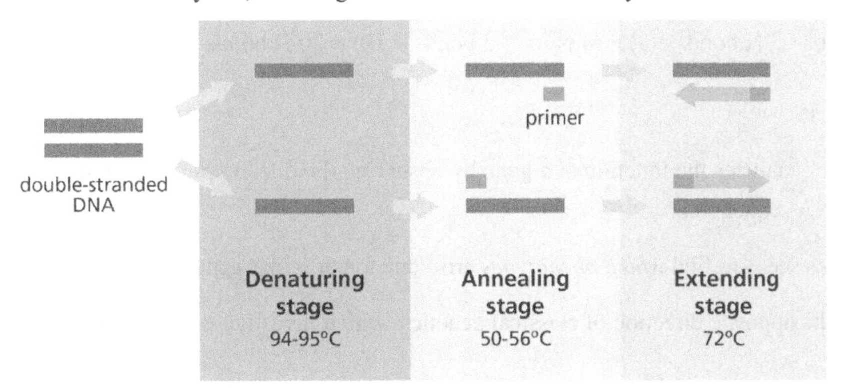

PCR amplification uses three steps for denaturing, annealing, and replicating DNA

57. A is correct.

DNA is double-stranded with A, C, G and T, while RNA is single-stranded with U replacing the T of DNA.

DNA uses the sugar of deoxyribose (i.e., the absence of ~OH group at the 2' in RNA), while RNA uses ribose (i.e., the presence of ~OH group at the 2').

58. B is correct.

Ligase is an enzyme used by the cell during DNA replication (and in other biochemical processes) that catalyzes the joining of two large molecules (e.g., DNA nucleotides) by forming a new chemical bond.

The newly formed bond is *via* a condensation reaction (joining) and usually involves dehydration with the loss of H_2O when the molecules (e.g., DNA, amino acids) are linked.

59. B is correct.

In DNA, thymine (T) base pairs with adenine (A) with two hydrogen bonds, while cytosine (C) base pairs with guanine (G) with three hydrogen bonds.

More energy is required to break three hydrogen bonds than two hydrogen bonds. A DNA sequence with increased C-G pairs has a higher melting point and requires more energy to denature (i.e., separate).

When bonded to its complementary strand, the DNA strand with GCCAGTCG has two T-A and six C-G pairs:

$$(2 \text{ pairs} \times 2 \text{ H bonds} = 4) + (6 \text{ pairs} \times 3 \text{ bonds} = 18) = 22 \text{ H bonds}$$

Thus, this DNA strand has the most hydrogen bonds and the highest melting point.

A: five T-A pairs and three C-G pairs:

$$(5 \text{ pairs} \times 2 \text{ H bonds} = 10) + (3 \text{ pairs} \times 3 \text{ bonds} = 9) = 19 \text{ H bonds}$$

C: four A-T pairs and four C-G pairs:

$$(4 \text{ pairs} \times 2 \text{ H bonds} = 8) + (4 \text{ pairs} \times 3 \text{ bonds} = 12) = 20 \text{ H bonds}$$

D: four A-T pairs and four C-G pairs:

$$(4 \text{ pairs} \times 2 \text{ H bonds} = 8) + (4 \text{ pairs} \times 3 \text{ bonds} = 12) = 20 \text{ H bonds}$$

60. C is correct.

Reverse genetics analyzes the function of a gene by observing the phenotypic effects of specific gene sequences obtained by DNA sequencing.

Reverse genetics seeks to find *which phenotypes* arise due to particular genetic sequences.

It proceeds in the opposite direction of classical genetics, which investigates the genetic basis of a phenotype.

61. D is correct.

Protein synthesis requires biochemical energy from ATP or GTP.

Two high-energy phosphate bonds (from ATP) provide the energy required to form one aminoacyl-tRNA involving the attachment of each amino acid to its tRNA.

Forming the *initiation complex* requires energy from one GTP.

For initiation, one high-energy phosphate bond (ATP) is required.

Elongation with the delivery of each new tRNA to the A site requires one GTP.

Translocation of the peptidyl-tRNA requires one GTP.

Termination does not require the hydrolysis of a high-energy phosphate bond (e.g., ATP, GTP).

For each amino acid added to the polypeptide chain, two high-energy phosphate bonds are used for "charging" the tRNA with the correct amino acid (2 GTP × 50 amino acids = 100).

For chain formation, one high-energy phosphate bond is required to carry the amino acid to the ribosome and another to translocate the ribosome (2 GTP × 49 peptide bonds = 98).

Total: 1 + 100 + 98 = 199

62. D is correct.

mRNA in *E. coli* cells is composed primarily of phosphodiester linkages between ribonucleotides.

63. B is correct.

DNA repair is a collection of processes by which a cell identifies and corrects damage to the DNA molecules encoding its genome.

Before replication of DNA, the cell methylates the parental strand for reference during any potential errors introduced during replication.

Normal metabolic activities and environmental factors such as UV light and radiation can cause DNA damage, resulting in many individual lesions per cell per day.

Many lesions cause structural damage to the DNA molecule and can alter the cell's ability to transcribe genes for the survival of its daughter cells after mitosis.

DNA repair process is constantly active as it responds to damage in the DNA structure, and methylation references the original strand when mismatches are detected during replication.

64. A is correct.

Methionine is the *start codon* of mRNA and is the first amino acid in eukaryotic proteins.

The mature protein may excise a portion of the original polypeptide, so methionine is not always the first amino acid in the mature protein after modification in the Golgi.

65. D is correct.

DNA in *E. coli* is composed of four bases (A, T, C, G), phosphodiester linkages connecting deoxyribonucleotide molecules; two strands base pair in an anti-parallel orientation, and phosphodiester linkages utilizing the 3'-OH.

66. B is correct.

3'–CAGUCGUACUUU–5' anticodon of the tRNA (known from question stem)

5'–GUCAGCAUGAAA–3' codon of the mRNA

3'–CAGTCGTACTTT–5' DNA

There is a *polarity* when nucleic acids base pair, whereby the 3' end of the tRNA anticodon corresponds to the 5' end of the mRNA codon. C pairs with G, and U pairs with A (base pairing is U to A in RNA).

mRNA sequence is 5'–GUCAGCAUGAAA–3'. The 3' end of the RNA hybridizes with the 5' end of DNA.

For complementary DNA, A pairs with T (not U in RNA), and the *polarity* of the strands is *antiparallel.*

An approach: since the 3' end of tRNA and the 3' end of DNA hybridize to the 5' of mRNA, the DNA sequence is the same orientation and similar to tRNA (i.e., replace T in DNA with U in tRNA).

By convention, nucleic acids are written with the 5' end on the left (top left in a double-stranded molecule) and read in the 5' to 3' direction.

67. A is correct.

Promoter is a region of 100–1000 base pairs long on the DNA that initiates transcription of a particular gene.

Promoters often are near the genes they transcribe, on the same strand, and upstream on the DNA (towards the 3' region of the antisense strand – template and non-coding strand).

Promoters contain specific DNA sequences and response elements that provide a secure initial binding site for RNA polymerase and transcription factors proteins.

Transcription factors have specific activator (or repressor) sequences of nucleotides that attach to specific promoters and regulate gene expressions.

In bacteria, the promoter is recognized by RNA polymerase and an associated sigma factor (i.e., a protein needed only for initiation of RNA synthesis), which are often brought to the promoter DNA by an activator protein's binding to its own nearby DNA binding site.

In eukaryotes, the process is complicated, with many factors needed to bind RNA polymerase II to a promoter.

68. A is correct.

Isoleucine-glycine is composed of two amino acids and therefore is a dipeptide.

69. A is correct.

Correct order of events in delivering a protein to its cellular destination:

signal sequence binds to a docking protein → membrane channel forms → chaperonins unfold

70. D is correct.

RNA polymerase synthesizes the new strand in the *anti-parallel orientation* with new nucleotides adding to the growing chain in the 5' to 3' direction.

71. B is correct.

Adenosine (A) bonds with thymine (T) by two hydrogen bonds.

Guanine (G) bonds with cytosine (C) by three hydrogen bonds.

72. B is correct.

Lagging strand is composed of Okazaki fragments.

Nucleotides (e.g., DNA and RNA) extend from the 3'-OH group.

The leading (i.e., continuous) *and* lagging (i.e., discontinuous) strands use the 3'-OH end as a nucleophile during the condensation (i.e., via dehydration) reaction for chain elongation.

A: 3' end of the *template strand.*

C: 5' end of a *lagging strand.*

D: 5' end of the *template strand*

73. C is correct.

Ribosomal subunits, radio-labeled with *heavy* carbon and *heavy* nitrogen, were placed in a test tube during bacterial protein synthesis.

The small and large subunits assemble to form a complete ribosome during translation.

After translation ceases, the complete ribosome dissociates into individual small and large subunits.

Since the sample used in centrifugation was taken after translation, the individual ribosomal subunits (not the assembled ribosomes) were present.

Centrifugation separates cellular components based on density, and since the subunits are different sizes, two different bands are expected in the centrifuge tube.

Understanding the size of the two ribosomal subunits in bacteria is required; bacteria have two subunits of the 30S and 50S, which assemble to form a 70S complex, and eukaryotes have 40S and 60s ribosomes, which assemble to form an 80S complex.

74. D is correct.

Translation is the protein production process whereby one amino acid adds to the end of a protein.

Ribosomes perform this mechanism.

The sequence of nucleotides in the template mRNA chain determines the sequence of amino acids in the generated amino acid chain.

Adding an amino acid occurs at the C-terminus of the peptide, and translation is amino-to-carboxyl directed.

75. D is correct.

Codon for histidine is 5'-CAU-3'. The anticodon in tRNA that brings histidine to the ribosome is 5'-AUG-3'.

76. B is correct.

The existing polypeptide chain is transferred to the *P site* during translation elongation as the ribosome moves in the 3' direction.

77. A is correct.

In polymerase chain reactions (*PCR amplification*), a primer hybridizes to the end of a DNA fragment.

A primer is the initiation site for DNA polymerase to bind and replicate the entire strand.

DNA replicates $5' \rightarrow 3'$.

The primer must be the complement of the $3'$ end because DNA polymerase reads the template strand $3' \rightarrow 5'$.

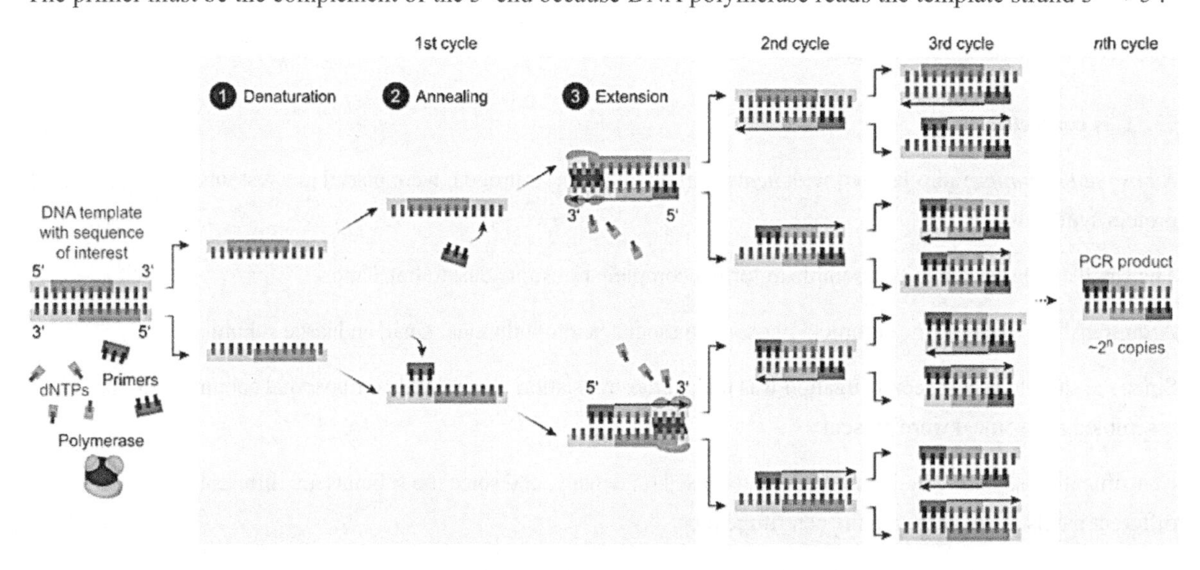

Polymerase chain with exponential product amplification during each cycle. First step heats the DNA to separate the two strands of the double helix. Step 2 cools the sample to allow annealing by complementary primers. Step 3 is chain elongation for the synthesis of DNA by RNA polymerase extending from the primers.

78. C is correct.

Genetic code is *not* ambiguous (i.e., each codon specifies one amino acid).

79. C is correct.

R-groups (i.e., amino acid side chains) portion of the polypeptide chain is responsible for establishing and maintaining the force to stabilize the secondary structure.

80. B is correct.

A ribosome made a tripeptide, MET-ARG-SER, attached to tRNA in the P site.

From the genetic code, the CGU codon is in the E site of the ribosome.

First base (5′ end)	Second base: U	Second base: C	Second base: A	Second base: G	Third base (3′ end)
U	UUU Phe	UCU Ser	UAU Tyr	UGU Cys	U
U	UUC Phe	UCC Ser	UAC Tyr	UGC Cys	C
U	UUA Leu	UCA Ser	UAA Stop	UGA Stop	A
U	UUG Leu	UCG Ser	UAG Stop	UGG Trp	G
C	CUU Leu	CCU Pro	CAU His	CGU Arg	U
C	CUC Leu	CCC Pro	CAC His	CGC Arg	C
C	CUA Leu	CCA Pro	CAA Gln	CGA Arg	A
C	CUG Leu	CCG Pro	CAG Gln	CGG Arg	G
A	AUU Ile	ACU Thr	AAU Asn	AGU Ser	U
A	AUC Ile	ACC Thr	AAC Asn	AGC Ser	C
A	AUA Ile	ACA Thr	AAA Lys	AGA Arg	A
A	AUG Met start	ACG Thr	AAG Lys	AGG Arg	G
G	GUU Val	GCU Ala	GAU Asp	GGU Gly	U
G	GUC Val	GCC Ala	GAC Asp	GGC Gly	C
G	GUA Val	GCA Ala	GAA Glu	GGA Gly	A
G	GUG Val	GCG Ala	GAG Glu	GGG Gly	G

81. D is correct.

A ribosome made a tripeptide, MET-ARG-SER, attached to tRNA in the P site.

Using the genetic code, it cannot be determined which codon is in the A site of the ribosome.

Notes for active learning

Evolution and Natural Selection – Detailed Explanations

1. D is correct.

Charles Darwin (1809-1882), during his trip to the Galapagos Islands in the 1830s, observed several species of finches that differed among islands.

2. A is correct.

Evolutionary relationships classify organisms:

Kingdom → Phylum → Class → Order → Family → Genus → Species

The largest group (i.e., kingdom) divides into smaller subdivisions.

Each smaller group has common characteristics. Of the answers, a genus is the smallest subdivision, and organisms in the same genus are more similar than organisms classified as the same family, order, class, or kingdom.

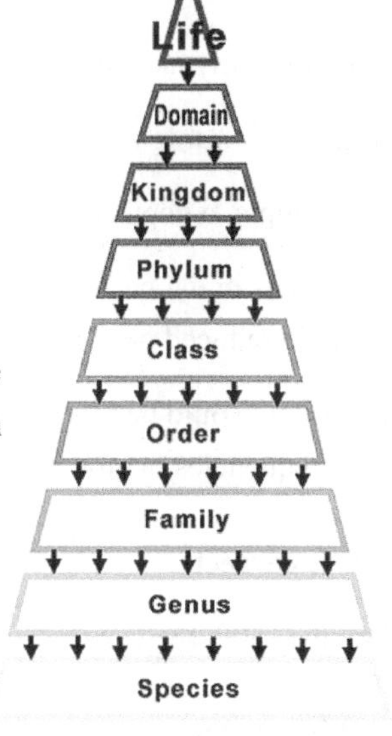

3. D is correct.

Mutations are the source of genetic variation for natural selection.

4. A is correct.

Chloroplast is a plant cell organelle that may have originated from cyanobacteria through *endosymbiosis*.

Endosymbiotic theory proposes that a eukaryotic cell engulfed a photosynthesizing cyanobacterium about one billion years ago. The photosynthesizing cyanobacterium became a permanent resident in the cell because it escaped the phagocytic vacuole in which it was contained.

Chloroplasts contain their DNA and ribosomes (like prokaryotic ribosomes) and undergo autosomal replication (i.e., replicating independently of the cell cycle), supporting this theory.

Cyanobacteria obtain energy through photosynthesis and have the color of the bacteria (i.e., blue).

Named blue-green algae, this is a misnomer as cyanobacteria are prokaryotes, while algae are eukaryotes.

By producing oxygen as a by-product gas of photosynthesis, cyanobacteria converted Earth's early reducing atmosphere into an oxidizing one, dramatically changing the composition of life by stimulating biodiversity and leading to the near-extinction of oxygen-intolerant organisms.

Endosymbiotic theory proposes that chloroplasts in plants, mitochondria in eukaryotes, and eukaryotic algae evolved from prokaryotic cyanobacterial ancestors.

Mitochondria evolved from free-living prokaryotic heterotrophs that, similarly to chloroplasts, entered eukaryotic cells and established a symbiotic relationship with the host (the theory of *endosymbiosis*).

Mitochondria contain circular DNA (similar in size and composition to prokaryotes), ribosomes (like prokaryotic ribosomes), and unique proteins in the organelle membrane (similar in composition to prokaryotes) and replicate independently, providing further evidence to support this theory.

5. D is correct.

Evolution is the long-term changes in a population's gene pool caused by environmental selection pressures.

I: *random mutation* creates new alleles selected for (or against) as a phenotypic variation for natural selection (i.e., survival of the fittest).

II: *reproductive isolation* of a population is a crucial component for speciation.

Geographically isolated populations often diverge to yield reproductive isolation leading to speciation.

III: *speciation* might happen in a population with no specific extrinsic barrier to gene flow.

For example, a population extends over a broad geography, and mating in the population is not random.

Individuals in the far west would have zero probability of mating with individuals in the far east range. This results in reduced *gene flow* but not total isolation. Such a situation may (or not) be sufficient for speciation.

Speciation would be promoted by different selective pressures at opposite ends of the range, which would alter gene frequencies in groups at different ranges so they would not be able to mate if they were reunited.

6. C is correct.

Darwin (1809-1882) hypothesized that the mechanism of evolution involves natural selection.

7. D is correct.

Prokaryotes are primarily *unicellular* organisms, although a few, such as mycobacterium, have multicellular stages in their life cycles or create large colonies like cyanobacteria.

Eukaryotes are often *multicellular* and are typically much *larger than prokaryotes*.

Eukaryotes have *internal membranous structures* (i.e., organelles) and a cytoskeleton composed of microtubules, microfilaments, and intermediate filaments, essential for cellular organization and shape.

8. D is correct.

Archaean Eon contains the oldest known fossil record, dating to about 3.5 billion years.

9. A is correct.

Urey and Miller demonstrated in 1953 that organic molecules might be created from inorganic molecules under the primordial earth conditions. They conducted an experiment that simulated conditions thought at the time to be on the early Earth and assessed for the occurrence of chemical origins of life.

Urey-Miller did not prove the existence of life on earth.

However, experiments showed over 20 different amino acids produced in Miller's original experiments.

10. B is correct.

Nature uses many methods for fertilization, development, and care of offspring.

Internal fertilization involves internal development and much care for offspring. These organisms (e.g., humans and many mammals) produce few offspring, but a large percentage reach adulthood.

External fertilization involves external development and little care for offspring. These organisms (e.g., many species of fish) produce large numbers of sperm and eggs because relatively few sperm and eggs interact to produce a zygote. Few zygotes survive without physical protection from predators, and millions of eggs and sperm must be released to perpetuate the species.

A: *protective coloring* might help for survival against predators, but not related to caring for the young.

C: *laying eggs* is not related to not caring for the young (most birds care for their young).

D: not relevant to the survival rate of the offspring.

11. C is correct.

Mutualism is when two species live in close association and both benefit.

Parasitism is a relationship between two organisms where one organism benefits while the other is harmed.

Commensalism involves a relationship between organisms where one benefits without affecting another.

Mimicry (in evolutionary biology) is the similarity of species, which protects one or both and occurs when a group (the mimics) evolves to share common characteristics with another group (the models). This similarity can be in appearance, behavior, sound, scent, or location, with mimics found in similar places to their models.

12. D is correct.

Disruptive selection shifts allele frequencies towards variants of extremes, leading to two subpopulations.

These subpopulations do not favor the intermediate variants of the original population and grow disparate over time, likely leading to speciation.

A: *sexual selection* gives an individual an advantage in finding a mate.

Sexual selection often acts opposite to the effects of natural selection (e.g., a brighter plume may make a bird vulnerable to predators but gives it an advantage during reproduction).

It is hypothesized that sexual selection leads to sexual dimorphism (i.e., phenotypic differences between males and females of the same species).

B: *stabilizing selection* is a shift in phenotypes towards intermediates by disfavoring variants at extremes.

Stabilizing selection reduces variation within the species and perpetuates similarities between generations.

C: *directional selection* is the population shift in allele frequencies towards variants of one extreme.

13. D is correct.

Similarity among the embryos of fish, amphibians, reptiles, and humans is evidence of *common ancestry*.

14. A is correct.

Mutualism (i.e., symbiotic) is a relationship between two organisms where both benefits. For example, soybeans depend on humans to survive while humans are provided with food. *Both species* benefit from the relationship.

Commensalism is a class of relationships where one organism benefits without affecting the other.

Mutualism (i.e., symbiotic) is a relationship between two organisms where both benefit.

Parasitism is a relationship between two organisms where one benefits while the other is harmed.

15. B is correct.

Natural selection leads to a population most adapted (*fittest*) to its current environment.

16. A is correct.

From an evolutionary perspective, *passing genetic information* to progeny is paramount.

17. D is correct.

Inherited traits determined by heredity are genes.

18. D is correct.

The evolutionary process of natural selection *works on existing genetic variation* within a population.

19. C is correct.

Genetic drift changes allele frequency within a population due to random sampling.

Allele frequency of a population is the fraction of the same alleles.

Offspring have the same alleles as the parents, and probability determines if an individual survives and reproduces.

Genetic drift may cause allele variants to disappear and thereby reduce genetic variation.

20. A is correct.

The characteristic of human height results from *polygenic* (i.e., many genes contribute) inheritance.

21. C is correct.

The oldest known *fossilized prokaryotes* were laid down approximately 3.6 billion years ago, about 1 billion years after the formation of the Earth's crust.

Eukaryotes appear in the fossil record later and may have formed from the aggregation of multiple prokaryotes.

The oldest known *fossilized eukaryotes* are about 1.7 billion years old.

continued…

However, some genetic evidence suggests eukaryotes appeared as early as 3 billion years ago.

Protists are a large and diverse group of eukaryotic microorganisms which belong to the kingdom Protista. There have been attempts to remove the kingdom from the taxonomy, but it is commonly used. Some professional organizations and institutions prefer the name Protista.

Protists are unicellular or they are multicellular without specialized tissues. Besides their relatively simple levels of organization, protists do not have much in common.

The straightforward cellular organization distinguishes protists from other eukaryotes (e.g., fungi, animals).

Protists live in almost any environment with liquid water.

Many protists, such as algae, are photosynthetic and are vital primary producers in ecosystems, particularly in the ocean as part of the plankton.

Protists include pathogenic species, such as the kinetoplastid *Trypanosoma brucei,* causing sleeping sickness, and species of the apicomplexan *Plasmodium,* causing malaria.

22. D is correct.

Morphological or physical similarity between organisms is insufficient for classifying the same species.

Species are organisms that mate and produce *viable* and *fertile* offspring (give rise to additional offspring).

Organisms appearing different (e.g., dog breeds) can be the same species if they mate and produce fertile offspring.

A: organisms can be the same species yet have different gene varieties (i.e., alleles) at the same gene locus.

For example, blue-eyed and green-eyed individuals can mate and produce fertile offspring.

B: *no relationship* between producing viable, fertile offspring and blood type.

C: *somatic cells* are body cells, not reproductive cells (i.e., gametes) or haploid (i.e., 1N or monoploid).

Somatic cells are diploid (2N) and undergo *mitosis* for cell division.

Gametes are haploid (1N) and undergo *meiosis* for cell division.

23. C is correct.

Gene pool is the population's total collection of alleles.

24. C is correct.

A pivotal point in Darwin's explanation of evolution is that any trait that confers an increase in the *probability* of its possessor surviving and reproducing is favored and spread through the population.

25. C is correct.

If an allele's frequency in a population is 0.7, the alternate allele is 0.3.

26. B is correct.

Natural selection is how mutations are selected for (or against) in the environment. If the resulting phenotype offers some degree of fitness, the genes are passed to the next generation.

A: *natural selection* includes selection pressures and needs a population with genetic variation (random mutations) to select the fittest organisms.

C: *Darwin's theory* depends on more than mere mutations. It is based on over-reproduction. Offspring are selected for (or against) when their genetic makeup is fit for the environment where the organism is located.

Organisms most fit (for their environment) and pass their genes (i.e., gametes) to the next generation. The result is survival (greatest reproduction) of the fittest organisms within the environment.

D: *Lamarck* proposed that if traits were used (e.g., stretching of a giraffe's neck), these acquired traits are passed to the next generation.

Acquired characteristics (phenotypic changes) do not affect the genes and are not passed to the next generation via the gametes (e.g., sperm and egg).

27. B is correct.

Fewer copies of an allele magnify the effect of *genetic drift*.

Genetic drift is negligible when there are many copies of an allele.

28. D is correct.

A population that survived a bottleneck and recovered to its original size has less genetic variation than before.

29. B is correct.

Founder effect and *population bottleneck* differ because the founder effect requires isolating a small group from a larger population.

30. B is correct.

Life originated in an atmosphere with *little or no oxygen.*

Until the Great Oxygenation Event (GOE) about 2.4 billion years ago, there was no atmospheric free oxygen.

Cyanobacteria appeared about 200 million years before the GOE began producing oxygen by photosynthesis.

Before the GOE, free oxygen produced was chemically captured by dissolved iron or organic matter.

The GOE was when oxygen sinks became saturated with oxygen produced by cyanobacterial photosynthesis. After GOE, excess free oxygen accumulated in the atmosphere.

Free oxygen is toxic to obligate anaerobic organisms. The rising concentrations eradicated most of Earth's anaerobic organisms. Cyanobacteria were responsible for one of Earth's most significant extinction events.

Free oxygen reacts with atmospheric methane (a greenhouse gas), which is oxidized to CO_2 and H_2O.

continued...

Free oxygen has been an essential constituent of the atmosphere ever since. Periods with much oxygen in the atmosphere are associated with the rapid development of animals.

Today's atmosphere contains about 21% oxygen, which is enough for the rapid development of animals.

31. B is correct.

Founder effect is the likely explanation that a population of humans has a higher rate of polydactyly (extra fingers or toes) than the human population.

32. C is correct.

Gene flow occurs through migration.

33. C is correct.

The first organisms had nothing else to eat.

Even with millions of organisms, one organism must eat many, which would have exhausted the supply.

34. B is correct.

Evolutionary fitness measures *reproductive success* (i.e., the hereditary succession of gene pools).

35. A is correct.

Lamarck's theory of evolution proposed that enhanced structures (e.g., a giraffe's neck) arise based on use.

Lamarck (1744-1829) had a false premise that favorable characteristics obtained by use were inheritable.

For example, giraffes stretch their necks to reach leaves on branches. He proposed that offspring inherit the trait (longer necks) based on use. However, only changes in the DNA of gametes (e.g., egg or sperm) are inherited.

B: de Vries (1848-1935) confirmed Mendel's observations with different plant species.

C: Mendel (1822-1884) defined classical genetics by experiments with inheritable traits (e.g., seed color, wrinkled vs. round seeds) in pea plants.

Mendel described the principles of dominance, segregation, and independent assortment. The unit of inheritance (i.e., genes) was unknown.

D: *Darwin's Theory of Natural Selection* states that *environmental pressures select the fittest organism* to survive and reproduce.

Natural Selection by Mendel is based on six principles.

1) **Overpopulation**: more offspring are produced than can survive from insufficient food, air, light, and space to support the population;

2) **Variations**: offspring have differences (i.e., variations) in characteristics compared to the population. Darwin did not know why, but de Vries later suggested that *genetic mutations* cause variations. Some mutations are *beneficial* fittest), but most are *detrimental*;

continued...

3) **Competition**: developing populations compete for necessities (e.g., food, air, light). Many young die, while the number of adults remains about constant for generations;

4) **Natural selection**: some organisms have phenotypes (i.e., variations) conferring an advantage over others;

5) **Inheritance of variations**: individuals reproduce and transmit favorable phenotypes to offspring. Favored alleles (i.e., variations of genes) eventually dominate the gene pool;

6) **Evolution of a new species**: natural selection (fittest) propagates favorable genes and phenotypes over generations.

Favorable changes result in significant changes in the gene pool for the evolution of a new species (i.e., organisms that reproduce and yield fertile offspring).

36. D is correct.

Non-poisonous butterflies evolve color changes to look like poisonous butterflies in *directional selection*.

37. A is correct.

Genetic variation would likely be decreased by stabilizing selection.

38. C is correct.

Asexual reproduction is more efficient than sexual reproduction in the number of offspring produced per reproduction, in the amount of energy invested in this process, and in the amount of time invested in the development of the young (before and after birth).

Asexual reproduction relies on *genetic mutation* for phenotypic variability to be passed to future generations since it produces genetic clones of the parent.

Sexual reproduction involves the process of meiosis – two rounds of cell division and the likelihood of cross-over (during prophase I).

A: new phenotype may be disadvantageous *or* advantageous.

B: a much greater probability of a mutation occurring with sexual reproduction (i.e., at the chromosomal level), known as chromosomal aberrations.

D: *sexual reproduction* requires more *energy* and *time* per progeny (i.e., offspring).

Species reproducing sexually have a selective advantage because of *gene recombination* during fertilization.

Fusing two genetically unique nuclei (haploid sperm and haploid egg nucleus) yields a unique (2N) zygote.

Fertilizing two unique gametes introduces phenotypic variability into a population.

This genetic and phenotypic variability may benefit or harm individuals in their environment.

Advantageous phenotypes will survive and pass genes to future generations consistent with natural selection (i.e., survival of the fittest).

39. D is correct.

Birds laying an intermediate number of eggs have the highest reproductive success, likely resulting from stabilizing selection.

40. D is correct.

Nucleotides are sugar (ribose for RNA or deoxyribose for DNA), a phosphate group, and a base.

Nitrogenous bases are guanine, adenine, cytosine, thymine (for DNA), or uracil (for RNA).

Adenine and guanine are purines, while thymine, cytosine, and uracil are pyrimidines.

A: *lipids* (i.e., fats) are composed of glycerol (i.e., 3-carbon chain) and (up to) three fatty acids.

B: *monosaccharides* are the monomers (e.g., glucose, fructose) of carbohydrates (e.g., glycogen, cellulose).

C: *nucleosides* have a nitrogenous base and sugar (without phosphate).

Nucleotides have a phosphate group, nitrogenous base, and sugar.

41. A is correct.

Sexual selection likely results from a female deer choosing to mate with males with the biggest antlers.

42. A is correct.

Embryos indicate that fossilized organisms reproduce sexually.

The development of an embryo involves two distinct reproductive cells fusing, characteristic of sexual reproduction. This single-cell zygote results from fertilizing the female egg cell with a male sperm cell.

43. D is correct.

Cambrian Explosion occurred around 542 million years ago with the rapid appearance of most major animal phyla. This was accompanied by significant diversification of other organisms, as the fossil record shows.

Before about 580 million years ago, most organisms were simple, composed of individual cells occasionally organized into colonies.

Over the following 70-80 million years, the rate of evolution accelerated by order of magnitude, and the diversity of life became similar to today.

44. C is correct.

During evolution, primates needed to walk on two legs (i.e., *bipedal*) to free their hands for other tasks.

Hands were used in creating weapons and tools to gather food and protect the young.

45. B is correct.

Eyes facing forward allow two fields of vision to overlap, enabling the perception of depth.

Animals without facing forward eyes could not likely judge the distance to objects (e.g., tree branches) due to flawed depth perception.

As primates moved into trees to escape predators, they needed to navigate tree branches, meaning evolution favored good depth perception.

46. D is correct.

Sexual reproduction increases fitness and allows for modifications in traits, which can help adapt to new living conditions in a changing environment.

Sexual reproduction adds to the diversity of the offspring.

All other answer choices characterize asexual reproduction.

47. D is correct.

Arboreal locomotion is the movement of animals in *trees.*

Some animals have evolved to move in habitats where trees are present.

Animals may only scale trees occasionally or become exclusively arboreal.

48. A is correct.

Australopithecus afarensis is an extinct species with hip, knee, and foot morphology distinctive to bipedalism.

Footprints show *Australopithecus afarensis* walked with an upright posture and a strong heel strike, which is early evidence of bipedalism.

49. D is correct.

Amniotic eggs are laid on land by certain reptiles, birds, and mammals.

Amniotic eggs differ from *anamniotic* eggs, typically laid in water (by fish and amphibians).

50. A is correct.

Gluteus muscles of the pelvis are important for propulsion and stability while walking.

Bipedal humans are different from quadrupedal apes in the lateral orientation of the ilium, which constitutes the bowl-shaped pelvis.

51. C is correct.

Homo sapiens evolved after the *Homo erectus* and are *modern humans*.

52. B is correct.

Neanderthals are closely related to modern humans, with differences based on DNA by 0.3%, but twice the greatest DNA difference among contemporary humans.

Genetic evidence suggests Neanderthals contributed to the DNA of anatomically modern humans, probably through interbreeding between 80,000 and 30,000 years ago.

Recent evidence suggests that Neanderthals practiced burial behavior and buried their dead.

Archaeological remains by Neanderthals include bones and stone tools.

Notes for active learning

Animal Behavior and Evolution – Detailed Explanations

1. A is correct.

Potato washing requires learning.

Learning behavior includes habituation, sensitization, classical conditioning, operant conditioning, observational learning, play, and insight learning.

Innate behaviors do not need prior experience or learning.

2. A is correct.

Behavior is the *internally coordinated responses* (i.e., actions or inactions) of organisms (individuals or groups) to internal or external stimuli. Behaviors can be *innate* (instinct) or *learned.*

Behavior is an act of an organism that changes its relationship to its environment; it provides outputs from the organism to the environment.

3. B is correct.

Evolution is the long-term changes in a population *gene pool* caused by environmental selection pressures.

Mutations are the source of genetic variation for natural selection.

Random mutations create new alleles selected for (or against) as a phenotypic variation for natural selection (i.e., survival of the fittest).

4. C is correct.

Operant conditioning is behavior modified by *antecedents* (i.e., before trained behavior) and consequences.

Operant conditioning is distinguished from *classical conditioning* (or *respondent conditioning*) because operant conditioning addresses reinforcement and punishment to change behavior.

Imprinting is *phase-sensitive* learning (learning during a life stage) rapid and independent of the consequences of behavior. Imprinting has a critical period.

Insight learning is the faculty of reason or rationality and involves a sudden realization distinct from cause-and-effect problem-solving. It manifests *spontaneously* and is a noteworthy event in the learning process.

Insight learning is *problem-solving* occurring suddenly by understanding relationships between parts of a problem rather than through test and error.

Classical conditioning differs from *operant conditioning* because the behavior is strengthened or weakened, depending on its consequences (i.e., reward or punishment).

Classical conditioning involves reflexive (reflex) behaviors elicited by prior exposure. It occurs when a conditioned stimulus is paired with an unconditioned stimulus.

Consequences do not maintain behaviors conditioned through classical conditioning.

5. A is correct.

Innate (or *instinct*) behavior is the inherent inclination towards a particular complex behavior. A truncated sequence of actions, without variation, is carried out in response to a clearly defined stimulus.

Instinctive behavior is *without prior experience* (i.e., absence of learning) and uses innate biological factors.

6. D is correct.

Innate (or *instinct*) behavior is the inherent inclination towards a particular complex behavior; a truncated sequence of actions, without variation, is carried out in response to a clearly defined stimulus.

Instinctive behavior is performed *without prior experience* (i.e., absence of learning) and expresses innate biological factors.

7. B is correct.

Moths communicate with predators, in this example, by sight. Animals communicate using four primary methods: visual, auditory, tactile, and chemical.

8. D is correct.

Classical conditioning differs from *operant conditioning* because the behavior is strengthened or weakened, depending on its consequences (i.e., reward or punishment).

Classical conditioning involves reflexive (reflex) behaviors elicited by prior exposure. It occurs when a conditioned stimulus is paired with an unconditioned stimulus.

Consequences do not maintain behaviors conditioned through classical conditioning.

9. C is correct.

Imprinting is *phase-sensitive* learning (learning during a life stage) rapid and independent of the consequences of behavior. Imprinting has a critical period.

10. A is correct.

Imprinting is *phase-sensitive* learning (learning during a life stage) rapid and independent of the consequences of behavior. Imprinting has a critical period.

11. A is correct.

Habituation diminishes a physiological or emotional response to a frequently repeated stimulus.

12. D is correct.

Classical conditioning differs from *operant conditioning* because the behavior is strengthened or weakened, depending on its consequences (i.e., reward or punishment).

Classical conditioning involves reflexive (reflex) behaviors elicited by prior exposure. It occurs when a conditioned stimulus is paired with an unconditioned stimulus.

Consequences do not maintain behaviors conditioned through classical conditioning.

13. C is correct.

Animals secrete *pheromones* (e.g., sex attractants) to influence the behavior of species members.

Animals *communicate* using four methods: visual, auditory, tactile, and chemical.

14. B is correct.

Imprinting is *phase-sensitive learning* (i.e., during a life stage), independent of the consequences of behavior.

Imprinting has a critical period.

15. C is correct.

Learning occurs when an external stimulus causes an animal to change behavior (e.g., response to stimuli).

16. A is correct.

Circadian rhythms are biological processes reoccurring every 24 hours.

Circadian clock drives these rhythms widely observed in plants, animals, fungi, and cyanobacteria.

17. D is correct.

Migrating birds that nest in the Northern Hemisphere tend to fly northward in the spring for the burgeoning insect populations, budding plants, and abundance of nesting locations. As winter approaches and the availability of insects and other food drops, the birds move south again.

Migration is based on seasons.

18. C is correct.

Kin selection is the evolutionary strategy favoring the reproductive success of an organism's relatives, even at a cost to the organism's survival and reproduction.

Kin altruism is unselfish behavior driven by *kin selection.*

Kin selection is *inclusive fitness*, combining the number of offspring produced with the number an individual can produce by supporting others (e.g., siblings).

For example, kin selection includes honeybees that do not reproduce by deferring to relatives, adopting orphans in animal populations, and familial caring for the young.

19. C is correct.

Hibernation is how animals conserve energy to survive adverse weather conditions or food scarcity.

Hibernation involves *physiological changes* such as decreased body temperature, heart rate, respiration rate, and slowed metabolism. It is a form of torpor (lethargy); metabolism is less than five percent.

20. B is correct.

Operant conditioning is behavior modified by *antecedents* (i.e., before trained behavior) and consequences. It is distinguished from *classical conditioning* (or *respondent conditioning*) because operant conditioning addresses reinforcement and punishment to change behavior.

Insight learning is problem-solving occurring suddenly by understanding relationships between parts of a problem rather than through test and error. It is the faculty of reason or rationality and involves a sudden realization distinct from cause-and-effect problem-solving.

Insight learning manifests spontaneously and is a noteworthy event in the learning process.

Classical conditioning differs from *operant conditioning* because the behavior is strengthened or weakened, depending on its consequences (i.e., reward or punishment).

Classical conditioning involves reflexive (reflex) behaviors elicited by prior exposure. It occurs when a conditioned stimulus is paired with an unconditioned stimulus.

Consequences do not maintain behaviors conditioned through classical conditioning.

Habituation diminishes a physiological or emotional response to a frequently repeated stimulus.

21. A is correct.

Fertility and reproduction in animals follow circadian and seasonal rhythms.

Reproductive rhythm aims to maximize mating opportunities and offspring birth during favorable seasons for climate and food availability. Their purpose is to increase offspring survival.

Chronobiology studies the rhythms of organisms and how external conditions influence them.

22. A is correct.

Courtship is mate-selection behavior (i.e., *rituals*).

Animal courtship occurs outside human observation, so it is the least documented animal behavior.

Animals *communicate* using four methods: visual, auditory, tactile, and chemical.

Courtship may include complicated protocols, vocalizations, beauty, or prowess.

23. D is correct.

Members of a society belong to the same species and interact closely.

Social animals (e.g., ants, termites) live together in large groups and often cooperate in many tasks.

24. B is correct.

Insight learning is the faculty of reason or rationality and involves a sudden realization distinct from cause-and-effect problem-solving. It manifests *spontaneously* and is a noteworthy event in the learning process.

Insight learning is *problem-solving* occurring suddenly by understanding relationships between parts of a problem rather than through test and error.

25. C is correct.

Animals require resources (e.g., food, water, biotic factors) for survival. An animal may benefit most by defending a territory if that area has more resources than the surrounding areas.

Competitive exclusion principle (*Gause's law of competitive exclusion* or *Gause's law*) states that two species competing for the same resources cannot coexist when ecological factors are constant.

26. D is correct.

Innate (or *instinct*) behavior is the inherent inclination towards a particular complex behavior.

A truncated sequence of actions, without variation, is carried out in response to a clearly defined stimulus.

Instinctive behavior is performed *without prior experience* (i.e., absence of learning) and expresses innate biological factors.

27. A is correct.

Social animals (e.g., ants, termites) live together in large groups and often cooperate in conducting many tasks.

Groups offer advantages such as greater protection from predation.

28. C is correct.

Nocturnality is an animal behavior characterized by *activity during the night* and *sleep during the day*.

Nocturnal creatures have advanced senses of hearing to avoid predators and communicate.

Diurnal animals are awake during the day and sleeping at night.

29. A is correct.

Animals *communicate* using four methods: visual, auditory, tactile, and chemical.

Some species rely more on one form to communicate; however, all use methods to show affection, ward off threats or attract mates.

Animals often use chemical communication (e.g., *pheromones*) to mark territory.

For example, animals (e.g., dogs, lions) make *scent posts* to mark their territory and set territory boundaries.

30. B is correct.

Operant conditioning is behavior modified by *antecedents* (i.e.; before trained behavior) and consequences.

Operant conditioning is distinguished from *classical conditioning* (or *respondent conditioning*) because operant conditioning addresses reinforcement and punishment to change behavior.

Imprinting is *phase-sensitive* learning (learning during a life stage) rapid and independent of the consequences of behavior. Imprinting has a critical period.

Habituation diminishes a physiological or emotional response to a frequently repeated stimulus.

Classical conditioning differs from *operant conditioning* because the behavior is strengthened or weakened, depending on its consequences (i.e., reward or punishment).

Classical conditioning involves reflexive (reflex) behaviors elicited by prior exposure. It occurs when a conditioned stimulus is paired with an unconditioned stimulus.

Consequences do not maintain behaviors conditioned through classical conditioning.

31. A is correct.

Animals *communicate* using four methods: visual, auditory, tactile, and chemical.

For example, changes in skin color and patterns are visual signals.

Animals secrete *pheromones* (e.g., sex attractants) to influence the behavior of species members.

32. C is correct.

Animals *communicate* using four methods: visual, auditory, tactile, and chemical.

For example, changes in skin color and patterns are visual signals.

Pheromones are *chemical signals* released by animals to influence other animals.

33. A is correct.

Imprinting is when environmental patterns (or objects) presented to a developing organism during a *critical period* in early life become accepted as permanent aspects of their behavior.

For example, a duckling passes through a critical period when its mother is the first large moving object it sees.

B: *instrumental conditioning* involves reward or reinforcement to stimuli to establish a conditioning response.

C: *discrimination* involves learning organisms that respond differently to slightly different stimuli.

D: *pheromones* (e.g., sex attractants) are secreted by animals to influence the behavior of species members.

Notes for active learning

Notes for active learning

Classification and Diversity – Detailed Explanations

1. D is correct.

Mnemonic: **D**arn **K**ing **P**hillip **C**ame **O**ver **F**or **G**ood **S**oup:

Domain → Kingdom → Phylum → Class → Order → Family → Genus → Species

Canis lupus indicates that the wolf's genus is *Canis,* and the species is *lupus*.

Family is more inclusive than genus or species, so any member of the species *lupus* is in the genus *Canis* of the Canidae family.

2. A is correct.

Class encompasses several orders.

Mnemonic: **D**arn **K**ing **P**hillip **C**ame **O**ver **F**or **G**ood **S**oup:

Domain → kingdom → phylum → class → **order** → family → genus → species

3. B is correct.

Homology serves as evidence of common ancestry. Homology is a relationship between structures or DNA derived from a common ancestor.

Homologous traits are traced by descent from a common ancestor.

Analogous organs have similar functions in two taxa, not in the last common ancestor but evolved separately.

Homologous sequences are *orthologous* if they descend from the same ancestral sequence separated by a speciation event.

When a species diverges into two species, the copies of a single gene in the resulting species are orthologous.

Orthology is strictly defined by ancestry.

*Orthologs (*i.e., orthologous genes) are genes in distinct species that originated by vertical descent from a single gene of the last common ancestor.

Due to gene duplication and genome rearrangement, the ancestry of genes is difficult to ascertain.

The strongest evidence that two similar genes are orthologous is usually a phylogenetic analysis of the gene lineage.

Orthologous genes often, but not always, have the same function.

4. A is correct.

Homology is a relationship between structures or DNA derived from a common ancestor.

Homologous traits descend from a common ancestor (e.g., the forelimb of a human and a dog).

Analogous organs, the opposite of homologous organs, have similar functions in two taxa, not in the last common ancestor but instead evolved separately.

Homologous sequences are *orthologous* if they descend from the same ancestral sequence separated by a speciation event. When a species diverges into two separate species, the copies of a single gene in the two resulting species are orthologous.

Orthologues (i.e., orthologous genes) are genes in distinct species that originated by *vertical descent* from a single gene of the last common ancestor.

Orthology is strictly defined by ancestry. Due to gene duplication and genome rearrangement, the ancestry of genes is difficult to ascertain.

The strongest evidence that two similar genes are orthologous is through phylogenetic analysis of gene lineage.

Orthologous genes often, but not always, have the same function.

	Analogous leg	Analogous flipper
Homologous mammals	Cat leg	Whale flipper
Homologous insects	Praying mantis leg	Water boatman flipper

Homologous (common ancestor) vs. analogous structures (similar function but evolved separately)

5. C is correct.

Homology is a relationship between structures or DNA derived from a common ancestor.

Homologous traits descend from a common ancestor (e.g., the forelimb of a human and a dog).

Analogous organs are the opposite of homologous organs and have similar functions in two taxa that were not in the last common ancestor but instead evolved separately.

Homologous sequences are *orthologous* if they descend from the same ancestral sequence separated by a speciation event.

When a species diverges into two species, copies of a single gene in the two resulting species are orthologous.

Orthologs (i.e., orthologous genes) are genes in distinct species that originated by vertical descent from a single gene of the last common ancestor.

Orthology is strictly defined by ancestry.

The strongest evidence that two similar genes are orthologous is usually a phylogenetic analysis of the gene lineage.

Orthologous genes often, but not always, have the same function.

D: wings of a pigeon and a bat represent *analogous structures*.

6. B is correct.

Taxonomy of humans:

> Domain: Eukaryota → Kingdom: Animalia → Phylum: Chordata → Subphylum: Vertebrata →
> Class: Mammalia → Order: Primates → Family: Hominidae → Genus: Homo →
> Species: *H. sapiens* → Subspecies: *H. s. sapiens*

7. B is correct.

Ants are not chordates.

Tunicates are marine invertebrates and members of the subphylum Tunicata within Chordata (i.e., phylum includes all animals with dorsal nerve cords and notochords).

Tunicates live as solitary individuals or replicate by budding and becoming colonies (each unit is a zooid).

Tunicates are marine filter feeders with a water-filled, sac-like body structure and two tubular openings, known as *siphons*, through which they draw in and expel water. They take in water through the *incurrent siphon* during respiration and feeding and expel filtered water through the *excurrent siphon*.

Most adult tunicates are sessile and permanently attached to rocks or other hard surfaces on the ocean floor; others swim in the pelagic zone (i.e., open sea) as adults.

8. B is correct.

Echinoderms are the invertebrate predecessors of the chordates and include starfish, sea urchins, and cucumbers. They are characterized by a primitive vascular system known as the water vascular system.

Adult echinoderms have radial symmetry, while larvae are bilaterally symmetrical. They move with structures known as tube feet, have no backbone, and are heterotrophic (i.e., they do not synthesize food).

Crayfish are in the phylum Arthropoda, which includes insects.

Arthropods are characterized by segmented bodies covered in a chitin exoskeleton and jointed appendages.

9. B is correct.

Kingdom encompasses many phyla.

Mnemonic: **D**arn **K**ing **P**hillip **C**ame **O**ver **F**or **G**ood **S**oup:

> Domain → kingdom → **phylum** → class → order → family → genus → species

10. D is correct.

Homo sapiens belong to the phylum Chordata. *Taxonomy of humans*:

> Domain: Eukaryota → Kingdom: Animalia → Phylum: Chordata → Subphylum: Vertebrata → Class: Mammalia → Order: Primates → Family: Hominidae → Genus: Homo → Species: *H. sapiens* → Subspecies: *H. s. sapiens*

11. B is correct.

Organisms of phylum *Chordata* have a dorsal notochord, while subphylum Vertebrata has a backbone.

Nonvertebrate chordates include amphioxus (lancelet) or unrelated tunicate worm.

Lancelet (or *amphioxus*) is the modern subphylum Cephalochordata and is vital in zoology – it provides indications about the origins of the vertebrates.

Lancelets are comparison points for tracing vertebrates' evolution. Lancets are the archetypal vertebrate form.

Lancelets split from vertebrates more than 520 million years ago; their genomes hold clues about evolution, specifically how vertebrates have adapted old genes for new functions.

Vertebrates include most of the phylum Chordata with about 64,000 species.

Vertebrates include amphibians, reptiles (e.g., lizards), mammals, birds, jawless and bony fish, sharks, and rays.

Shark and lamprey eel are vertebrates with cartilaginous skeletons.

12. A is correct.

Cell, tissue, organ, organism, population, and community represent the correct ordering of the levels of complexity at which life is studied, from simplest to most complex.

13. A is correct.

Notochord is *ventra*l to the *neural tube* and forms during gastrulation.

The notochord induces *neural plate formation* (during neurulation) to synchronize neural tube development (precursor to the central nervous system).

The notochord is a flexible rod-shaped structure in embryos of all chordates. It is composed of cells derived from the mesoderm and defines the primitive axis of the embryo.

In lower chordates, this chord remains throughout the life of the animal.

In higher chordates (e.g., humans), the notochord exists during embryonic development and disappears.

If the notochord persists, it functions as the primary axial support. In most vertebrates, it becomes the nucleus pulposus of the intervertebral disc.

B: *notochord remains* in the lower chordates, such as the amphioxus and the tunicate worm. It is not vestigial (not a genetically determined structure that lost its ancestral function) because it disappears.

D: *echinoderms* are the invertebrate predecessors of chordates and include starfish, sea urchins, and cucumber. Echinoderms do *not* possess a notochord.

14. D is correct.

Chordates are animals that, for at least some of their life cycle, possess:

1) a notochord

2) a dorsal neural tube

3) pharyngeal slits

4) an endostyle

5) a post-anal tail

Chordate phylum includes the subphyla Vertebrata (e.g., mammals, fish, amphibians, reptiles, birds), Tunicata (e.g., salps, sea squirts), and Cephalochordata (e.g., lancelets).

Vertebrata subphylums have a backbone, but it is not a shared characteristic of chordates.

Chordates are a phylum that shares a bilateral body plan and have at some stage:

Notochord is a relatively stiff rod of cartilage extending inside the body.

Among vertebrate sub-group chordates, the notochord develops into the spine. This helps the animal swim by flexing its tail in aquatic species.

Dorsal neural tube (for vertebrates, including fish) develops into the spinal cord, the leading communications trunk of the nervous system.

Pharyngeal slits comprise the throat immediately behind the mouth (modified fish gills). In some chordates, they are part of a filter-feeding system extracting food from its environment.

Endostyle groove in the ventral wall of the pharynx to store iodine and precursor of the vertebrate thyroid gland. In filter-feeders, it produces mucus to gather food particles, which help transport food to the esophagus.

Post-anal tail is a muscular tail extending behind the anus.

15. B is correct.

Migratory birds nesting on islands is not behavioral, temporal, or geographical isolation leading to speciation. The birds are migratory and are not geographically isolated.

16. D is correct.

Sponges are Porifera (i.e., pore or Ostia-bearing) phylum animals.

Like other animals, they are multicellular, heterotrophic, and lack cell walls. Sponges lack tissues and organs and have no body symmetry, differentiating them from other animals.

Heterotrophy means obtaining food and energy by consuming other organic substances rather than through sunlight or inorganic compounds.

17. B is correct.

Homology is a relationship between structures or DNA derived from a common ancestor.

Homologous traits are explained by descent from a common ancestor.

Analogous organs have similar functions in two taxa, not in the last common ancestor but evolved separately.

Homologous sequences are *orthologous* when descended from ancestral sequences separated by speciation.

When a species diverges into two species, copies of a single gene in the two resulting species are *orthologous*.

Orthologues (i.e., orthologous genes) are genes in distinct species that originated by vertical descent from a single gene of the last common ancestor.

Orthology is defined by ancestry.

Due to gene duplication and genome rearrangement, the ancestry of genes is difficult to ascertain.

The strongest evidence that two similar genes are orthologous is usually a *phylogenetic analysis* of *gene lineage*.

Orthologous genes often, but not always, have the same function.

continued...

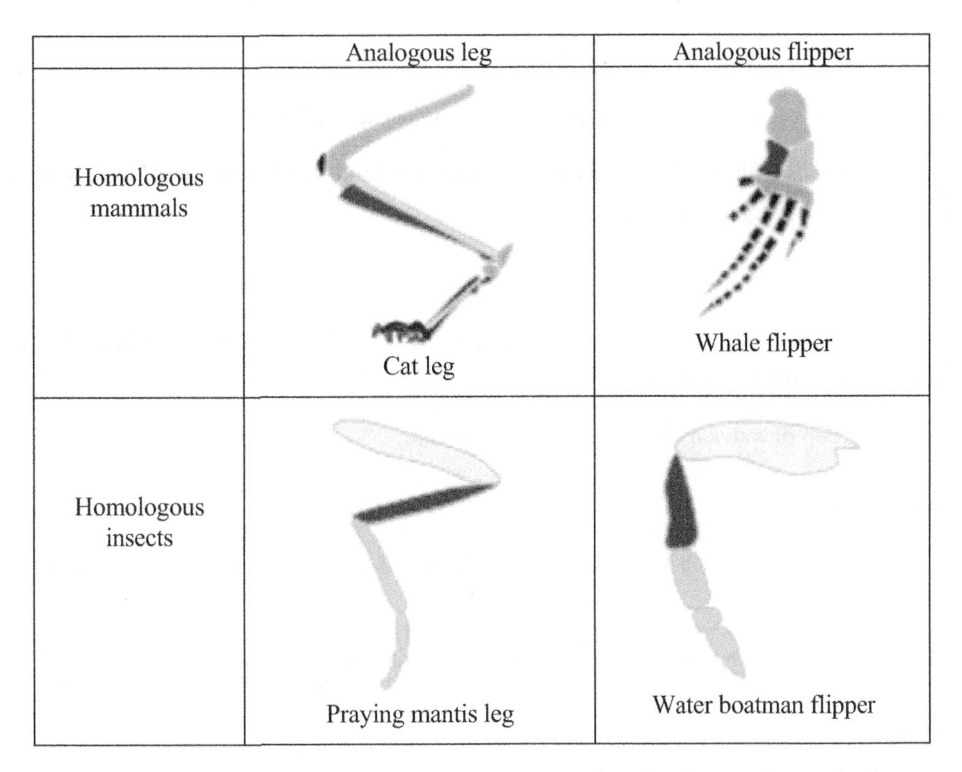

Homologous (common ancestor) vs. analogous structures (similar function but evolved separately)

18. C is correct.

Arthropods are invertebrate animals with an exoskeleton, segmented body, and jointed appendages and include insects, arachnids, myriapods, and crustaceans.

19. A is correct.

Animal cells do *not* have cell walls, distinct from plant cells.

Another distinct feature of plant cells is the presence of chloroplasts in the structure.

20. C is correct.

Annelids are a large phylum of segmented worms, each segment having the same set of organs.

Coelom is a cavity lined by a mesoderm-derived epithelium. Organs formed inside a coelom can grow, freely move, and develop independently of the body wall while protected by fluid cushions.

Organisms are classified into three groups:

1) *Coelomates* are animals with a fluid-filled body cavity (i.e., coelom) and complete lining (peritoneum derived from mesoderm), allowing organs to be attached and suspended while moving freely within the cavity.

Coelomates include most bilateral animals, including all vertebrates.

2) *Pseudocoelomates* are animals with a pseudocoelom fully functional body cavity (e.g., roundworm).

Pseudocoelomate *organs* are held loosely and not as well organized as coelomates.

continued...

Mesoderm-derived tissue partly lines the fluid-filled body cavity.

Pseudocoelomates are *protostomes*, but not all protostomes are pseudocoelomates.

3) *Acoelomates* are animals with no body cavity (i.e., flatworms). Semi-solid mesodermal tissues between the gut and body wall hold their organs in place.

21. B is correct.

From embryological studies, ancient chordates were closely related to the ancestors of echinoderms, marine animals such as sea stars, and sea urchins.

Sea anemones are a group of water-dwelling, predatory animals.

22. C is correct.

Echinoderms are marine animals such as sea stars, sea urchins, and sand dollars characterized by radial (usually five-point) symmetry.

Most echinoderms can regenerate tissue, organs, and limbs and reproduce asexually.

23. A is correct.

Cnidaria is a phylum of animals with over 10,000 species exclusively in aquatic and marine environments.

Cnidaria bodies consist of a *non-living jelly-like substance* sandwiched between two layers of epithelium that are mostly one cell thick.

Their distinguishing feature is *cnidocytes*, specialized cells mainly for capturing prey.

Cnidaria has two basic body forms: *swimming medusae* and *sessile polyps*; each is radially symmetrical, with mouths surrounded by tentacles that bear cnidocytes.

Both forms have a single orifice and body cavity used for digestion and respiration.

Many cnidarian species form colonies of single organisms with Medusa-like or polyp-like zooids or both.

B: *echinoderms* are a phylum of marine animals, and adults have radial (usually five-point) symmetry (e.g., sea urchins, sand dollars, starfish, and sea cucumbers).

24. C is correct.

Chordates are animals with a *notochord* (stiff rod of cartilage that extends inside the body), *dorsal neural tube*, and *pharyngeal slits*, which are openings of the pharynx to allow aquatic organisms to extract oxygen from water and excrete carbon dioxide (i.e., gills).

25. A is correct.

A hollow *nerve cord* (a single hollow nerve tissue tract) constitutes the central nervous system of chordates.

26. B is correct.

Cephalization is an evolutionary trend when nervous tissue becomes concentrated toward one end of an organism over many generations. This process produces a head region with sensory organs.

The process of cephalization is intrinsically connected with a change in symmetry. Cephalization accompanied the shift to bilateral symmetry in flatworms.

In addition to a concentration of sense organs, annelids place the mouth in the head region. This process is tied to developing an anterior brain in the chordates from the notochord.

An exception to the trend of cephalization throughout evolutionary advancement is the phylum Echinodermata.

Echinodermata, despite having a bilateral ancestor, developed with 5-point symmetry) and no concentrated neural ganglia or sensory head region.

Some echinoderms have developed bilateral symmetry secondarily.

27. B is correct.

Deuterostomes differ from protostomes in embryonic development.

In deuterostomes, the first opening (i.e., blastopore) becomes the anus. In protostomes, it becomes the mouth.

Chordates, echinoderms, and hemichordates are deuterostomes.

28. A is correct.

Pharyngeal pouches are filter-feeding organs in fish that develop into gills used for respiration.

29. D is correct.

Corals are marine invertebrates (phylum Cnidaria) typically in compact colonies with identical individual *polyps*. The group includes the reef builders of tropical oceans secreting calcium carbonate, forming a hard skeleton.

A coral "head" is a colony of myriad genetically identical polyps. Each polyp is a spineless animal, typically a few millimeters in diameter and a few centimeters in length.

Tentacles surround a central mouth opening, and an *exoskeleton* is excreted near the base.

Over many generations, colonies create a large skeleton structure.

Individual heads grow by the asexual reproduction of polyps.

Corals breed *sexually* by *spawning:* polyps of the same species release gametes simultaneously for several nights, cycling around full moons.

30. B is correct.

The first amphibians developed from lobe-finned fish about 370 million years ago during the Devonian period.

Lobe-finned fish had multi-jointed leg-like fins that allowed crawling at the bottom of the sea. Their bony fins evolved into limbs, becoming the ancestors of tetrapods, including amphibians, reptiles, birds, and mammals.

31. D is correct.

Notochord is a flexible rod essential in vertebrate development and skeletal element of developing embryos.

The notochord is related to cartilage, serving as the axial skeleton of the embryo until other elements form.

32. D is correct.

Chordates are animals that, for at least some period of their life cycles, possess the following: a notochord, a dorsal neural tube, pharyngeal slits, an endostyle, and a post-anal tail.

Notochord is a flexible rod-shaped structure in embryos of chordates. It is composed of mesoderm-derived cells that define the embryo axis.

Notochord is a relatively stiff cartilage rod extending along the body's inside.

Among the vertebrate sub-group of chordates, the notochord develops into the spine, and in aquatic species, this helps the animal swim by flexing its tail.

In lower chordates, the notochord remains throughout life.

In higher chordates (e.g., humans), the notochord exists only during embryonic development and disappears.

If it persists throughout life, it functions as the primary axial support, while in most vertebrates, it becomes the nucleus pulposus of the intervertebral disc.

Notochord is ventral to the neural tube and forms during gastrulation.

The notochord *induces neural plate formation* (during neurulation) to synchronize neural tube development (precursor to the central nervous system).

33. C is correct.

Earthworms are part of the Annelid phylum. *Pseudocoelom* is a fluid-filled cavity between the body wall and intestine of certain invertebrates, such as roundworms and hookworms.

All other statements are true.

34. C is correct.

Notochords are similar to cartilage, made of type II collagen. Collagen makes notochords soft and flexible.

The notochord is a flexible rod between the nerve cord and the digestive tract.

35. B is correct.

Cnidaria bodies consist of a non-living jelly-like substance sandwiched between two layers of epithelium that are mostly one cell thick.

Cnidaria has two body forms: swimming medusae and sessile polyps, each *radially symmetrical* with mouths surrounded by tentacles with cnidocytes.

Echinoderms are a phylum of marine animals, and adults have radial (usually five-point) symmetry (e.g., sea urchins, sand dollars, starfish, and sea cucumbers).

36. A is correct.

Chordates share several key features, such as a notochord, a dorsal hollow nerve cord, pharyngeal slits, and a post-anal tail.

Of the characteristics visible on a cat, a tail extending beyond the anus makes it a chordate.

37. B is correct.

Vertebral column is the backbone or spine, a segmented series of bones separated by intervertebral discs.

38. B is correct.

Ovoviviparous fish (e.g., guppies, angel sharks) have eggs that develop inside the mother's body after *internal fertilization*, whereby each embryo develops within its egg.

Yolk nourishes the embryo, which receives little or no nourishment from the mother.

Viviparous fish retain the eggs and nourish the embryos. They have a structure analogous to the placenta (mammals), connecting the mother's blood with the embryo.

39. C is correct.

Chordates are defined by the presence of a *notochord.*

Not all chordates are vertebrates, have paired appendages, or have backbones.

Chordates are *deuterostomes* where the first opening (i.e., blastopore) becomes the anus.

Chordates are a phylum that shares a bilateral body plan and have at some stage:

> ***Notochord*** is a relatively stiff rod of cartilage extending inside the body.
>
> Among vertebrate sub-group chordates, the notochord develops into the spine. This helps the animal swim by flexing its tail in aquatic species.
>
> ***Dorsal neural tube*** (for vertebrates, including fish) develops into the spinal cord, the leading communications trunk of the nervous system.
>
> ***Pharyngeal slits*** comprise the throat immediately behind the mouth (modified fish gills). In some chordates, they are part of a filter-feeding system extracting food from its environment.
>
> ***Endostyle groove*** in the ventral wall of the pharynx to store iodine and a possible precursor of the vertebrate thyroid gland. In filter-feeders, it produces mucus to gather food particles, which help transport food to the esophagus.
>
> ***Post-anal tail*** is a muscular tail extending behind the anus.

40. A is correct.

Chordates are animals with a notochord, a dorsal neural tube, pharyngeal slits, endostyle, and a post-anal tail for at least some of their life cycles.

41. B is correct.

Hominoids are called *apes*, but *ape* is used differently.

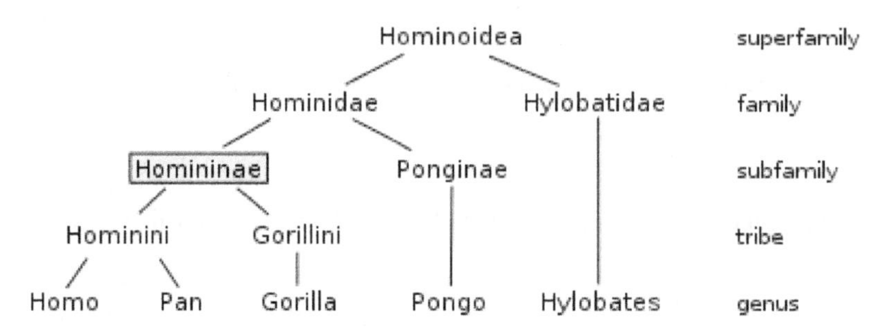

Homininae cladogram divides into genus homo, pan and gorilla

Until 1970, Hominidae meant humans only, with non-human great apes assigned to the family Pongidae.

Later discoveries led to revised classifications, with the great apes then united with humans (now in subfamily Homininae) as members of the family Hominidae

By 1990, molecular biology techniques classified gorillas and chimpanzees as more closely related to humans than orangutans.

Gorillas and chimpanzees are in the subfamily Homininae.

Hominines are a subfamily of Hominidae that includes humans, gorillas, chimpanzees, bonobos, and hominids which arose after the evolutionary split from orangutans.

Homininae cladogram has three main branches, which lead to gorillas, chimpanzees, bonobos, and humans.

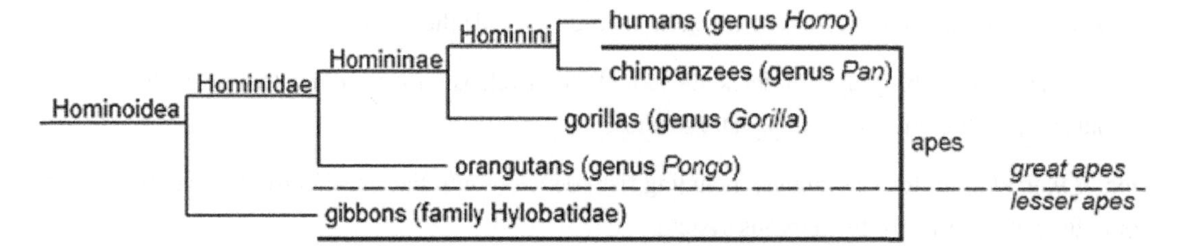

Homininae cladogram includes gorillas, chimpanzees, and humans

42. D is correct.

Fish evolved with *jawless fish*, followed by *bony fish with a jaw*.

Lastly, fish with leg-like fins, which allowed for movement along the seabed, evolved into limbs of *tetrapods*.

43. B is correct.

Jaws and limbs are characteristic of *vertebrates*.

44. A is correct.

Yolk nourishes the embryo, which receives little or no nourishment from the mother.

Amniotic fluid, surrounded by the amnion, is a liquid environment around the egg, protecting it from shock.

Embryonic membranes include:

1) ***chorion*** lines the inside of the shell and permits gas exchange;

2) ***allantois*** is a saclike structure developed from the digestive tract and functions in respiration, excretion, and gas exchange with the external environment;

3) ***amnion*** encloses *amniotic fluid* as a watery environment for embryogenesis and shock protection;

4) ***yolk sac*** encloses the yolk and transfers food to the developing embryo.

45. C is correct.

External fertilization is male sperm fertilizing an egg outside the female's body, as seen in amphibians and fish.

Mammals, further in the evolution of vertebrate groups, use internal fertilization for reproduction.

46. A is correct.

Prehensile refers to an appendage or organ adapted for holding or grasping.

47. D is correct.

Mammals are *endothermic* (warm-blooded) vertebrates with *body hair* and the ability to feed babies with *milk*.

In the embryonic development of vertebrates (e.g., mammals), *pharyngeal pouches* form that develop into essential structures such as the eardrum and thymus gland.

48. A is correct.

Hominoids are called *apes*, but *ape* is used differently.

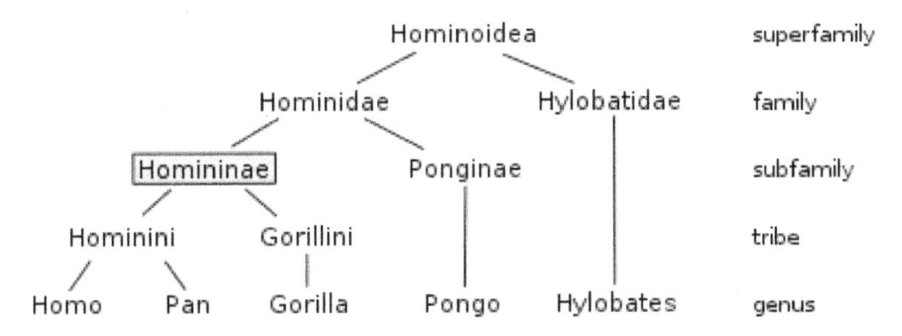

Homininae cladogram divides into genus homo, pan and gorilla

Until 1970, Hominidae meant humans only, with non-human great apes assigned to the family Pongidae.

Later discoveries led to revised classifications, with the great apes then united with humans (now in subfamily Homininae) as members of the family Hominidae

continued...

By 1990, molecular biology classified gorillas and chimpanzees as more closely related to humans than orangutans.

Gorillas and chimpanzees are in the subfamily Homininae.

Hominines are a subfamily of Hominidae that includes humans, gorillas, chimpanzees, bonobos, and hominids which arose after the evolutionary split from orangutans.

Homininae cladogram has three main branches, which lead to gorillas, chimpanzees, bonobos, and humans.

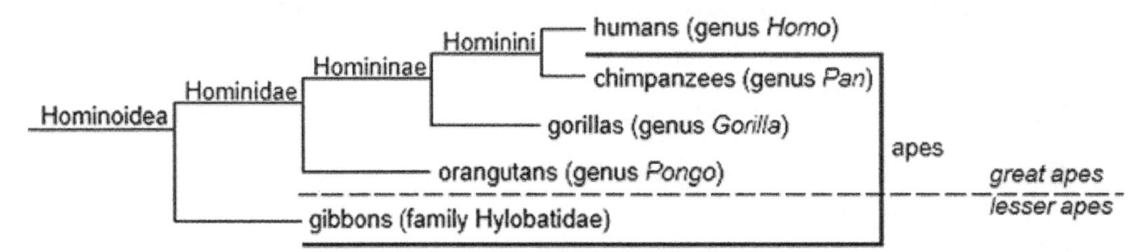

Homininae cladogram includes gorillas, chimpanzees, and humans

49. C is correct.

Cartilaginous fishes have a skeleton made of cartilage rather than bone.

Sharks, skates, rays, and sturgeons have cartilaginous skeletons, while hagfish have cartilaginous skulls.

50. A is correct.

Old World monkeys are primates in the clade of Catarrhini. They are native to Africa and Asia today, inhabiting environments from tropical rainforest to savanna, shrubland, and mountainous terrain.

Old World monkeys include familiar species of nonhuman primates (e.g., baboons, macaques). They are medium to large and range from arboreal (i.e., locomotion in trees) to fully terrestrial (e.g., baboons).

New World monkeys are the five families of primates in Central and South America and portions of Mexico. They are small to mid-sized primates.

New World monkeys differ from Old World monkeys in several aspects.

The prominent phenotypic distinction is the nose, commonly used to distinguish between groups.

New World monkeys have noses flatter than the narrow noses of Old-World monkeys and have side-facing nostrils.

New World monkeys are the only monkeys with prehensile tails.

Old-World monkeys have shorter, non-grasping tails.

51. C is correct.

A reptile's body temperature is determined by the temperature of its surrounding environment, meaning it could fluctuate more often than endothermic (*warm-blooded*) animals.

Birds are *endothermic*, so their body temperature remains constant and is warmer than reptiles.

52. D is correct.

Earthworms are soft-bodied segmented worms with nephridia, paired organs in each worm segment.

Nephridia remove nitrogenous waste.

53. D is correct.

Monotremes are mammals laying eggs instead of birthing live young like marsupials and placental mammals.

The surviving species of monotremes are indigenous to Australia and New Guinea, though evidence suggests they were once widespread.

The existing monotreme species are the *platypus* and four species of echidnas (i.e., spiny anteaters).

54. B is correct.

Legs and limbs indicate that the animal is *segmented.*

55. D is correct.

Lemurs are a clade of *strepsirrhine primates* characterized by a *moist nose tip.*

Lemurs are primarily *nocturnal animals* and are on the island of Madagascar.

56. A is correct.

Birds have a *complex respiratory system.*

Upon inhalation, 75% of the fresh air bypasses the lungs and flows directly into a posterior air sac extending from the lungs, connects with air spaces in the bones, and fills them with air.

25% of the air goes directly into the lungs.

When birds exhale, the used air flows out of the lung, and the stored fresh air from the posterior air sac is simultaneously forced into the lungs.

The bird's lungs receive fresh air during inhalation and exhalation.

Sound production uses the *syrinx*, a muscular chamber incorporating multiple tympanic membranes that diverge from the trachea's lower end.

In some species, the *trachea* is elongated to increase *vocalization volume* and *perceived size.*

57. D is correct.

Grasping hands of primates (i.e., having opposable thumbs) are an adaptation to life in the trees.

Thumbs help primates grasp objects (e.g., tree branches) firmly.

58. B is correct.

Chordates are both vertebrates and invertebrates.

Chordates share features, such as a:

notochord,

dorsal hollow nerve cord,

pharyngeal slits, and

post-anal tail.

In vertebrate chordates, the notochord is replaced by a *vertebral column*.

59. B is correct.

Radial symmetry is present in organisms with symmetry around a central axis.

Radial symmetry is in *starfish* or *sea urchins*, whose body parts extend equally outward from a center point.

60. C is correct.

Deuterostome is distinguished by embryonic development, whereby the first opening (i.e., blastopore) becomes the anus.

Protostomes develop with the first opening (i.e., blastopore) as the *mouth*.

Deuterostome mouth develops at the opposite end of the embryo from the blastopore. A digestive tract develops in the middle connecting the two.

Humans are deuterostomes.

Invertebrates are *protostomes.*

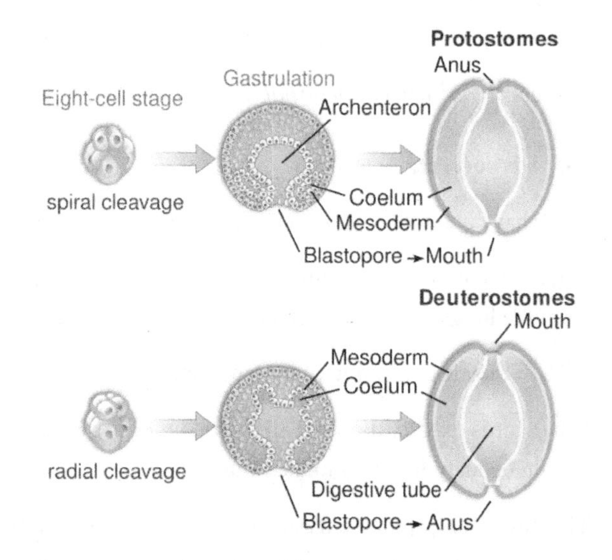

Protostomes (mouth at blastopore) vs. deuterostomes

61. A is correct.

Shapes of forelimbs are an expected variant for vertebrates using these appendages for utility.

62. C is correct.

Homo habilis (or *Australopithecus habilis*) is a species of the *Hominini* tribe, which lived from 2.33 to 1.44 million years ago.

There has been controversy regarding its placement in the genus *Homo* rather than *Australopithecus*; its brain size is 550-687 cm^3, rather than 363-600 cm^3.

Recent findings on brain size support its traditional placement in the genus *Homo* and the theory that *Homo habilis* is the common ancestor.

63. B is correct.

Feathers are the most critical characteristic separating birds from other living animals.

Birds are the only *chordates* with feathers.

Other chordates, such as mammals, have *fur or hair.*

64. B is correct.

Double-loop circulatory system is one in which blood flows through the heart twice.

Pulmonary circulation involves blood flowing between the heart and lungs.

Systemic circulation is blood movement from the heart to the body and back.

Lungs are essential for *double-loop circulatory systems.*

65. A is correct.

Cladograms of animals' support segmentation evolving more than once in different branches.

Cephalization is an evolutionary trend whereby nervous tissue (over many generations) becomes concentrated toward one end of an organism to produce a head region with sensory organs.

66. D is correct.

Green algae are classified as *plants* because they have *gene segments* similar to land plants, use chlorophyll *a*, and have cellulose cell walls.

67. C is correct.

Evidence suggests that green algae were the first plants.

Land plants evolved from *filamentous green algae*, which invaded land about 410 million years ago

Land plants and green algae have *cellulose* in their cell walls and share many *photopigments for photosynthesis.*

Notes for active learning

Energy Flow, Nutrient Cycles, Ecosystems and Biomes – Detailed Explanations

1. A is correct.

Ecosystem is a community of organisms (e.g., plants, animals, microbes) with nonliving (i.e., *abiotic*) components of their environment (e.g., air, water, minerals). It is the network of interactions among organisms and between organisms and their environment.

Nutrient cycles and *energy flows* link *biotic* (i.e., living) and *abiotic* (i.e., nonliving) components.

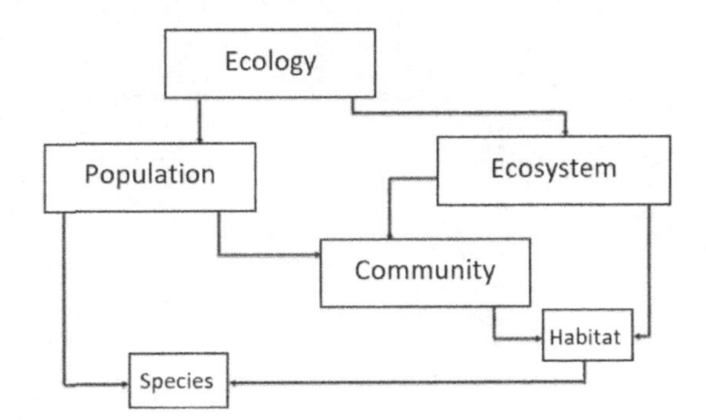

Relationship between organisms and their environment. Population, ecosystem, community, habitat, and species relationship are highlighted.

Ecology is the study of relationships between living organisms and between their environment.

Population is a group of organisms of the same species living in the same area.

Community is a group of populations living and interacting in an area.

Habitat is the environment in which a species lives.

Species are a group of organisms that can breed and produce fertile offspring.

2. B is correct.

Weather is the immediate conditions (e.g., hourly, daily, weekly), while *climate* is the average conditions.

3. A is correct.

Symbiosis is the close and often long-term interaction between species.

Historically, some biologists proposed symbiosis as *persistent mutualisms* (i.e., all organisms benefit).

Biologists and ecologists now propose symbiosis as *persistent biological interactions*; mutualistic (+/+), commensalism (+/0), or parasitic (+/–).

4. C is correct.

Climate zones are distinct in an east-west direction around Earth and are classified by climate parameters.

Climate zones are primarily determined by *variations in temperature* related to *latitude* and *altitude*.

Angle of the sun's rays contributes to differences in climate zones.

5. A is correct.

Greenhouse effect is a natural phenomenon that maintains Earth's temperature range.

Greenhouse gases on Earth are water vapor (36–70%), CO_2 (9–26%), methane (4–9%), and ozone (3–7%).

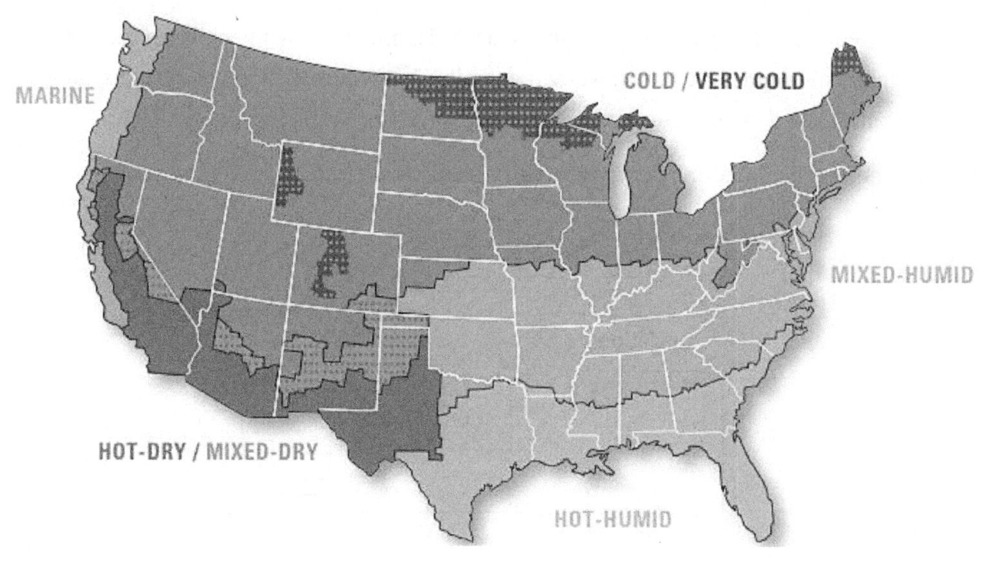

U.S. climate zones

6. D is correct.

Convection is movement caused by hotter (i.e., less dense) air rising and colder (i.e., denser) air sinking under the influence of gravity, consequently resulting in heat transfer.

Global wind patterns in the atmosphere are created by *convection* (i.e., air movement based on density).

When *warm air rises* and cools in a low-pressure zone, it may not hold the water it contains as vapor. Some water vapor condenses to form clouds or precipitation.

When *cool air descends*, it warms.

7. D is correct.

Wetlands ecosystems have saturated ground surfaces either permanently or temporarily.

8. C is correct.

Niche describes when each species has separate, unique physical and environmental conditions.

Biological aspects of an organism's niche are *biotic factors* (i.e., living) required for survival.

Abiotic factors (i.e., nonliving) include soil, sunlight, water, and minerals.

Ecological niche is how organisms (or populations) respond to the distribution of resources and competitors (e.g., growing with abundant resources while predators are scarce) and how it alters those factors (e.g., limiting access by other organisms, being a food source for predators and a consumer of prey).

9. C is correct.

Niche is when each species has separate, unique physical and environmental conditions.

Niche is the range of *physical and biological conditions* in which an organism lives and how it obtains resources for survival and reproduction.

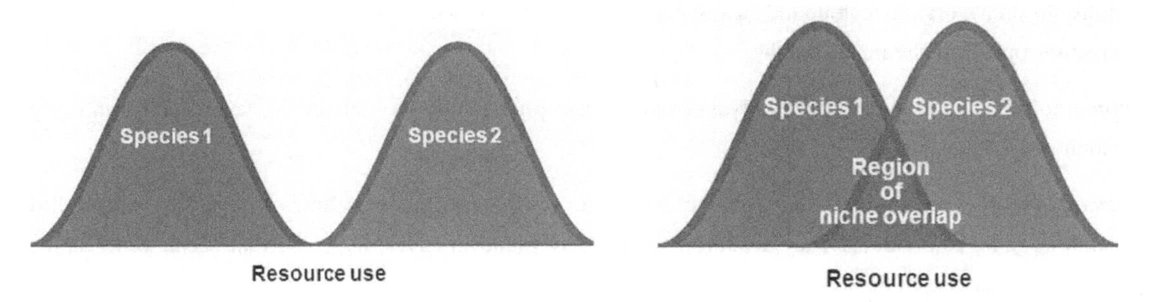

Resource partitioning results in competition for scarce resources when niche regions overlap

10. B is correct.

Competitive exclusion principle (*Gause's law of competitive exclusion* or *Gause's law*) states that two species competing for the same resources cannot coexist when ecological factors are constant.

Domination occurs when one species has even a slight advantage. One competitor overcomes another, leading to extinction or behavioral shift toward a different ecological niche.

11. D is correct.

Primary producers (i.e., *autotrophs*) produce energy from inorganic compounds in an ecosystem. Primary producers often use *photosynthesis* (e.g., plants and cyanobacteria).

Autotrophs (e.g., plants) support the ecosystem and feed heterotrophs.

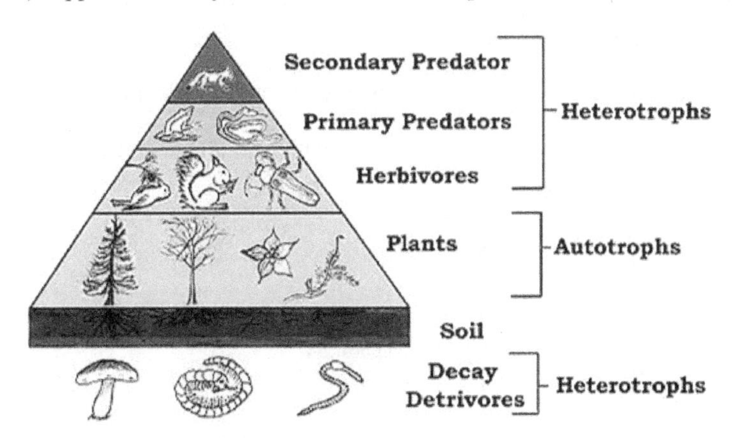

Trophic levels as positions on a food web. Autotrophs support the ecosystem and feed heterotrophs.

12. D is correct.

Primary producers (i.e., *autotrophs*) produce energy from inorganic compounds in an ecosystem. Primary producers often use *photosynthesis* (e.g., plants and cyanobacteria). Plants are primary producers.

Autotrophs support the ecosystem and feed heterotrophs.

Autotrophs create organic compounds using energy from the sun or inorganic compounds. They are divided into photoautotrophs and chemoautotrophs.

Photoautotrophs (e.g., algae, plants, cyanobacteria) use photosynthesis, converting solar energy into organic compounds.

Chemoautotrophs are bacteria that oxidize inorganic compounds such as ammonia, nitrite, and sulfide to generate organic compounds. They are rare and typically found in caves, hydrothermal ocean vents, and other environments lacking light.

Archaea (single-cell prokaryotes) may produce biomass from oxidizing inorganic compounds (i.e., chemoautotrophs). For example, processes in *deep ocean hydrothermal vents*.

Decomposers are fungi and other organisms that produce biomass from oxidizing organic materials. They absorb and metabolize nutrients (i.e., saprotrophic nutrition from dead or decaying material).

13. A is correct.

Open ocean waters are separated from cold, nutrient-rich interior water by *density differences* restricting water mixing and reducing nutrient supply, which becomes the limiting factor for productivity.

Open oceans have negligible nutrients from land and little upwelling to supply nutrients from deep oceans.

14. B is correct.

Habitat is an ecological area inhabited by a species. It is the natural environment in which an organism lives or the physical environment encompassing a population.

Niche describes when each species has separate, unique physical and environmental conditions.

Niche is the range of *physical and biological conditions* in which an organism lives and how it obtains resources for survival and reproduction.

Niche breadth is the range of habitat by an organism.

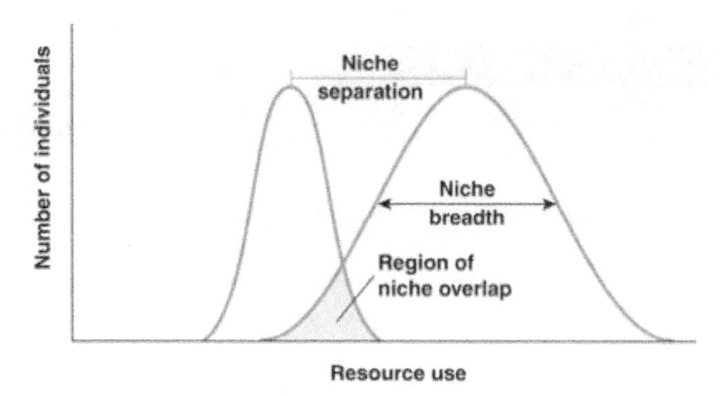

Niches may overlap and introduce competition for scarce resources

15. A is correct.

Food web is a graphical model depicting linked *food chains by* feeding relationships in an ecosystem.

Food web and energy flow relationship examples

Food chain is a *linear succession* whereby another eats each species.

16. A is correct.

Mutualism is when two organisms of different species exist in a relationship, each benefit.

B: *parasitism* is a non-mutual symbiotic relationship between species, where one species (i.e., the parasite) benefits at the expense of the other (i.e., the host).

C: *commensalism is* when two organisms of different species exist in a relationship, each benefit.

D: *omnivorism* is a human diet consuming meat, eggs, dairy, and produce traced to an organic farm.

17. A is correct.

Predation is a biological interaction when a predator (i.e., a hunting organism) feeds on prey.

A predator may (or *may not*) kill its prey before feeding, but the act of predation often results in the prey's death and the eventual absorption of the prey's tissue through consumption.

Given an alternative, *predators* (e.g., lions, tigers, wolves) may engage in *scavenging* feeding.

Mutualism (+/+) is a symbiosis of *persistent biological interactions.*

18. B is correct.

Biomass is the mass (i.e., a body of matter without defined shape) of living organisms in an area (or ecosystem). Biomass can include microorganisms, plants, or animals.

The mass can be expressed as the average mass per unit area or as the total mass in the community. How biomass is measured depends on why it is being measured.

Species biomass is the mass of one or more species.

Community biomass is the mass of the species in the community.

Trophic levels show a succession of the flow of *food energy* and *feeding relationships*. It is a food chain or ecological pyramid occupied by groups with similar feeding modes.

Trophic level 1	Producers
Trophic level 2	Primary consumers
Trophic level 3	Secondary consumers
Trophic level 4	Tertiary consumers

Food chain is the hierarchy in which organisms in an ecosystem are grouped into trophic (nutritional) levels.

Ecological pyramid represents the biomass or the energy flow in an ecosystem.

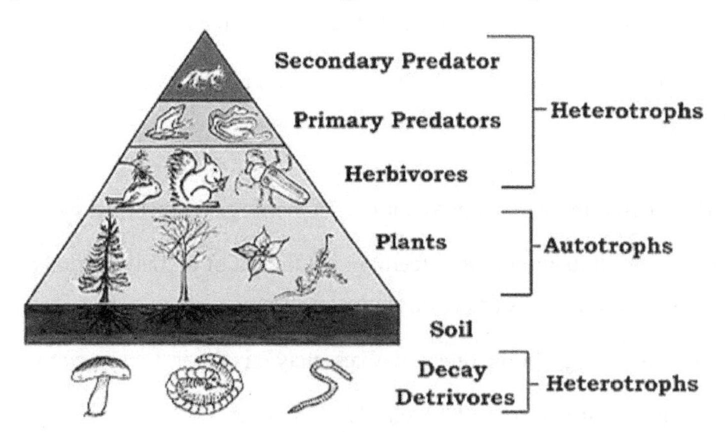

Trophic levels as positions on a food web. Autotrophs support the ecosystem and feed heterotrophs.

19. C is correct.

Herbivory is an animal anatomically and physiologically adapted to eating plants.

As a result of their plant diet, herbivorous animals typically have mouthparts adapted to rasping or grinding.

For example, foliage or marine algae is the main component of herbivores.

20. D is correct.

Parasitism (+/–) is a non-mutual symbiotic relationship between species, where one species (i.e., the parasite) benefits at the expense of the other (i.e., the host).

A: *synnecrosis* is a rare symbiosis when the interaction between species is detrimental to both. It is short-lived because the interaction eventually causes death. Evolution selects against synnecrosis and is uncommon.

B: *predation* is a biological interaction when a predator (i.e., hunting organism) feeds on prey.

Predators may not kill their prey before feeding, but predation often results in the prey's death and eventual absorption of their tissue through consumption.

The remains of prey may become a food source for scavengers.

Scavengers feed on dead organisms that they did not kill.

Organisms (e.g., lions, tigers, wolves) considered predators may engage in scavenging feeding behavior when given the alternative.

C: *mutualism* (+/+) is when two organisms of different species exist in a relationship, each benefit.

21. C is correct.

Omnivores consume meat, eggs, dairy, and produce.

Autotrophs support the ecosystem and feed heterotrophs. They create organic compounds using energy from the sun or inorganic compounds.

Autotrophs divide into photoautotrophs and chemoautotrophs.

Photoautotrophs (e.g., algae, plants, cyanobacteria) use photosynthesis to convert solar energy into organic compounds.

Chemotrophs are organisms that obtain energy by oxidation of electron donors in their environments. These molecules can be organic or inorganic.

Chemotrophs can be either *autotrophic* or *heterotrophic*.

Herbivores are animals anatomically and physiologically adapted to eating plants. As a result of their plant diet, herbivorous animals typically have mouthparts adapted to rasping or grinding.

22. D is correct.

Ecosystems include food production, solar energy (photosynthesis), and O_2 production (e.g., photosynthesis). They are the network of interactions among organisms and between organisms and their environment.

23. C is correct.

Autotrophs support the ecosystem and feed heterotrophs. Autotrophs create organic compounds using energy from the sun or inorganic compounds. They divide into *photoautotrophs* and *chemoautotrophs*.

Photoautotrophs (e.g., algae, plants, cyanobacteria) use photosynthesis, converting solar energy into organic compounds.

Heterotrophs obtain nutrients and energy by consuming organic substances.

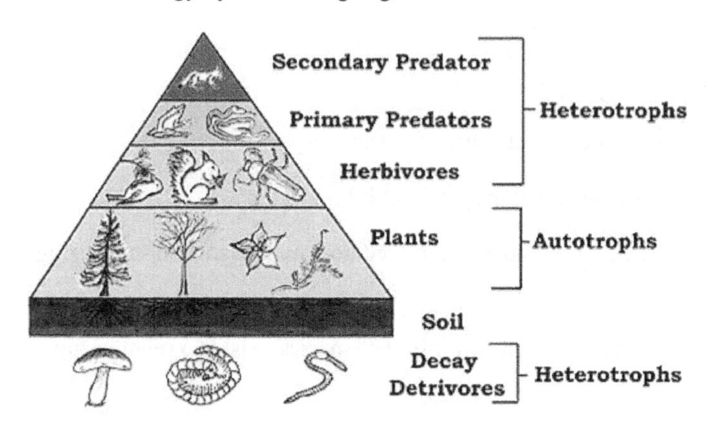

Trophic levels as positions on a food web. Autotrophs support the ecosystem and feed heterotrophs.

24. C is correct.

Primary succession is one of two biological and ecological succession of plant life, occurring in an environment devoid of vegetation and usually lacking soil (e.g., lava flow). It is the gradual growth of an ecosystem over a longer period.

Secondary succession occurs on a substrate that supports vegetation before an ecological disturbance from less cataclysmic events (e.g., floods, hurricanes, tornadoes), which destroy plant life.

25. B is correct.

Heterotrophs obtain nutrients and energy by consuming organic substances.

Autotrophs are *producers*.

Heterotrophs are *consumers* and rely on producers.

26. B is correct.

Primary succession is one of two biological and ecological succession of plant life, occurring in an environment devoid of vegetation and usually lacking soil (e.g., lava flow).

Primary succession is the gradual growth of an ecosystem over a more extended period.

Secondary succession occurs on a substrate that supports vegetation before an ecological disturbance from less cataclysmic events (e.g., floods, hurricanes, tornadoes), which destroy plant life.

27. B is correct.

The snail is a typical detritivore.

Detritivores are heterotrophs that obtain nutrition from decomposing (waste or detritus) plants, dead organisms, and feces and contribute to decomposition and the nutrient cycles. Detritivores are not to be confused with other decomposers such as bacteria, fungi, and protists, which cannot ingest minute lumps of matter.

Decomposers absorb and metabolize nutrients (i.e., saprotrophic nutrition from dead or decaying material).

28. A is correct.

Matter recycles through the biosphere because biological systems do not deplete it but transform it.

29. D is correct.

Clearing and farming are physical disturbances to the ecosystem.

Climax community is a biological community of plants, animals, and fungi that has reached a *steady-state* through ecological succession (i.e., vegetation in an area over time).

Equilibrium occurs because the climax community has species best adapted to average conditions in that area.

30. A is correct.

Ecosystems include food production, solar energy (photosynthesis), and O_2 production (e.g., photosynthesis). They are the network of interactions among organisms and between organisms and their environment.

Biomes are geographically and climatically defined as contiguous with similar conditions, such as communities of plants, animals, and soil organisms.

31. B is correct.

Tundra is a biome where low temperatures and short growing seasons hinder tree growth. The vegetation includes dwarf shrubs, grasses, mosses, and lichens.

Desert is a barren land where little precipitation occurs, and consequently, living conditions are hostile to plant and animal life.

32. C is correct.

The bird is the carnivore, while the insect is the consumer (heterotroph).

33. B is correct.

Tundra is a biome where low temperatures and short growing seasons hinder tree growth. The vegetation includes dwarf shrubs, grasses, mosses, and lichens.

Desert is a barren land where little precipitation occurs, and consequently, living conditions are hostile to plant and animal life.

Boreal forest (or *taiga*) is a biome characterized by coniferous (i.e., softwood) forests mainly consisting of pines, spruces, and larches and is the world's largest terrestrial biome.

34. A is correct.

Decomposers are fungi and other organisms that produce biomass from oxidizing organic materials. They absorb and metabolize nutrients (i.e., saprotrophic nutrition from dead or decaying material).

Scavengers feed on dead organisms that they did *not* kill. Often, the remains of the prey become a food source for scavengers.

35. D is correct.

Climate is the average conditions, *while the weather* is the immediate conditions (e.g., hourly, daily, weekly).

36. C is correct.

Nitrogen fixation is when atmospheric nitrogen (N_2) is converted into ammonium (NH_4). It is necessary for life because nitrogen is required for nucleotides of DNA and RNA and amino acids of proteins.

Diazotrophs are prokaryotic (i.e., bacteria and archaea) microorganisms that can fix nitrogen.

Some higher plants and animals (e.g., termites) have symbiotic relationships with diazotrophs.

37. C is correct.

Primary productivity is the rate at which producers (autotrophs) produce organic matter.

38. B is correct.

Biomes are climatically and geographically defined as *contiguous areas* with *similar climatic conditions* such as communities of animals, plants, and soil organisms and are often called ecosystems.

Factors such as plant structures define biomes (e.g., shrubs, trees, and grasses), leaf types (e.g., broadleaf and needleleaf), plant spacing (e.g., forest, woodland, savanna), and climate.

Biomes, unlike ecozones, are not defined by genetic, taxonomic, or historical similarities.

Biomes are often identified by patterns of ecological succession and climax vegetation.

39. A is correct.

North Pole and the South Pole are not classified into major biomes.

40. B is correct.

Predation is a biological interaction when a predator (i.e., a hunting organism) feeds on prey. A predator may (or may not kill) its prey before feeding on them, but the act of predation often results in the prey's death and the eventual absorption of the prey's tissue through consumption.

Scavengers feed on dead organisms that they did not kill. Often, the remains of the prey become a food source for scavengers.

Organisms (e.g., lions, tigers, wolves) considered predators may engage in scavenging feeding behavior when given the alternative.

41. B is correct.

Aphotic zone is the area of a lake or ocean with little or no sunlight, the depths beyond which less than 1 percent of sunlight penetrates. Below the photic zone is the dark aphotic zone, where photosynthesis cannot occur.

Benthic zone is the lowest ecological zone in water bodies and usually involves sediments on the seafloor. These sediments are essential in providing nutrients for the organisms that live in the benthic zone.

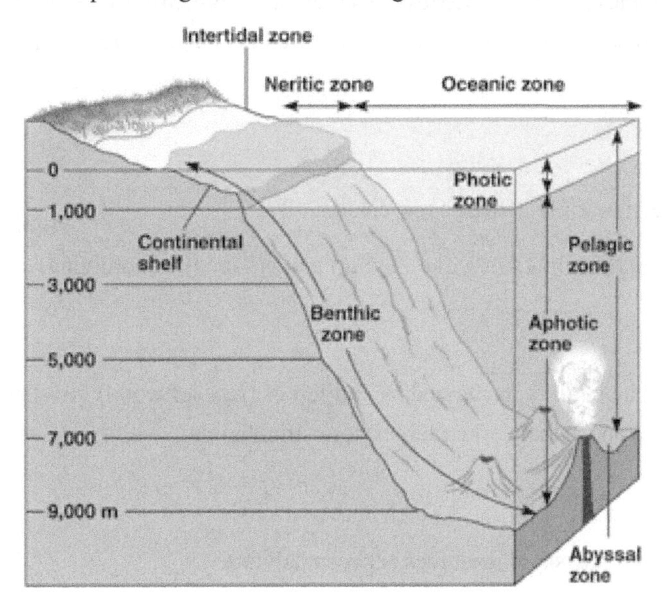

Deep ocean zones include photic, pelagic, aphotic, and abyssal zones

Phytoplankton (microalgae), like terrestrial plants, contain chlorophyll and require sunlight to live and grow.

Most phytoplankton is buoyant and floats in the ocean's upper layers, where sunlight penetrates the water.

Phytoplankton is the base of many aquatic food webs whereby shrimp, jellyfish, and whales feed on them.

Zooplankton is heterotrophic (sometimes detritivores) plankton – organisms drifting in oceans, seas, and freshwater bodies. Individual zooplankton is usually microscopic, but some (e.g., jellyfish) are larger and visible to the unaided eye.

42. C is correct.

Transpiration is when water moves in a plant and evaporates from aerial parts, such as leaves, stems, and flowers.

43. D is correct.

In aquatic ecosystems, *nitrogen* and *phosphorus* are the most important, often in short supply relative to the needs of plants, algae, and microbes.

Elements like iron, manganese, and copper are needed in small amounts.

44. A is correct.

Phytoplankton (microalgae), like terrestrial plants, contain chlorophyll and require sunlight to live and grow.

Most phytoplankton is buoyant and floats in the ocean's upper layers, where sunlight penetrates the water. Phytoplankton is the base of many aquatic food webs whereby shrimp, jellyfish, and whales feed on them.

Zooplankton is heterotrophic (sometimes detritivores) plankton – organisms drifting in oceans, seas, and freshwater bodies. Individual zooplankton is usually microscopic, but some (e.g., jellyfish) are larger and visible to the unaided eye.

45. C is correct.

Energy flows in one direction while nutrients recycle.

Nutrient cycles and *energy flows* link *biotic* (i.e., living) and *abiotic* (i.e., nonliving) components.

46. B is correct.

Boreal forest (or *taiga*) is a biome characterized by coniferous (i.e., softwood) forests mainly consisting of pines, spruces, and larches and is the world's largest terrestrial biome.

47. C is correct.

Freshwater ecosystems naturally share resources between habitats.

At lower elevations, rivers and streams bring salts and nutrients from the mountains to lakes, ponds, and wetlands. Eventually, they bring those nutrients to the ocean.

48. A is correct.

Wetlands are areas filled with water most of the year. It might not always be wet.

Ponds and *lakes* are usually kept filled with water from many sources. They receive more water than they give off through evaporation.

Lake and ponds are distinguished by *depth* and *surface area.*

Lakes usually are much deeper than ponds and have a larger surface area.

Ponds have water in the photic zone, meaning ponds are shallow enough to allow sunlight to reach the bottom.

49. D is correct.

Estuaries are partly enclosed coastal bodies of brackish water (i.e., saline levels of 0.05 to 3% between fresh and saltwater).

Estuaries form when rivers or streams flow in and connect freely to the open sea. They form a transition zone between the river and maritime environments and have marine influences (e.g., tides, waves, and saline water) and river influences (e.g., freshwater and sediment).

Inflows of seawater and freshwater provide nutrients in the water column and sediment, making *estuaries* among the most *productive natural habitats*.

50. A is correct.

Aphotic zone is the area of a lake or ocean with little or no sunlight, the depths beyond which less than 1 percent of sunlight penetrates. Below the photic zone is the dark aphotic zone, where photosynthesis cannot occur.

51. C is correct.

Abiotic factors (i.e., nonliving) include soil, sunlight, water, and minerals.

Biotic factors are living components affecting other organisms. Biotic factors need food and metabolic energy for proper growth.

52. D is correct.

Estuaries are partly enclosed coastal bodies of brackish water (i.e., saline levels of 0.05 to 3% between fresh and saltwater).

Estuaries form when rivers or streams flow in and connect freely to the open sea. They form a *transition zone* between rivers and maritime environments and have marine influences (e.g., tides, waves, and saline water) and river influences (e.g., freshwater and sediment).

The inflows of seawater and freshwater provide nutrients in the water column and sediment, making estuaries among the most *productive natural habitats*.

53. D is correct.

Scavengers feed on dead organisms that they did not kill. Often, the remains of the prey become a food source for scavengers.

Detritivores are heterotrophs that obtain nutrition from decomposing (waste or detritus) plants, dead organisms, and feces and contribute to decomposition and the nutrient cycles.

Detritivores are not to be confused with other decomposers such as bacteria, fungi, and protists, which cannot ingest minute lumps of matter.

Decomposers absorb and metabolize nutrients (i.e., saprotrophic nutrition from dead or decaying material).

54. A is correct.

Open ocean (or *pelagic zone*) is the area of the ocean outside of coastal areas.

The open ocean lies beyond the continental shelf: extending from the Arctic to the Antarctic. It is from the surface to the deepest ocean parts and encompasses the entire water column. It accounts for 64% of the ocean and 45% of Earth.

55. B is correct.

A: *paleontology* studies prehistoric life and includes the study of fossils to determine organisms' evolution.

C: *microbiology* is the scientific study of microscopic organisms, unicellular (i.e., single-cell), multicellular (i.e., cell colony), or acellular (i.e., lacking cells).

Microbiology encompasses sub-disciplines of *mycology* (i.e., fungi), *virology*, *parasitology*, and *bacteriology*.

D: *entomology* is the study of insects (a branch of arthropodology), a branch of zoology.

56. B is correct.

Species make up *populations* that comprise *communities*.

57. D is correct.

Photic zone (sunlight zone) is the depth of the water in a lake or ocean exposed to sufficient sunlight for photosynthesis. It extends from the surface to a depth where light intensity falls to one percent.

The thickness of the photic zone depends on the extent of intensity loss in the water column. It can vary from a few inches in highly turbid lakes (i.e., seasonal effects) to around 600 feet in the ocean.

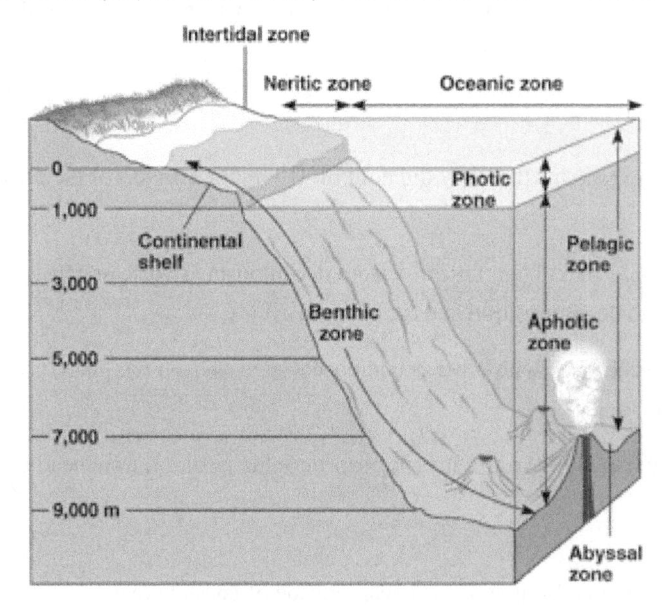

Deep ocean zones include photic, pelagic, aphotic, and abyssal zones

58. D is correct.

Mutualism is when organisms of different species exist in a relationship where each benefit (+/+ relationship).

Symbiosis includes *mutualistic*, *parasitic*, or *commensal* relationships. Mutualism is one *type* of symbiosis.

Most lichens' bodies differ from those of either fungus or alga growing separately.

The fungus surrounds the algal cells, often enclosing them within complex fungal tissues.

continued...

Algal cells are photosynthetic and reduce atmospheric CO_2 into organic carbon sugars to feed both symbionts.

Both partners mainly gain water and mineral nutrients from the atmosphere through rain and dust.

The fungal partner protects the alga by retaining water, serving as a larger capture area for mineral nutrients and, in some cases, providing minerals obtained from the substrate.

If a cyanobacterium is another symbiont in addition to green alga (tripartite lichens), they can fix atmospheric nitrogen, complementing the activities of the green alga.

A: *nematodes* (i.e., roundworms) are unlike cnidarians or flatworms because nematodes have tubular digestive systems with openings at each end.

Nematodes are obligate aquatic organisms consisting of cylindrical unsegmented worms. They are free-living saprophytes or parasites.

B: *bread mold* is a *saprophyte* that feeds on dead and decaying material.

C: t*apeworms* are *parasites* extracting nutrition (they benefit) from the host while the host is depleted (host harmed) of nutrients.

This is a +/– relationship.

59. A is correct.

Heterotrophic organisms obtain nutrients and energy by consuming organic substances.

Autotrophic organisms synthesize food from inorganic environmental substances (e.g., light, chemical energy).

Autotrophs are the basis of the ecosystem and feed heterotrophs. Autotrophs create organic compounds using energy from the sun or inorganic compounds. They can be divided into photoautotrophs and chemoautotrophs.

Photoautotrophs (e.g., algae, plants, cyanobacteria) use photosynthesis to convert solar energy into organic compounds.

Chemoautotrophs are bacteria that oxidize inorganic compounds such as ammonia, nitrite, and sulfide to generate organic compounds. They are rare and typically found in caves, hydrothermal ocean vents, and other environments lacking light.

60. D is correct.

Extracellular digestion allows for the digestion of food outside of the cell, permitting the ingestion of large pieces of food.

Intracellular digestion is limited to small particles to be taken into individual cells.

Complex animals typically have digestive tract enzymes that act on the food material.

Notes for active learning

Populations, Communities and Conservation Biology – Detailed Explanations

1. D is correct.

Sustainable development minimizes environmental impact. Sustainable buildings preserve precious natural resources and improve the quality of life. Buildings should consider design, construction, or operation, reducing or eliminating negative impacts and positively impacting climate and the natural environment.

Several features can make a development *green*, including:

Efficient use of energy, water, and other resources; renewable energy, such as solar energy

Pollution and waste reduction measures and enabling re-use and recycling

Good indoor environmental air quality

Use of materials that are non-toxic, ethical, and sustainable

Consideration of the environment in design, construction, and operation

Design enables adaptation to a changing environment

2. A is correct.

Community is a population of species occupying the same geographical area. In ecology, a community is an association of populations of two or more species simultaneously occupying the same geographical area.

Ecosystem is a community of organisms (e.g., plants, animals, microbes) with nonliving (i.e., *abiotic*) components of their environment (e.g., air, water, minerals). Ecosystems are the network of interactions among and between organisms and their environment.

Habitat is an *ecological area* inhabited by a species. It is the natural environment in which an organism lives or the physical environment encompassing a population.

3. B is correct.

Population density measures population per unit area.

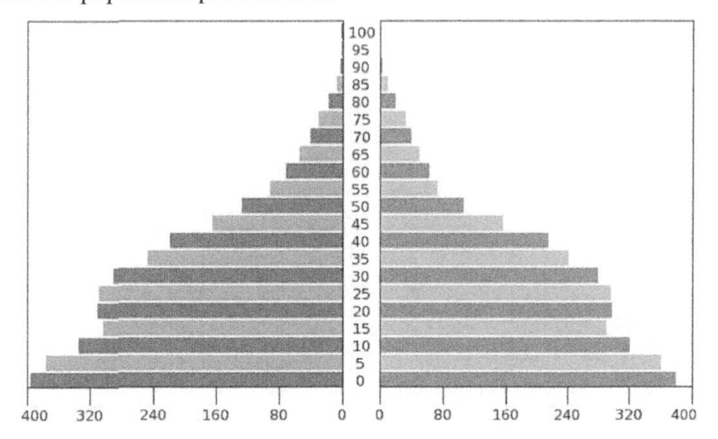

Population density plots age vs. population (in thousands) with male (left) and female comparison

4. D is correct.

Sustainable development meets people's needs without compromising future generations' ability to meet their natural resources and environmental quality needs.

Preventing long-term environmental harm ensures that people can benefit from its use in the future.

5. C is correct.

Range (or *distribution*) of a population is the geographical area.

Dispersion is the variation in local *density* within a range.

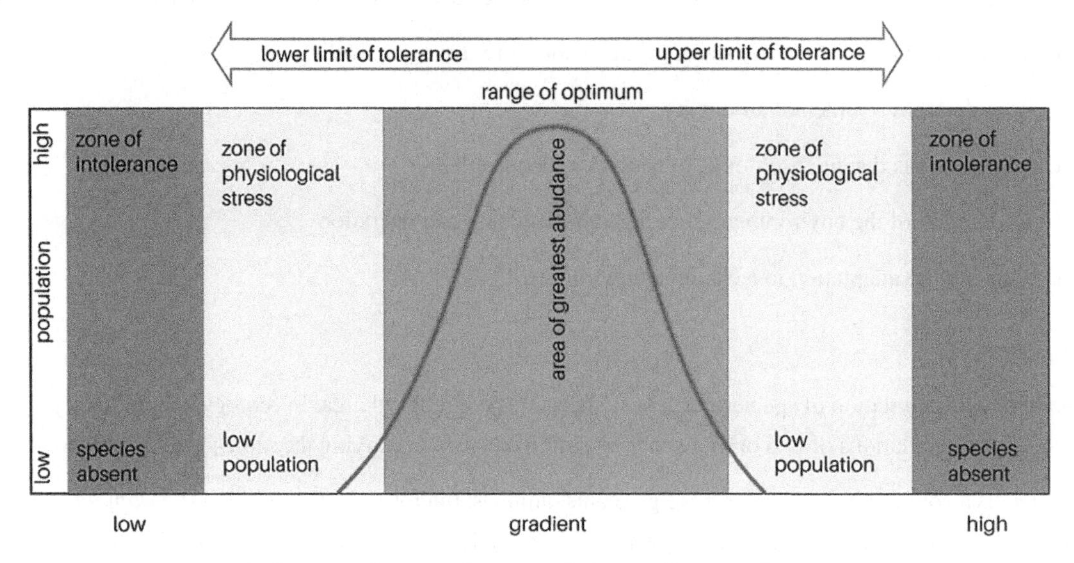

Range of tolerance plots population vs. bifurcated range of optimum stress

6. C is correct.

Observation involves noting characteristics *without* engagement or intervention by the researcher.

7. A is correct.

Demography uses statistics such as births, deaths, income, the incidence of disease, and education, illustrating the changing structure of human populations.

Population growth rate is how the number of people changes in a given period; the flow of people in and out, births, and deaths affect the number of individuals within a population.

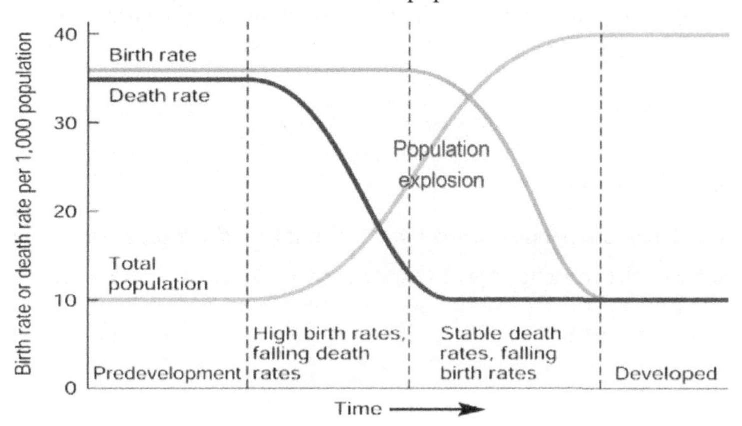

Birth rate and death rate affect population size transitioning from high to low rates with increasing population

8. B is correct.

Population density measures population per unit area (e.g., people per square mile).

9. C is correct.

Biotic factors are living components affecting other organisms.

For example, animals consume other organisms and organic food. Biotic factors need food and metabolic energy for proper growth.

Biotic factors include human influence.

10. A is correct.

Coal, natural gas, oil, and energy are derived from fossil fuels, including minerals (e.g., copper, magnesium). Non-renewable resources are not replenished at a sufficient rate for sustainable economic extraction.

Non-renewable resources require tens of thousands to millions of years and specific conditions to form.

Renewable resources replenish over time through biological reproduction or other naturally recurring processes. They are integral to Earth's natural environment and the largest components of its ecosphere.

Renewable resources may be the source of power for renewable energy. However, renewal and sustainability will not be sustainable when resource consumption exceeds the renewal rate.

11. A is correct.

Ecological models trace the interaction between and interdependence of factors within and across all population levels. It highlights people's interactions with physical and environmental factors.

12. B is correct.

The Dust Bowl was a period of severe dust storms that significantly damaged the ecology and agriculture of the American and Canadian prairies during the 1930s; severe drought and a failure to apply dryland farming methods to prevent the aeolian processes (wind erosion) caused the phenomenon.

Crops began to fail with the onset of drought in 1931, exposing the bare, over-plowed farmland. It began to blow away without deep-rooted prairie grasses to hold the soil in place. The eroding soil led to massive dust storms and economic devastation—especially in the Southern Plains.

13. C is correct.

Immigration is moving *into* an area.

Carrying capacity is the maximum population size the environment can sustain based on resources. If a population grows larger than the carrying capacity, species may die due to a lack of environmental resources.

Emigration is moving *out* of an area.

14. D is correct.

Animal training is not a method used by ecologists to study the environment.

15. A is correct.

Slower growth rate means fewer new individuals in a population. Increased birth rate and decreased death rates lead to a rise in growth rate, whereas decreased birth rate slows down the population growth rate.

	High stationary	**Early expanding**	**Late expanding**	**Low stationary**	**Declining**
	Stage 1	Stage 2	Stage 3	Stage 4	Stage 5
Birth rate	High	High	Falling	Low	Rising again
Death rate	High	Falls rapidly	Falls slowly	Low	Low
Natural output	Stable or slow increase	Very rapid increase	Increase slows down	Falling and then stable	Stable or slow increase

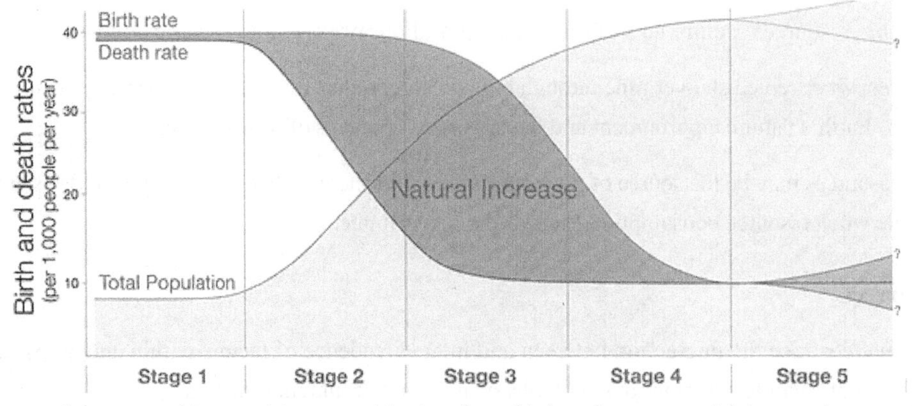

Five stages of demographic transition transitioning from high to low rates with increasing population

16. C is correct.

Desertification is land degradation when a relatively dry land region becomes increasingly arid, typically losing its bodies of water and vegetation, and wildlife. It is caused by factors such as climate change and human activities. The immediate cause is the removal of most vegetation.

Desertification is driven by drought, climatic shifts, tillage for agriculture, overgrazing, deforestation for fuel, and harvesting of construction materials. Desertification is a global ecological and environmental problem.

B: *monoculture* is the agricultural practice of growing a single crop for many consecutive years. It is widely used in industrial agriculture, and its implementation has allowed for large harvests from minimal labor.

However, monocultures quickly spread pests and diseases, making a uniform crop susceptible to a pathogen.

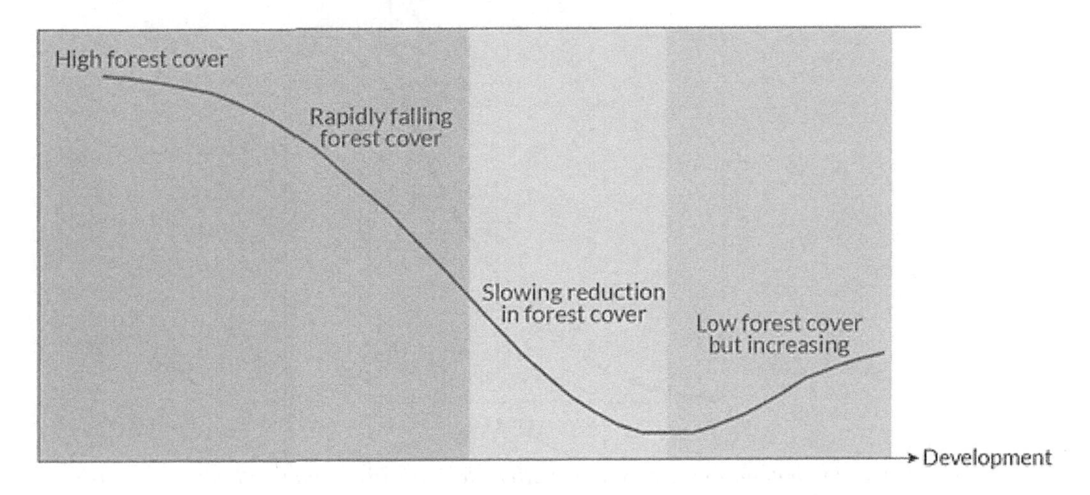

Four stages of forest transition model plotting forest cover vs. development

Stage 1 *Pre-transition*: high forest cover. No or slow loss of forest. (left panel on the graph)

Stage 2 *Early transition*: deforestation rates increasing.

Stage 3 *Late transition*: low forest cover but a slowing rate of deforestation

Stage 4 *Post-transition*: low forest cover but increasing through reforestation. (right panel on the graph)

17. A is correct.

Exponential growth is a process that increases quantity over time.

Exponential growth graphs exhibit *a steep curve up*.

Animals require resources (e.g., food, water, biotic factors) for survival.

The number of microorganisms in culture increases exponentially until an essential nutrient is exhausted, which impedes the organisms' growth.

Typically, the first organism divides into two, who split to form four, eight, etc.

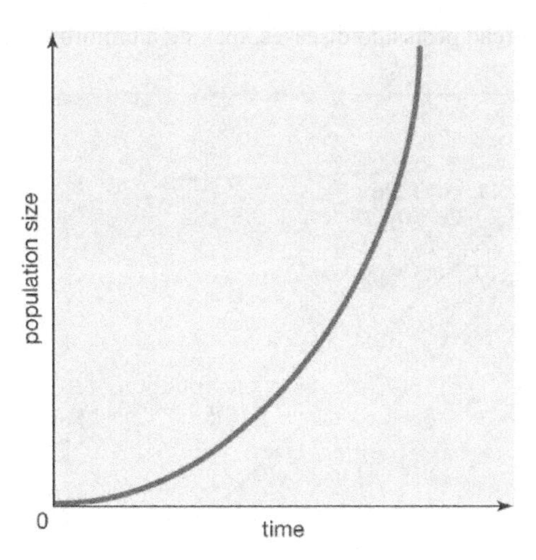

Exponential growth plotting population size vs. time with a steep positive slope indicating increasing numbers

18. C is correct.

Desertification is land degradation when a relatively dry land region becomes increasingly arid, typically losing its bodies of water and vegetation, and wildlife. It is caused by factors such as climate change and human activities. The immediate cause of desertification is the removal of most vegetation.

Desertification is driven by factors (alone or in combination) such as drought, climatic shifts, tillage for agriculture, overgrazing, deforestation for fuel, and harvesting of construction materials.

Desertification is a significant global ecological and environmental problem.

B: *monoculture* is the agricultural practice of growing a *single crop* for many consecutive years. It is widely used in industrial agriculture, and its implementation has allowed for large harvests from minimal labor.

However, monocultures quickly *spread pests and diseases*, making a uniform crop susceptible to a pathogen.

Stage 1 Pre-transition: high forest cover. No or slow loss of forest.

Stage 2 Early transition: deforestation rates increasing.

Stage 3 Late transition: low forest cover but a slowing rate of deforestation

Stage 4 Post-transition: low forest cover but increasing through reforestation.

19. B is correct.

Decreased birth rate and *emigration* (i.e., outflow) cause population size to *decrease*.

20. D is correct.

Soil erosion gradually removes a field's top layer of soil from natural elements such as water, wind, and farming activities.

Irrigation controls the amount of water released by supplying it at regular intervals for farming, which is an effective way of maintaining the quality of the soil.

21. D is correct.

Demographic transition is the shift from high birth and death rates to low birth and death rates as a country develops from a pre-industrial to an industrialized economic system.

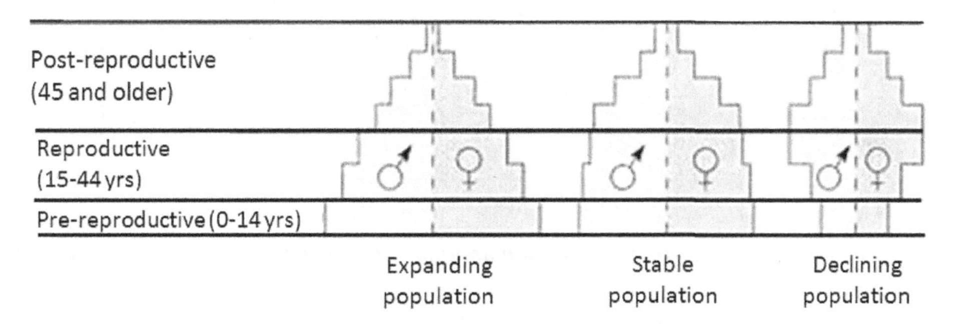

Age structure diagrams: pyramid (left) for expanding, bell-shaped (center) for stable, urn-shaped (right) for declining population profiles

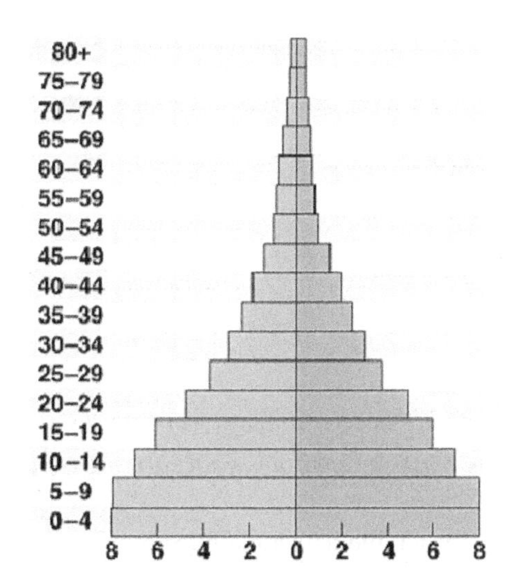

An expansive population pyramid plots age vs. percent. Males on the left. The graph is skewed towards younger members when the demographic transition is incomplete

22. A is correct.

Births and *immigration* (inflows) *increase* population size.

23. D is correct.

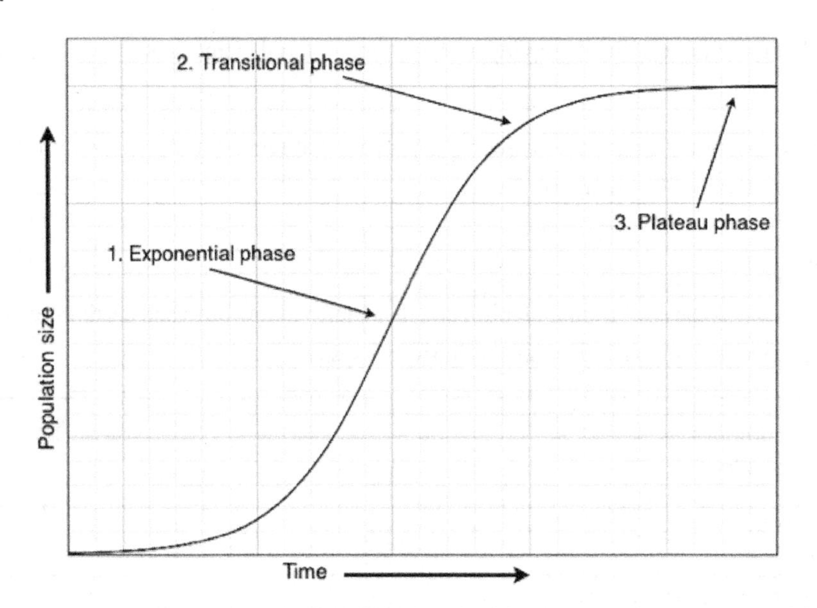

Sigmoidal (S)-shaped logistic growth curve of population growth with environmental resistance. The exponential phase has an accelerating growth rate. The exponential phase is marked by a steep positive slope, transitional phase with a slightly positive slope, and plateau phase with flat curve profiles

Exponential growth is a process that increases quantity over time; the graph exhibits a steep curve up.

Logistic curve (or *function*) is a common *sigmoid function* (S-shape) concerning population growth.

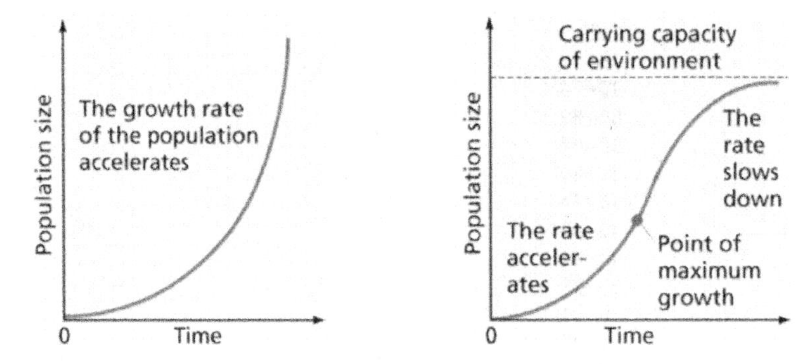

Exponential (unrestricted) growth (left) has accelerating growth patterns and logistic (restricted) growth (right) where the rate decreases as environmental carrying capacity is achieved

Animals require resources (e.g., food, water, biotic factors) for survival.

The number of microorganisms in culture increases exponentially until an essential nutrient is exhausted, which impedes the organisms' growth.

24. A is correct.

Using predators and parasites for pest management is a sustainable resource in ecology.

25. B is correct.

Exponential growth is a process that increases quantity over time. The graph exhibits a steep curve up.

Animals require resources (e.g., food, water, biotic factors) for survival. The number of microorganisms in culture increases exponentially until an essential nutrient is exhausted, which impedes the organisms' growth. Typically the first organism divides into two, who split to form four, eight, etc.

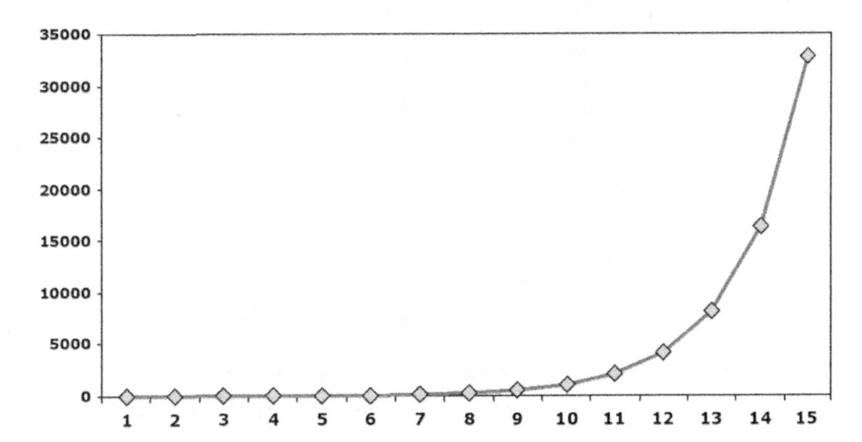

Exponential growth with population vs. generation plotted shows accelerated growth rates

26. C is correct.

DDT (or d*ichlorodiphenyltrichloroethane*) was a modern synthetic pesticide used in the United States (beginning in the 1940s) to control insects on food crops and in buildings for pest control.

DDT was discontinued in 1972 because of its harmful effects on humans and wildlife.

27. D is correct.

Renewable resources can be regenerated or replenished. A renewable resource is a natural resource that can replenish over time through biological reproduction or other naturally recurring processes.

Renewable resources are a part of Earth's natural environment and the largest components of its ecosphere.

Renewable resources may be the source of power for renewable energy.

Renewal and sustainability are not ensured if the renewable resource consumption exceeds its renewal rate.

28. C is correct.

Density-dependent limiting factors affect the size or growth due to variation in population density. Dense populations are more strongly affected than less crowded ones.

Density-dependent limiting factors include food availability, disease, living space, predation, and migration.

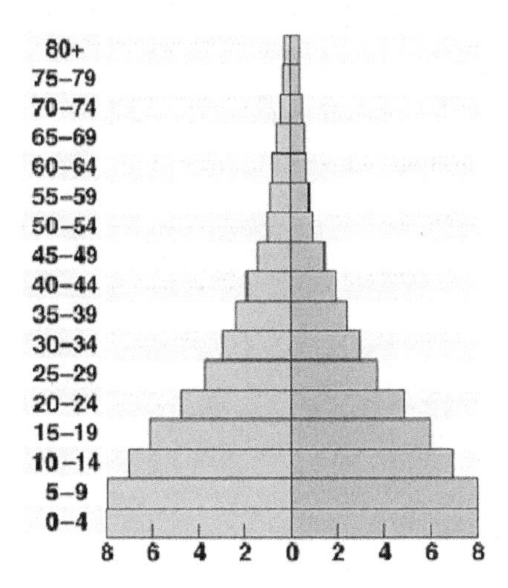

An expansive population pyramid plots age vs. percent. Males on the left. The graph is skewed towards younger members when the demographic transition is incomplete

29. D is correct.

Carrying capacity is the maximum population size the environment can sustain indefinitely based on the available resources. If a population grows larger than the carrying capacity, species may die due to a lack of environmental resources.

30. B is correct.

Biological magnification is any concentration of a toxin, such as pesticides, in the tissues of tolerant organisms at successively higher levels in a food chain.

Biomagnification is when an organism's chemical concentration exceeds its food concentration when the primary exposure route occurs from the diet.

Higher-level predators (e.g., fish, birds, marine mammals) build up greater dangerous amounts of toxic materials than animals lower on the food chain.

DDT was banned in 1972 as a suspected carcinogen (i.e., cancer causing agent).

31. B is correct.

Exponential growth is a process that increases quantity over time. The graph exhibits a steep curve up.

Animals require resources (e.g., food, water, biotic factors) for survival. The number of microorganisms in culture increases exponentially until an essential nutrient is exhausted, which impedes the organisms' growth.

Typically, the first organism divides into two, who split to form four, eight, etc.

32. A is correct.

Photochemical smog is air pollution resulting from the interaction of sunlight with certain chemicals in the atmosphere. One of the primary components of photochemical smog is *ozone*.

Smog is air pollution that reduces visibility and was first labeled in the early 1900s to describe a mix of smoke and fog. The smoke usually came from burning coal. Smog was common in industrial areas and remains a familiar sight in cities today.

The atmospheric pollutants or gases that form smog are released into the air when fuels are burnt. Smog is formed when sunlight and its heat react with these gases and fine particles in the atmosphere.

Particulate matter is a mixture of tiny particles and liquid droplets. Particle pollution comprises several components: acids (nitrates and sulfates), organic chemicals, metals, and soil or dust particles.

Greenhouse gas absorbs infrared radiation (net heat energy) emitted from Earth's surface and reradiates it back to Earth's surface, thus contributing to the greenhouse effect. Carbon dioxide, methane, and water vapor are the most important greenhouse gases.

Ozone layer is a region in the Earth's stratosphere that contains high ozone (O_3) concentrations and protects the Earth from the sun's harmful ultraviolet radiations.

33. A is correct.

Acid rain is any form of precipitaion when acidic components (e.g., sulfur dioxide, nitrogen oxides) fall to the ground form the atmosphere. These compounds rise into the atmosphere, reacting with water and oxygen and falling to the ground as precipitation.

34. C is correct.

Logistic curve (or *function*) is a standard *sigmoid function* (S-shape) concerning population growth. The initial growth stage is approximately exponential. As saturation begins, growth slows, and at maturity, growth stops.

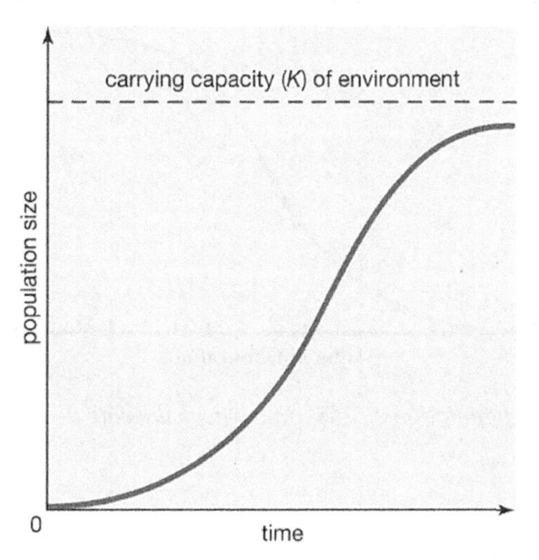

Logistic growth plotting population size vs. time where the rate decreases at carrying capacity

Exponential growth is a process that increases quantity over time; the graph exhibits a *steep curve up*.

35. C is correct.

Limiting factors in an ecosystem are typically food, water, habitat, and mate. The availability factors will affect the carrying capacity of an environment. As the population increases, food demand increases as well. Since food is a limited resource, organisms will begin competing for it.

36. A is correct.

Acid rain is a chemical reaction with sulfur dioxide, and nitrogen oxides are released into the air. These compounds rise into the atmosphere, reacting with water and oxygen and falling to the ground as precipitation.

37. D is correct.

The vapors given off when gasoline evaporates and the substances produced when gasoline is burned (carbon monoxide, nitrogen oxides, particulates, and unburned hydrocarbons) contribute to air pollution.

Burning gasoline produces carbon dioxide (CO_2), a greenhouse gas.

Lead gasoline (prohibited in 1996) releases suspended particles into the air. Motor-vehicle emissions have been reduced by banning lead gasoline for motor vehicles.

However, lead is used in general-aviation gasoline for piston-engine aircraft. Lead poisoning causes immense societal harm: brain damage, chronic illness, lowered IQ, and elevated mortality.

38. D is correct.

Density-dependent limiting factors affect the size or growth due to variation in population density.

Dense populations are more strongly affected than less crowded ones.

Density-dependent limiting factors include food availability, disease, living space, predation, and migration.

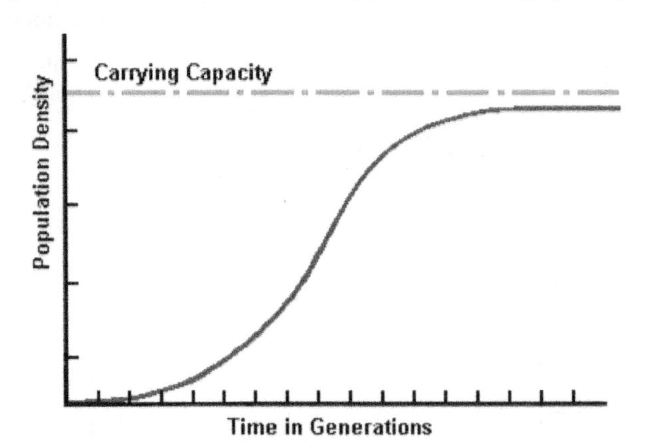

Logistic growth plotting population size vs. time where the rate decreases at carrying capacity

39. A is correct.

Particulate matter is a mixture of tiny particles and liquid droplets. Particle pollution comprises several components: acids (nitrates and sulfates), organic chemicals, metals, and soil or dust particles.

40. B is correct.

Carrying capacity is the maximum population size the environment can sustain indefinitely based on the available resources. If a population grows larger than the carrying capacity, species may die due to a lack of environmental resources.

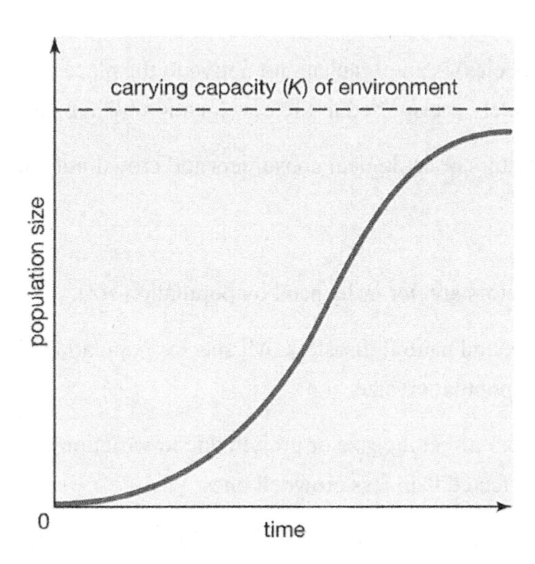

Logistic growth plotting population size vs. time where the rate decreases at carrying capacity

41. A is correct.

Species diversity is the adequate number of different species represented in a collection of individuals.

B: *genetic diversity* refers to the total number of genetic characteristics in the genetic makeup of a species.

It is distinguished from genetic variability, which describes the tendency of genetic characteristics to vary.

Genetic diversity serves as a way for populations to adapt to changing environments.

C: *ecosystem diversity* refers to the diversity of a place at the level of ecosystems (i.e., biotic and abiotic factors).

D: *biodiversity* refers to variation in species rather than ecosystems.

42. B is correct.

Density-dependent limiting factors affect the size or growth due to variation in population density. Dense populations are more strongly affected than less crowded ones.

Density-dependent limiting factors include food availability, disease, living space, predation, and migration.

43. D is correct.

Species diversity is the adequate number of different species represented in a collection of individuals.

B: *genetic diversity* refers to the total number of genetic characteristics in the genetic makeup of a species.

Genetic diversity is distinguished from *genetic variability*, which describes the tendency of genetic characteristics to vary. It serves as a way for populations to adapt to changing environments.

44. A is correct.

Drought is a prolonged period of abnormally low rainfall, leading to a water shortage. This limiting factor does not apply to marine animals.

45. A is correct.

Introduced species (or exotic species) is an organism not native to the place or area it is introduced. Instead, it has been accidentally or deliberately transported to the new location by human activity.

Introduced species may be predators or ecological consumers and crowd out native species.

46. B is correct.

Density-independent limiting factors are *not* influenced by population size.

Factors include weather, climate, and natural disasters. All species populations in the ecosystem will be similarly affected, regardless of population size.

Density-dependent limiting factors affect the size or growth due to variation in population density. Dense populations are more strongly affected than less crowded ones.

Density-dependent limiting factors include food availability, disease, living space, predation, and migration.

47. D is correct.

Higher birth and lower death rates increase the number of individuals, thus increasing competition.

Fewer resources and higher population density lead to increased competition.

A decrease in population size can reduce competition.

48. C is correct.

Habitat is the natural environment in which an organism lives or the physical environment encompassing a population. It is an ecological area inhabited by a species.

Habitat fragmentation divides large habitats into smaller, isolated patches due to *habitat loss* by human activity and natural causes. This negatively affects biodiversity and reduces the suitable habitat for certain species.

49. C is correct.

Habitat is an ecological area inhabited by a species. It is the natural environment in which an organism lives or the physical environment encompassing a population.

50. A is correct.

Density-independent limiting factors are *not* influenced by population size. Factors include weather, climate, and natural disasters. Species populations in the ecosystem are similarly affected, regardless of population size.

The spray program affected the mosquito population as a density-independent limiting factor.

51. D is correct.

Density-dependent limiting factors affect the size or growth due to variation in population density.

Dense populations are more strongly affected than less crowded ones. Density-dependent limiting factors include food availability, disease, living space, predation, and migration.

Density-independent limiting factors are *not* influenced by population size. Factors include weather, climate, and natural disasters. All species populations in the ecosystem will be similarly affected, regardless of population size.

52. A is correct.

Hot spots are regions of species in a single geographic region (i.e., endemism). Ecological hot spots tend to occur in tropical environments where species richness and biodiversity are higher than in ecosystems closer to the poles.

For example, biodiversity hotspots are forest habitats, as they constantly face destruction and degradation due to illegal logging, pollution, and deforestation.

53. B is correct.

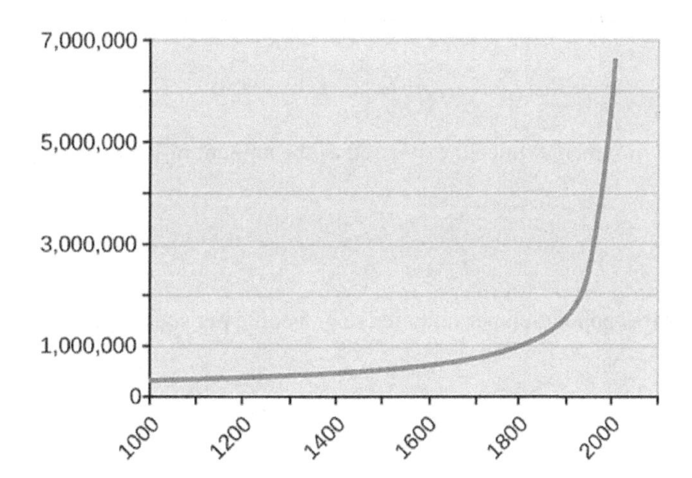

World population from 1000 AD. Graph plots population (in thousands) vs. year

54. A is correct.

Ecosystems include interactions between species. Protecting the entire ecosystem preserves this equilibrium.

55. C is correct.

Biodiversity conservation protects and preserves the wealth and variety of species, habitats, ecosystems, and genetic diversity.

Introduced species (or exotic species) is an organism not native to the place or area it is introduced. Instead, it has been accidentally or deliberately transported to the new location by human activity. Introduced species may be predators or ecological consumers and crowd out native species.

56. C is correct.

Demographic transition is the shift from high birth and high death rates to low birth and low death rates as a country develops from a pre-industrial to an industrialized economic system.

	High stationary	**Early expanding**	**Late expanding**	**Low stationary**	**Declining**
	Stage 1	Stage 2	Stage 3	Stage 4	Stage 5
Birth rate	High	High	Falling	Low	Rising again
Death rate	High	Falls rapidly	Falls slowly	Low	Low
Natural output	Stable or slow increase	Very rapid increase	Increase slows down	Falling and then stable	Stable or slow increase

Five stages of demographic transition transitioning from high to low rates with increasing population

57. B is correct.

Demography is the statistical study of human populations. Demographers use census data, surveys, and statistical models to analyze populations' size, movement, and structure.

58. D is correct.

Ecological footprint is environmental impact expressed as the amount of land required to sustain the use of natural resources.

59. C is correct.

Population density measures population per unit area (e.g., people per square mile).

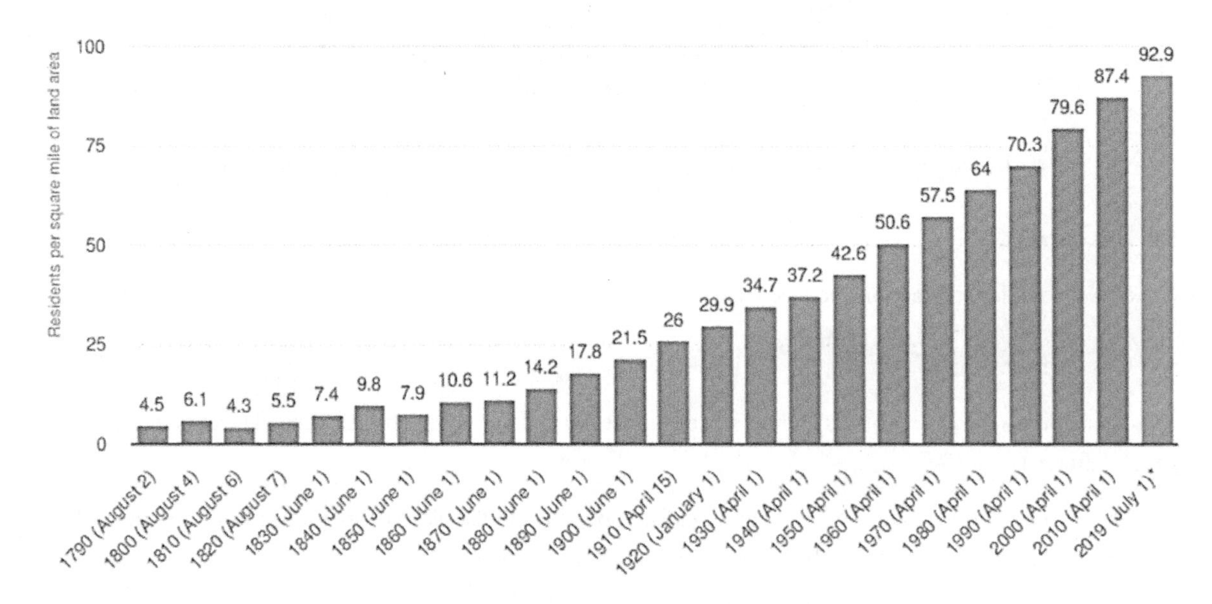

Population density of the United States from 1790 to 2019 in residents per square mile of land area

60. C is correct.

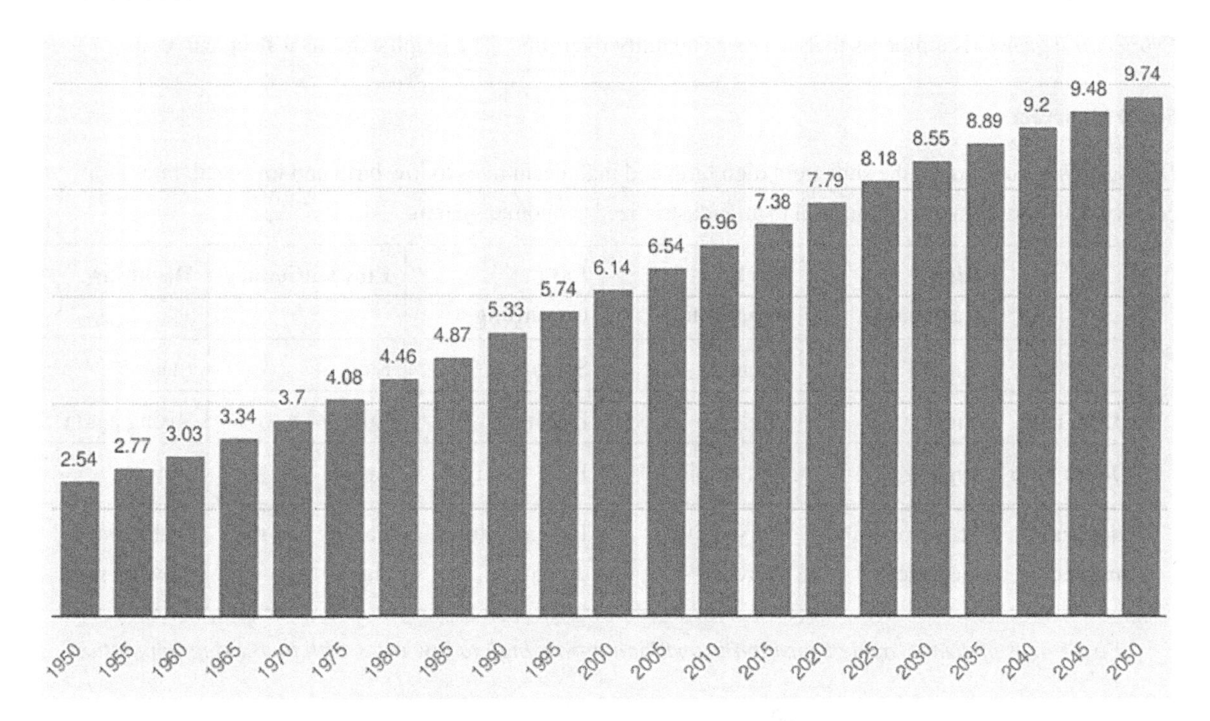

World population from 1950 to 2020 in billion

61. C is correct.

Demographic transition is the shift from high birth and high death rates to low birth and low death rates as a country develops from a pre-industrial to an industrialized economic system.

62. D is correct.

Introduced species (or exotic species) is an organism not native to the place or area it is introduced. Instead, it has been accidentally or deliberately transported to the new location by human activity. Introduced species may be predators or ecological consumers and crowd out native species.

63. B is correct.

Monoculture farming grows the same crop or plant yearly in a field. This requires standardized planting, maintenance, and harvesting, resulting in greater yields and lower costs but can lead to quicker buildup and *spread of pests and diseases.*

64. C is correct.

Density-independent limiting factors are *not* influenced by population size. Factors include weather, climate, and natural disasters. All species populations in the ecosystem will be similarly affected, regardless of population size.

Predation is a biological interaction when a predator (i.e., a hunting organism) feeds on prey.

Exponential growth is a process that increases quantity over time. The graph exhibits a steep curve up.

65. C is correct.

Exponential growth is a process that increases quantity over time. The graph exhibits a steep curve up.

66. D is correct.

Demographic transition is the shift from high birth and high death rates to low birth and low death rates as a country develops from a pre-industrial to an industrialized economic system.

	High stationary	**Early expanding**	**Late expanding**	**Low stationary**	**Declining**
	Stage 1	Stage 2	Stage 3	Stage 4	Stage 5
Birth rate	High	High	Falling	Low	Rising again
Death rate	High	Falls rapidly	Falls slowly	Low	Low
Natural output	Stable or slow increase	Very rapid increase	Increase slows down	Falling and then stable	Stable or slow increase

Five stages of demographic transition transitioning from high to low rates with increasing population

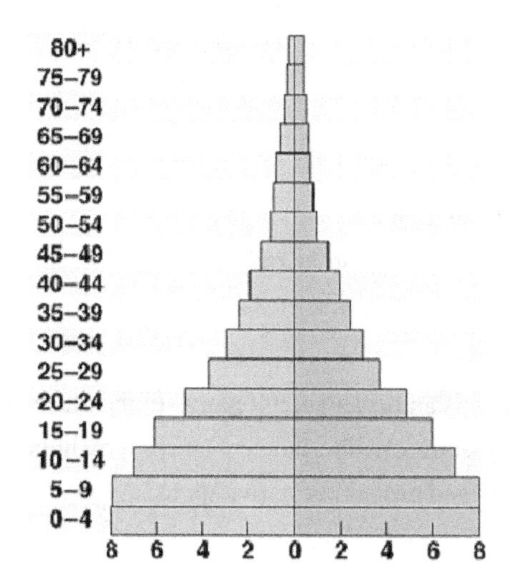

An expansive population pyramid plots age vs. percent. Males on the left. The graph is skewed towards younger members when the demographic transition is incomplete

67. A is correct.

Ecology uses scientific research to identify the cause and best practices to solve problems.

68. D is correct.

Global warming refers to the rise in the average temperature of the Earth's climate system.

The graph in the question shows that the land-surface air temperature has increased over the last century.

69. B is correct.

Biodiversity is the biological variety and variability of life on Earth. Biodiversity measures variation at the genetic, species, and ecosystem levels. Terrestrial biodiversity is usually greater near the equator, resulting from the warm climate and high primary productivity.

Genetic diversity refers to the total number of genetic characteristics in the genetic makeup of a species.

Genetic variability is the tendency of genetic characteristics to vary. It serves as a way for populations to adapt to changing environments.

70. A is correct.

Hot spots are regions of species in a single geographic region (i.e., endemism). These regions are sensitive to human intervention, and many habitats and species are at a high risk of extinction.

Ecological hot spots tend to occur in tropical environments where species richness and biodiversity are higher than in ecosystems closer to the poles.

For example, biodiversity hotspots are forest habitats, as they constantly face destruction and degradation due to illegal logging, pollution, and deforestation.

71. D is correct.

Ecological succession in a rocky, barren area to a final climax community is:

> lichen → mosses → annual grasses → perennial grasses → shrubs →
> deciduous trees (e.g., thick shade trees such as oak and hemlock).

72. A is correct.

Climax community is when a biological community of plants, animals, and fungi reaches a steady-state through *ecological succession* (i.e., vegetation development in an area over time).

Equilibrium is when the climax community comprises species best adapted to average conditions.

For example, the climax community is grasslands in the Midwest, while deciduous forests are in the northeast.

B: *climax community* is mainly dependent on *environmental factors*.

Temperature, soil, and rainfall determine which organisms survive and thrive.

C: *biomes* are geographically and climatically defined as contiguous with similar conditions, such as communities of plants, animals, and soil organisms.

Many species live in a biome.

D: *pioneer species* are hardy species and the first to colonize previously disrupted ecosystems,

Pioneer species are the earliest species in a biome and initially colonize it (e.g., lichen on rocks). They begin a chain of ecological succession leading to a biodiverse steady-state ecosystem.

Notes for active learning

AP Biology Review provides a comprehensive review of topics tested on the AP Biology exam. The content covers foundational principles and concepts necessary to answer exam questions.

This review book will increase your score.

Visit our Amazon store

AP Chemistry, Biology and Physics online practice tests

Our advanced online testing platform allows you to take AP practice questions on your computer to generate a Diagnostic Report for each test.

By using our online AP tests and Diagnostic Reports, you will:

Assess your knowledge of subjects and topics to identify your areas of strength and weakness

Learn important scientific topics and concepts for comprehensive test preparation

Improve your test-taking skills

To access AP questions online
at special pricing for book owners, visit:
http://ap.sterling-prep.com/bookowner.htm

Frank J. Addivinola, Ph.D.

The lead author and chief editor of this preparation guide is Dr. Frank Addivinola. With his outstanding education, laboratory research, and decades of university science teaching, Dr. Addivinola lent his expertise to develop this book.

Dr. Frank Addivinola conducted original research in developmental biology as a doctoral candidate and pre-IRTA fellow in Molecular and Cell Biology at the National Institutes of Health (NIH). His dissertation advisor was Nobel laureate Marshall W. Nirenberg, Chief of the Biochemical Genetics Laboratory at the National Heart, Lung, and Blood Institute (NHLBI). Before NIH, Dr. Addivinola researched prostate cancer in the Cell Growth and Regulation Laboratory of Dr. Arthur Pardee at the Dana Farber Cancer Institute of Harvard Medical School.

Dr. Addivinola holds an undergraduate degree in biology from Williams College. He completed his Masters at Harvard University, Masters in Biotechnology at Johns Hopkins University, and five other graduate degrees at the University of Maryland University College, Suffolk University, and Northeastern University.

During his extensive teaching career, Dr. Addivinola taught numerous undergraduate and graduate-level courses, including biology, biochemistry, organic chemistry, inorganic chemistry, anatomy and physiology, medical terminology, nutrition, and medical ethics. He received several awards for his research and presentations.

Frank R. Addivinola, Ph.D.

Made in the USA
Las Vegas, NV
10 December 2024